Fundamentals of
Inorganic, Organic and
Biological Chemistry

JOSEPH I. ROUTH, Ph.D.

Professor of Biochemistry
State University of Iowa

Fourth Edition, Illustrated

W. B. Saunders Company

Philadelphia   1959   London

The Library of Congress has cataloged this book as follows:

Routh, Joseph Isaac, 1910— Fundamentals of inorganic, organic, and biological chemistry. 4th ed. Philadelphia, Saunders, 1959. 384 p. illus. 21 cm.

1. Chemistry. QD33.R86 1959 (540) 59-5964 ‡

To My Wife

THE NURSE WHOSE IDEAS AND
EXPERIENCE MADE THIS BOOK POSSIBLE

Preface to Fourth Edition

In recent years, the importance of chemistry in nursing and medicine has increased markedly. The rapidly developing fields of radiochemistry, organic and pharmaceutical chemistry, and biological chemistry have emphasized the need for constant revision of textbook material. Accordingly, in the preparation of the fourth edition, these fields have received the greatest attention. In addition, the author has incorporated changes suggested by students and instructors who use the book.

It is not possible in this book to discuss all of the recent developments in the application of nuclear energy to the production of power plants, self-propelled vehicles, biological research, medicine, and industry. Nevertheless, a cross section of these advances has been included in this edition. Other changes in the inorganic section include a discussion of ion exchange resins in water softeners, the preparation and use of normal solutions, and extensive revision of the material on ionization of electrolytes and hydrolysis of salts.

An attempt has been made to improve the presentation of the material on organic chemistry by omitting obsolete sections, increasing the emphasis on the application of organic compounds to nursing and medicine, and changing structural formulas to conform to current chemical practice.

Many of the recent developments in biological chemistry have been incorporated in this edition. Increased attention has been given to the reactions and schemes involved in the metabolism of the major foodstuffs. The correlation between these metabolic processes has received greater emphasis.

The illustrations used in the previous edition have been critically reviewed, with the result that many have been replaced. Most of the new illustrations have been prepared in the author's laboratory.

The author is pleased to acknowledge the valuable assistance obtained from the suggestions and criticisms received from students and instructors. He also wishes to express his appreciation to his publishers for their constant interest and efforts to improve the textbook.

JOSEPH I. ROUTH

Contents

Chapter 1

INTRODUCTION 1

Chapter 2

SOME FUNDAMENTAL CONCEPTS 7

Chapter 3

ATOMS AND MOLECULES 14

Chapter 4

VALENCE AND CHEMICAL EQUATIONS 36

Chapter 5

OXYGEN, OXIDATION AND REDUCTION....................... 52

Chapter 6

WATER.. 70

Chapter 7

SOLUTIONS 82

Chapter 8

ACIDS, BASES, AND SALTS................................... 102

vii

Chapter 9

ELECTROLYTES AND IONIZATION 115

Chapter 10

INTRODUCTION TO ORGANIC CHEMISTRY 127

Chapter 11

ALIPHATIC COMPOUNDS 136

Chapter 12

CYCLIC COMPOUNDS 165

Chapter 13

CARBOHYDRATES 191

Chapter 14

THE LIPIDS 204

Chapter 15

PROTEINS 219

Chapter 16

ENZYMES AND DIGESTION 233

Chapter 17

CARBOHYDRATE METABOLISM 251

Chapter 18

FAT METABOLISM 260

Chapter 19

PROTEIN METABOLISM 266

Chapter 20

THE BLOOD 276

Chapter 21

THE URINE. 291

Chapter 22

VITAMINS 304

Chapter 23

NUTRITION 330

Chapter 24

HORMONES 339

APPENDIX 363

INDEX. 367

LONG FORM OF THE PERIODIC TABLE ⎫
INTERNATIONAL ATOMIC WEIGHTS ⎬ . . . . *Inside Back Cover*
⎭

Chapter 1

Introduction

The activity of chemists in many fields of research has ushered us into an era of scientific achievement that seemed out of reach at the beginning of the century. Although remarkable advances have been made in industry, the most exciting developments are concerned with advances in medical science. Therapeutic agents that once required years of development and clinical trial are now given early opportunity to prove their merit. Research teams screen chemical compounds for beneficial action on bacteria and laboratory animals prior to their release for clinical testing. Sulfanilamide, when developed in 1935, received only a fraction of the screening and therapeutic trial afforded prednisolone, a steroid more potent than cortisone. A healthy competition exists between agencies that attempt to produce more potent, less toxic drugs; and the results of their extensive study and trial eventually benefit the entire population. The over-all effect of this chemical research is to make available cheaper, safer and more effective therapeutic agents. Improved sulfa drugs, antibiotics, analgesic compounds, tranquilizers, and cortisone-like steroids are products of this research. The recently developed drugs with an insulin-like action that can be taken orally are further examples of research teamwork.

Another recent development in the field of chemistry involves the application of radioactive isotopes in diagnostic and therapeutic procedures. Cobalt bombs for applying radiation to cancerous tissue, radio-iodine used in diagnosis and therapy of the thyroid gland, and radioactive phosphorus used in the location of breast cancers and brain tumors are examples.

Chemists in industry have also made considerable progress in the past few years. Constant improvements in the properties of plastics and synthetic fibers have resulted from their research. Rocket research has produced new alloys and propellants, and has opened an entirely new field in physics and chemistry.

History of Chemistry

In an attempt to trace the origin of chemistry, we are carried back to the very beginning of civilization. It is said that chemistry originated in the Egyptian temples where priests experimented in the preparation of medicines.

From early records it appears that alchemy, the attempts to transmute the base metals into silver and gold, had its origin in the Greek colony of Alexandria at the beginning of the Christian era. When the Arabians overran Egypt in the seventh century, they learned about chemistry from the Egyptians. Alchemy was carried into Spain by the Arabians, and by the fourteenth century its study extended throughout the civilized world. In a broad sense alchemy represents the chemistry of the Middle Ages. The all important objective of the alchemist was to transform common metals into gold. It was their belief that this could be accomplished by means of the philosophers' stone, a mysterious substance they spent their lives to prepare. Countless experiments were performed employing all manner of material and crude chemical methods. Several pieces of chemical apparatus were developed and a few important chemical compounds were discovered by the alchemists. In their attempts to transform other metals into gold many individuals, especially royalty, were relieved of articles of jewelry to act as "seed."

The fifteenth, sixteenth, and seventeenth centuries were marked by important advances in chemistry and medicine. The experimental method finally replaced superstition and mysticism as a means of attacking problems in these fields. A new era of medical chemistry began, marked by the advent of the iatrochemist, or physician chemist (Fig. 1). This group of men believed that the prime purpose of chemistry was to prepare medicines and not to transmute base metals into gold. The most renowned of the medical chemists was Paracelsus, the son of a Swiss physician. He believed that man is made of chemical elements and that life processes are essentially chemical in nature. He stated that the health of the body depended upon the correct proportion of these chemical elements and that a change in the proportions caused illness which could be cured by the administration of chemical medicine. He vigorously advocated the value of experimenta-

Figure 1. A medical alchemist or iatrochemist.

tion in chemistry and medicine and actively criticized the earlier beliefs and superstitions of medical lore. It is probably safe to state that Paracelsus exerted a more profound influence over the development of the experimental approach to problems in chemistry and medicine than any other man in his time.

Fields of Chemistry

Originally the two major fields of chemistry were inorganic and organic. In recent years, subdivisions such as physical, analytical, biochemistry and radiochemistry have been developed. Inorganic chemistry is concerned with a study of lifeless material such as metals and minerals whereas organic chemistry is a study of matter associated with living things. Physical chemistry is a study of fundamental laws and theories of chemistry, while radiochemistry is concerned with atomic structure, nuclear reactions, and radioactive isotopes. Biochemistry or biological chemistry is the chemistry of living processes in health and disease. The most fundamental fields of chemistry are inorganic, organic and biological, the fundamentals of which compose the subject matter of this book.

Importance of Chemistry

A reasonable knowledge of chemistry enables us to understand the thousands of chemical changes that are constantly occurring. Our main interest is a consideration of the chemistry of the body in health and disease. The food we eat is an important weapon in the proper treatment of many abnormal conditions in the body. An acquaintance with the chemical nature of food and the chemical processes of digestion, absorption, and metabolism will increase your value as a nurse.

The majority of diseases are treated with chemicals called *drugs,* which change the chemical reactions in the body in an attempt to restore normal conditions. A better understanding of the effect of drugs may be gained through application of your knowledge of chemistry. It is a well-known fact that drugs are valuable agents in the treatment of disease, but they may be exceedingly harmful when administered promiscuously in the form of patent medicines. The American people find it difficult to resist the temptation of self-medication and pay millions of dollars each year for preparations whose continued use may produce harmful effects.

The present-day progress of medical science is very rapid, and a great share of this progress is due to the skill of the research chemist. Hence, a basic knowledge of chemistry will enable you to keep abreast of recent medical discoveries made through chemistry.

The human body has often been referred to as a laboratory in which chemical changes are constantly occurring. To run the gamut from birth to death involves more reactions than are understood at the present time. Nevertheless, a knowledge of the fundamental principles of the chemical changes that occur in the body will enable you as a nurse to treat diseases of the body more intelligently.

Suggested Method of Study

Chemistry is a science and its study, like any other science, requires a different method of approach than the liberal arts courses with which we are familiar. Many of you are just beginning a study of chemistry while others may have had chemistry in high school and a few may have taken a course in college chemistry. Your attitude toward chemistry depends not only on your previous experience in the subject, but may be influenced to a large extent by the opinion of other students. The familiar hue and cry that chemistry is a "tough" course and should be avoided like the plague is heard on every campus. Many of you may feel rather apprehensive because you are required to take a course in chemistry. But it is a well-known fact that fear can be overcome by knowledge, and the study of chemistry is certainly no exception to this rule.

By far the most universally accepted method of study of students in grade school, high school, and college is memorization. Most of us are endowed with the mental ability to memorize facts, and details concerning the facts. In grade school, the facts were made interesting and repeated so often that they were relatively easy to memorize. In too many high schools a premium is placed on the individual's ability to memorize, and his power of "memorization" directly affects his grades.

You are now faced with an entirely different task, that of learning a specific profession. Many of the courses which you will take, such as chemistry, physiology, bacteriology, pharmacology, and so on, are professions within themselves and require years of study for their mastery. Thus, you will soon find that it is impossible to memorize all the facts and details that are known about any one scientific subject. If you attempt to learn chemistry as you did History, Latin, or English in high school your mind will become confused with nonessential details.

How, then, should we approach the study of chemistry? It is realized that each individual has different methods of learning and that no single plan of study could be adopted by everyone. In chemistry, as in any other science, there are certain fundamental principles or concepts upon which whole sections of the subject are based. If we thoroughly understand the underlying principles, it is not too difficult to fill in the necessary details of the subject. Chemistry cannot be understood by merely reading an assigned section in a textbook. It requires a little more effort to recognize the fundamental principles upon which each section is based, but it results in an understanding that can never be achieved by memorization. A good study habit to develop early in your professional life is to prepare an outline of the most important points that are covered in your lecture and reading material. If you understand the subject, it will be easy to condense the principal thoughts into outline form. *Literally speaking, study with a pencil in your hand and use it constantly to practice formulas and equations that illustrate fundamental facts.* Another good study habit whose importance cannot be stressed too strongly is that of consistent application. Even though the temptation to let a course "slide" for a week or two is sometimes irresistible, it is a pernicious habit and should not be allowed to develop. You will find that the practice of studying for each session of a course as it occurs throughout the week pays dividends in increased knowledge, self-confidence, and better grades. In all of your major subjects, make an effort to recognize the important points that are stressed, without getting lost in a mass of details.

Chapter 2

Some Fundamental
Concepts

Certain fundamental concepts are essential to all fields of chemistry. These may be considered tools of the trade of chemistry. Before entering into a detailed study of a particular field, its tools should be mastered.

Chemistry is the science which deals with the composition of substances and with the changes which they may undergo. It is also concerned with the properties of substances and with their energy relationships. All substances are forms of matter, and *matter* is anything that possesses weight and occupies space. Matter exists in three states: solid, liquid, and gaseous, depending on the temperature and pressure. The relationship between matter and energy is very close. *Energy* is defined as the ability to do work. It exists in many different forms, each of which may be converted into any of the other forms. Heat, light, motion, sound, and electricity are all familiar forms of energy. *Chemical energy* is the energy that is stored up in chemical substances, and is released during chemical changes. Sometimes these energy changes become the most important part of a chemical reaction; for example the combustion of fuel in the furnace to produce heat or the "burning" of foods in the body to produce heat and energy. It should be kept in mind that every chemical change is accompanied by a change in energy.

Physical and Chemical Properties

We usually recognize substances by their appearance, taste, odor, feel, and other characteristics which serve to identify them. These characteristics are called the properties of the substance and are

Nuclear?

divided into two classes: physical and chemical. *Physical properties* are concerned with substances as they exist in nature; the chemical properties of a substance are made manifest only when the substance undergoes a chemical change. Such characteristics as the physical state (solid, liquid or gaseous), crystalline form, odor, taste, color, luster, and solubility are common physical properties. The *chemical proper-ties* of a substance are characteristic of the manner in which they react with other substances, e.g., oxygen, water, acids, and bases.

Properties, then, are the signs by which we recognize substances. If we study the physical and chemical properties of two substances and find they are identical, then the substances must be the same; if the properties are different, we are concerned with two different sub-stances.

Physical and Chemical Change

Substances are constantly undergoing physical and chemical changes. *Physical changes* are changes in the condition or state of a substance; they do not result in the formation of new substances nor involve a change in composition. An example of a physical change would be the breaking of a bottle. Although there has been a marked change, the substance is still glass. No new substance has resulted, nor have we produced a change in the composition of the glass. If we file a piece of iron into small pieces, we observe a definite change; yet the particles are readily identified as iron for they have the same properties as the original piece.

If we expose the iron filings to moisture, however, the iron will soon be changed into rust. A magnet will no longer attract the particles

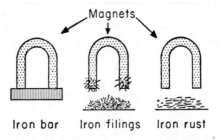

Figure 2. The failure of the magnet to attract the iron rust indicates that a chemical change has occurred.

(Fig. 2), the metallic luster is gone, the properties are different from those of the original substance; we therefore conclude that a new substance has been formed. When we heat a piece of wood in a test tube, we observe that dense fumes are formed and a black charred mass remains behind. The rusting of iron and the destruction of wood by heat are examples of chemical changes. We might then define *chemical changes* as those that result in the formation of new substances and involve changes in the composition of the substance.

Elements, Compounds, and Mixtures

All of the chemical substances we know may be divided into three classes: elements, compounds, and mixtures. *Elements* are considered as basic units of matter which cannot be decomposed by ordinary chemical methods. There are 102 of these elements and they are considered to be the building stones of all matter. Iron, oxygen, gold, neon, copper, and nitrogen are examples of elements.

By proper combination of these basic substances, we may prepare thousands of more complex substances. These substances are called *compounds* and are composed of two or more elements combined chemically and in definite proportions. If a compound is decomposed or broken down into its constituent elements, we can determine its composition. Water may be decomposed into its constituents, the elements hydrogen and oxygen, by passing an electric current through it. Iron rust, which is iron oxide, may be broken down into its constituent elements, iron and oxygen, by a suitable chemical procedure. It will be shown later that every chemical compound contains its constituent elements in definite proportions by weight. A given amount of water always contains a definite amount of hydrogen combined with a definite amount of oxygen. In this way, we can readily recognize any chemical compound if we know its composition.

The remaining class of substances is called *mixtures*. A mixture is made up of two or more substances that are not combined chemically and may be present in any proportion. The ingredients in a mixture can usually be separated by physical methods without changing the chemical identities of the individual substances that are present. Most of our natural and prepared foods are mixtures, as are many of the therapeutic agents used in medicine. Air is a very important mixture, consisting mainly of the gaseous elements oxygen and nitrogen.

The Metric System

In chemistry and many related scientific fields a system of measurement that differs from our ordinary system is employed. This is called the metric system and is used by the scientist in expressing units of weight, volume, and temperature. It is more readily mastered and convenient because it is based on a decimal system in which the divisions and multiples are in a ratio of tens. Considerable confusion would be avoided if the metric system was universally adopted. As a start in this direction many pharmaceutical manufacturers have adopted this system for their products, and the U.S. Army has recently installed the system for arms and ammunition.

The standard unit of length is called the *meter*, which was originally based on one ten-millionth of the distance from the equator to the north pole. The meter is equivalent to 39.37 inches. The *centimeter* is one-hundredth the length of a meter; the *millimeter* is one-thousandth of a meter or one-tenth of a centimeter. There are approximately 30 centimeters in a foot or about 2.5 centimeters in an inch.

These units of length are abbreviated: m. (meter), cm. (centimeter), and mm. (millimeter), and their relation to each other can be stated simply as follows: 1 m. = 100 cm. = 1000 mm.

The standard unit of weight is the *kilogram*, which is the weight of a block of platinum-iridium kept by the International Bureau of Weights and Measures. A kilogram weighs approximately 2.2 pounds. The *gram* is one-thousandth the weight of a kilogram and the milligram is one-thousandth the weight of a gram. These units are abbreviated as follows: kg. (kilogram), gm. (gram), and mg. (milligram). In modern vitamin therapy, quantities are often expressed in micrograms. A microgram is one-thousandth of a milligram and is abbreviated μg., often called a *gamma*. We may represent these relationships as follows: 1 kg. = 1000 gm.; 1 gm. = 1000 mg.; 1 mg. = 1000 μg.

The *liter* is the unit of volume; it is the volume occupied by a kilogram of pure water at 4° centigrade (the temperature at which a volume of water weighs the most). A liter is slightly more than a quart. A milliliter is one-thousandth of a liter and for all practical purposes is the same as a cubic centimeter. Ordinarily we say that a liter is equal to 1000 cubic centimeters. A *microliter*, sometimes called a *lambda* (λ), is one-thousandth of a milliliter. Modern micro methods often require microliter quantities for analysis. A fluid ounce is approximately 30 cubic centimeters; a teaspoon holds about 4 cubic centimeters. The units of volume are abbreviated as follows: l. (liter), ml. (milliliter), cc. (cubic centimeter), and μl. (microliter).

A comparison of the metric and English systems of measurement is shown in Figure 3. The units of the metric system may be represented in tabular form as follows:

UNITS OF LENGTH

Millimeter	=	0.001	meter
Centimeter	=	0.01	meter
Decimeter	=	0.1	meter
Meter	=	1.0	meter
Dekameter	=	10	meters
Hectometer	=	100	meters
Kilometer	=	1000	meters

UNITS OF WEIGHT

Microgram	=	0.001	milligram
Milligram	=	0.001	gram
Gram	=	1.0	gram
Kilogram	=	1000	grams

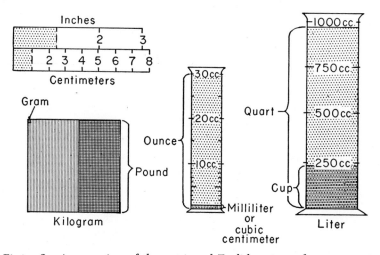

Figure 3. A comparison of the metric and English systems of measurement.

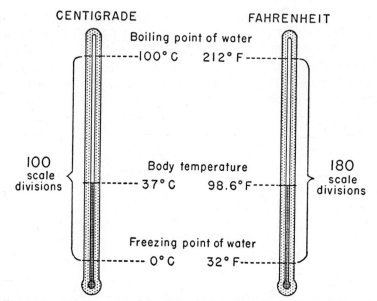

Figure 4. A comparison of the Fahrenheit and centigrade thermometers. It is apparent that 100 scale divisions centigrade equals 180 scale divisions Fahrenheit. Therefore, 1 scale division centigrade equals $\frac{9}{5}$ scale division Fahrenheit, and 1 scale division Fahrenheit equals $\frac{5}{9}$ scale division centigrade.

UNITS OF VOLUME

Microliter	=	0.001 milliliter
Milliliter	=	0.001 liter
Liter	=	1.0 liter

SOME APPROXIMATE EQUIVALENTS

1	inch	=	2.5 centimeters
1	foot	=	30 centimeters
1.1	yard	=	1 meter
15	grains	=	1 gram
1	avoir. ounce	=	30 grams
1	pound	=	450 grams
2.2	pounds	=	1 kilogram
1	fluid ounce	=	30 cubic centimeters
1	quart	=	950 cubic centimeters
1	teaspoon	=	4 cubic centimeters
1	tablespoon	=	15 cc. = $\frac{1}{2}$ fluidounce

We are accustomed to expressing temperature measurements on the common Fahrenheit scale. On this scale, the temperature at which water freezes is 32 degrees (32°), while water boils at 212° F. In scientific work, this system has been replaced by the simpler centigrade scale, which is based on the freezing and boiling points of water. The freezing point was taken as 0° C. and the boiling point as 100° C. A comparison of these two thermometers is shown in Figure 4.

A temperature on one scale may readily be converted to the corresponding temperature on the other scale. To convert degrees Fahrenheit to degrees centigrade: add 40, multiply by $\frac{5}{9}$, and subtract 40 from the result. As an example, let us convert 32° F. to degrees centigrade:

$$32° \text{ F.} + 40 = 72$$
$$72 \quad \times \quad \tfrac{5}{9} = \tfrac{360}{9} = 40$$
$$40 \quad - 40 = 0° \text{ C.}$$

To convert degrees centigrade to degrees Fahrenheit: add 40, multiply by $\frac{9}{5}$, and substract 40 from the result. For example, let us convert 100° C. to degrees Fahrenheit:

$$100° \text{ C.} + 40 = 140$$
$$140 \quad \times \quad \tfrac{9}{5} = \tfrac{1260}{5} = 252$$
$$252 \quad - 40 = 212° \text{ F.}$$

It is often more difficult to change a negative or below-zero temperature from one scale to another. For example in the conversion of —15° F. to degrees centigrade:

$$-15° \text{ F.} + 40 = +25 \text{ (algebraic sum)}$$
$$+25 \quad \times \quad \tfrac{5}{9} = \tfrac{125}{9} = +14$$
$$+14 \quad - 40 = -26° \text{ C. (algebraic sum)}$$

Other methods of conversion from one temperature scale to another may be used, although the one explained seems easier to remember. In both conversions, you add 40 to the original temperature, multiply by either $\frac{5}{9}$ or $\frac{9}{5}$ and subtract 40 from the result. If you choose a common point like the boiling point of water, 212° F. and 100° C., it can be seen that the Fahrenheit value is higher than the centigrade; therefore, you would have to use the largest factor $\frac{9}{5}$ to convert centigrade to Fahrenheit. Conversely, since the centigrade value is lower than the Fahrenheit, you would use the factor $\frac{5}{9}$ to convert Fahrenheit to centigrade.

Another method that is commonly used to convert readings on one scale to the other is as follows:

$$C = \frac{5}{9} \ (F \ - \ 32°)$$
$$F = \frac{9}{5} \ C + 32°$$

Review Questions

1. Name several instances in which electrical energy is converted into other forms of energy for use in the hospital.
2. List several of the physical properties that would be helpful in the identification of the following substances: iron, copper, ether, lead, charcoal, gasoline, and silver.
3. How do you distinguish between a physical and a chemical change?
4. Which of the following are physical changes and which are chemical changes?

Lighting a match	Chopping wood
Boiling water	Souring of milk
Making a cake	Frying of meat
Ripening of fruit	Breaking a plate

5. Give three examples of the use of uncombined elements in medicine.
6. Differentiate between compounds and mixtures.
7. A 3-inch bandage is equivalent in width to how many millimeters?
8. What is the weight in kilograms of a 10-pound plaster cast?
9. A bottle that contains 16 tablespoons of cough syrup contains _____ cc. or _____ ounces.
10. A micropipette holds 10μl. How many pipettes would be required to fill a teaspoon?
11. Room temperature is usually about 75° Fahrenheit. What would be the reading on the centigrade scale?
12. Dry ice has a temperature of −80° centigrade. This is equivalent to what temperature on the Fahrenheit thermometer?
13. "A good nurse is worth her weight in gold." If gold sells at $500 a pound and the nurse weighs 50 kg., how much is she worth? $_____.

Chapter 3

Atoms and Molecules

The early Greek philosophers were concerned with the limits into which matter could be subdivided. They reasoned that repeated division of matter would ultimately end in chemically indivisible particles to which they gave the name *atoms*. By the beginning of the nineteenth century, several chemical elements such as oxygen, hydrogen, gold, and copper had been discovered. The elements were established as basic substances of chemistry and it was found by experiment that, when elements combined to form compounds, a definite weight of each element always united with a definite weight of the other elements.

Dalton's Atomic Theory

In an attempt to explain the speculations and observations concerning atoms, elements, and compounds, John Dalton, an English scientist, proposed his atomic theory in 1803. His ideas were generally accepted and are known as the *atomic theory.* He began by assuming that all elements are composed of minute invisible particles called *atoms*. The atom may then be considered the smallest unit of an element, and since there are 102 different elements, it is reasonable to assume that there can be only 102 different atoms. Dalton stated further that all atoms of the same element had the same properties and the same weight, but that they differed from the atoms of all the other elements in these respects. In chemical changes, the atoms could combine to form small particles of compounds, or they could separate or change

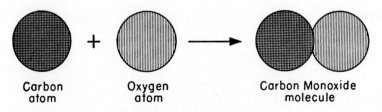

Carbon   Oxygen   Carbon Monoxide
atom   atom   molecule

Figure 5. The union of an atom of carbon with an atom of oxygen to form a molecule of carbon monoxide.

places in these compounds. When the atoms enter into chemical combination, the weight of the individual atoms does not change.

We may, therefore, regard an atom as the smallest particle of an element that can take part in a chemical change.

Atomic Weight

A single atom is so small that it would be impossible to weigh it accurately. While it has never been possible to weigh a single atom of each of the elements, it is possible by complex methods to obtain the weight of equal numbers (several million) of the different atoms. The 102 different atoms could then be arranged in order of their relative weights. Such a series would be useful if the *atomic weight* of each atom could be expressed as a numerical value. Oxygen was used as a standard reference element because it is the most abundant, and is one with which almost all the other elements will combine. An atom of oxygen was found to be approximately 16 times as heavy as the lightest atom, hydrogen, so its atomic weight was set at 16. The atomic weight of hydrogen then became 1.008. It was determined that an atom of nitrogen weighed $\frac{14}{16}$ as much as an atom of oxygen, giving it an atomic weight of 14. The sulfur atom was twice as heavy as the oxygen atom, therefore sulfur has an atomic weight of 32. A complete table of atomic weights will be found in the Appendix.

Molecules

The atomic theory states that in chemical changes the atoms can combine to form small particles of compounds. Each small particle of a compound contains a definite number of atoms. This means that

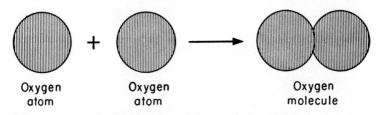

Oxygen   Oxygen   Oxygen
atom   atom   molecule

Figure 6.   The union of two oxygen atoms to form a molecule of oxygen. Like
most gases, oxygen is found in nature in this molecular form.

each unit particle of a compound must have the same number and
kinds of atoms as all the other unit particles. These small unit particles
of which every compound is composed are called *molecules*. The
molecule can be considered the indivisible unit for compounds, much
as the atom is the unit particle for elements.

The simplest compound would be one whose molecule contains one
atom of each of the two elements that unite to form the compound. An
example of such a simple compound is carbon monoxide (Fig. 5),
whose molecule is composed of 1 atom of carbon and 1 atom of
oxygen. Every molecule of water contains 2 atoms of hydrogen and
1 atom of oxygen.

The majority of molecules are composed of two or more different
atoms; however, some atoms of the same element are capable of
uniting with each other to form a molecule of that element. This is
particularly true of elements that are gases at room temperature (oxygen, hydrogen, nitrogen, and chlorine). Such gases always exist in
molecular form when in the free state, each molecule containing 2
atoms of the element. For example, a molecule of oxygen may be
represented as in Figure 6.

This combination of atoms to make molecules of gas is very important in chemical reactions in which a gas such as oxygen or hydrogen
is formed.

Molecular Weight

The molecular weight of a compound is the sum of the atomic
weights of all the atoms present in one molecule of the compound. A
molecule of carbon dioxide contains 1 atom of carbon and 2 atoms of
oxygen. Since the atomic weight of carbon is 12 and the atomic weight
of oxygen is 16, the molecular weight may be calculated as follows:

ELEMENT	ATOMIC WEIGHT
Carbon	12
Oxygen	16
Oxygen	16
Carbon dioxide	44 $=$ Molecular weight

A molecule of sulfuric acid contains 2 atoms of hydrogen, 1 atom of sulfur, and 4 atoms of oxygen. The atomic weight of hydrogen is 1.008, although for convenience in ordinary chemical calculations it is taken as 1.0. The molecular weight of sulfuric acid is 98 as shown by the calculation:

ELEMENT	ATOMIC WEIGHT
Hydrogen	1
Hydrogen	1
Sulfur	32
Oxygen	16
Oxygen	16
Oxygen	16
Oxygen	16
Sulfuric acid	98 $=$ Molecular weight

Each atom of hydrogen, carbon, sulfur, or oxygen in these compounds has a weight of its own and must be used in a calculation of the molecular weight each time it occurs in the compound.

If the molecular weight of a compound can be represented as the sum of the atomic weights of all the atoms in the molecule, then every compound must have a constant composition. A compound is always made up of definite proportions by weight of its constituent elements; this is known as the *law of definite proportions*. For example, specimens of water collected from any source always contain 2 parts by weight of hydrogen to 16 parts by weight of oxygen. If water is formed from a mixture of hydrogen and oxygen gas, the compound formed will always contain 2 parts of hydrogen to 16 parts of oxygen by weight, and any excess of hydrogen or oxygen gas will remain uncombined.

The atomic weight of an element or the molecular weight of a compound may be expressed in any units. If they are expressed in grams, we have the *gram atomic weight* of the element and the *gram molecu-*

lar weight of the compound. Therefore, the gram molecular weight is the sum of the gram atomic weights of the atoms in the molecules. Thus, sulfur dioxide has a gram molecular weight of 64; sulfuric acid, 98; and water, 18. Avogadro, an Italian physicist, stated that a gram molecular weight of any compound which exists as a gas contains the same number of molecules as a gram molecular weight of any other gaseous compound. Extensive study of this theory resulted in a chemical law that has practical application in expressing the concentration of solutions. For example, 64 gm. of sulfur dioxide contains the same number of molecules as 98 gm. of sulfuric acid or 18 gm. of water.

The Structure of the Atom

Atoms are made up of positive electrical units called *protons*, and negative electrical units called *electrons*. Any one atom contains the same number of electrons as it does protons. A third type of particle called the *neutron* is also present in the atom. The neutron is electrically neutral and possesses a mass approximately equal to that of a proton. It is very convenient to consider the neutron as a combination of a proton and an electron, although its structure is not that simple and its mass is not exactly equal to the sum of the masses of a proton and an electron.

Every atom consists of a *nucleus* surrounded by electrons which revolve about it at relatively great distances, much as the planets revolve about the sun. The nucleus is a small, compact mass made up of protons and neutrons. It is positively charged because it contains a number of free protons in excess of those combined with electrons in neutrons. Since atoms contain an equal number of electrons and protons, the number of electrons revolving around the nucleus must be exactly equal to the excess protons in the nucleus. The nitrogen atom, for example, has 7 electrons revolving around its nucleus; therefore, it must have 7 uncombined protons (positive charges) in the nucleus.

The number of revolving or *"planetary" electrons* in an atom is equal to the *atomic number* of the atom. The excess positive charges (protons) in the nucleus are also equal to the atomic number. If we are told that the atomic number of oxygen is 8, we can conclude that the oxygen atom has 8 planetary electrons and 8 uncombined protons in the nucleus.

The mass of an atom consists almost entirely of the heavy protons

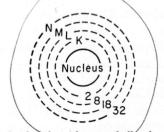

Figure 7.   The first four electron shells of an atom.

and neutrons in the nucleus. Electrons possess a negligible mass, $\frac{1}{1837}$ that of a proton, and may be disregarded in a consideration of the weight of an atom. Each proton or neutron contributes one unit to the weight of the atom. The *atomic weight* of an atom is thus equal to the total number of protons and neutrons in the nucleus.

The planetary electrons revolve in concentric rings or shells about the nucleus in a fashion similar to that in which planets revolve in definite orbits around the sun. Only 2 electrons can occupy the shell or orbit closest to the nucleus. The next nearest shell can hold up to 8 electrons. As many as 18 electrons can occupy the third orbit. The electron shells of an atom are designated as K, L, M, N, and so on as they move away from the nucleus. Figure 7 illustrates the maximum number of electrons that can exist in the four shells closest to the nucleus.

The lightest atom, the hydrogen atom, has a nucleus of 1 proton with 1 planetary electron rotating about it in the first orbit. In Figure 8 the nucleus is represented as a small circle, containing protons ($+$) and neutrons ($\pm$). The ($+$) represents the positively charged protons, while the ($\pm$) represents the union of a proton and an electron within the nucleus. Planetary electrons are shown as shaded circles and the orbit or shell in which they revolve as a large circle. The atomic number and atomic weight of hydrogen may readily be determined from the diagram. Since there is 1 planetary electron rotating about the nucleus, the atomic number is 1; the atomic weight is also 1 because there is 1 proton in the nucleus.

At present it is not possible to represent the true picture of the structure of an atom. A three-dimensional scheme in which the electron orbits are drawn in different planes comes closer to an accurate structure than those represented in Figure 8. Since diagrams of the larger atoms would appear like a hopelessly tangled ball of yarn if represented in three-dimensions, the simplified version will be used.

Helium, the second lightest element, has 2 protons and 2 neutrons in its nucleus, with 2 planetary electrons revolving in the first orbit. These two electrons complete this shell. By inspection of Figure 8, we can see that helium has an atomic number of 2 and an atomic weight of 4 (2 protons + 2 neutrons).

Carbon is an example of an element whose planetary electrons rotate in the first and second orbits. Its nucleus contains 6 protons. Six planetary electrons rotate around the nucleus. Since the first orbit can hold only 2 electrons, the other 4 must revolve in a new orbit at a greater distance from the nucleus. A glance at the diagram reveals an atomic number of 6 and an atomic weight of 12 for carbon.

A more complicated atom such as sodium is also represented in Figure 8. The nucleus consists of 11 protons and 12 neutrons with 11

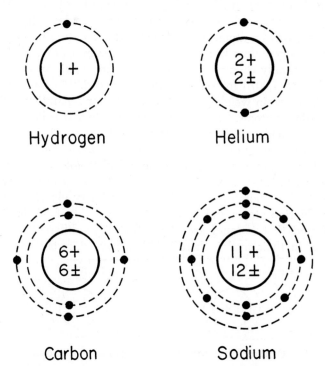

Figure 8. The structure of the atoms of a few common elements.

planetary electrons rotating about it. As the first two shells are completely filled by 10 electrons, the remaining electron occupies the third orbit, which is still farther from the nucleus. The atomic number of sodium is 11, the atomic weight is 23. Atoms of elements with higher atomic weights can be illustrated in a similar fashion, but become more and more difficult to represent as they approach nobelium which has an atomic weight of 253 and an atomic number of 102.

Isotopes

From inspection of the table of atomic weights in the Appendix, we can see that few elements have atomic weights that can be expressed in whole numbers. It is known that atoms of the same element show variations in their mass, because they have different numbers of neutrons in their nucleus. These atoms of different weights are called isotopes. The actual atomic weight of an element represents the average weight of its atoms. For example, there are two forms of hydrogen atoms, one heavier than the other but occurring less often than the ordinary hydrogen atom. An ordinary hydrogen atom has 1 proton, a heavy hydrogen atom has 1 proton and 1 neutron (Fig. 9). The mixture in naturally occurring hydrogen has an atomic weight of 1.008 compared to 1.0078 for the lighter form and 2.0143 for the heavier. This difference in weight is used as a basis for separation of isotopes from ordinary atoms. The heavy hydrogen atom is called *deuterium*, and water made of heavy hydrogen and oxygen is called "heavy water." All samples of water contain a small amount of heavy water.

Another example is heavy chlorine, which has 2 extra neutrons in its nucleus (Fig. 10). The chlorine gas that is used in water purification or in the laboratory is a mixture of ordinary chlorine atoms and heavy chlorine atoms and has an atomic weight of 35.46. It should be stressed that *isotopes* are atoms that have different numbers of neutrons in their nuclei, therefore they have different weights than

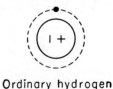

Ordinary hydrogen   Heavy hydrogen

Figure 9.   The atomic structure of two isotopes of hydrogen.

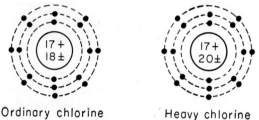

Ordinary chlorine   Heavy chlorine

Figure 10.   The atomic structure of two isotopes of chlorine.

ordinary atoms. However, these isotopes have the same number of protons and electrons and behave alike chemically. All of the 102 elements have two or more isotopes, and about 300 stable isotopes have been found occurring in natural mixtures similar to hydrogen and chlorine.

Radioactive Elements

After the discovery of x-rays by Röntgen in 1895, Becquerel investigated several fluorescent substances as possible sources of similar penetrating rays. He found that all uranium compounds gave off penetrating rays, which he called Becquerel rays. The production of radiation from uranium compounds was called radioactivity.

Madame Curie (Fig. 11) and her husband Pierre investigated this new property of radioactivity and tested all other known elements for radioactive properties. They found that thorium was a radioactive element and discovered two new radioactive elements, polonium and radium. The radioactivity of radium was two to three million times that of uranium.

Rutherford studied the radiations given off by radium by placing some of the radioactive material in the bottom of a thick lead well. The lead shielded out stray radiations and allowed him to focus the rays on a photographic plate. Under the influence of a magnetic field, the rays were deflected in such a way that three types of radiations were observed (Fig. 12). Rutherford named the rays alpha, beta, and gamma, and found they were given off by all the radioactive elements he studied.

1. Alpha rays, which consist of alpha particles, are positively charged helium atoms or the nucleus of the helium atom with 2 positive charges.

Figure 11. Marie Sklodowska was born in Poland in 1867. Her father, a professor of physics and mathematics in Warsaw, greatly influenced her early education. On moving to Paris she met and married Pierre Curie, then a graduate student at the University. Together they isolated polonium and later radium from pitchblende. For their work on radioactivity and their discovery of radium they shared in the 1903 Nobel Prize in Physics. After the death of her husband, in 1906, Mme. Curie succeeded him as professor of physics at the University of Paris.

2. Beta rays are made up of beta particles, which are streams of electrons. They are more penetrating than alpha rays, and are of an opposite electrical charge.

3. Gamma rays are similar to x-rays but are more penetrating. They do not consist of individual particles but are electromagnetic waves.

Another important characteristic of radioactive elements is the instability of their nuclei. The nucleus is apparently not satisfied with its proportion of protons and neutrons and is continually giving off alpha and beta particles until a stable arrangement is achieved. For example, a radium atom is successively changed into nine other elements, with a total loss of five alpha particles and four beta particles before it finally reaches a stable arrangement as an isotope of lead with an atomic weight of 206. Since radioactive elements are constantly undergoing disintegration or natural decay, it is reasonable to assume that eventually all the radioactivity of a given element will be dissipated. By counting the number of alpha particles emitted per second from a sample of radium containing a known number of radium atoms, it has been calculated that half of the radium atoms will have decayed in about 1590 years. The time necessary for half the weight of a sample of radioactive element to decay or disintegrate is called the *half-life* of that element. Using radium as an example again, at the end of 1590 years, one half of an original sample would remain; at the end of another 1590 years, one fourth of the original sample would be left; and at the end of another 1590 years, one eighth of the sample would remain. The half-life of radioactive elements varies considerably. Uranium has a half-life of approximately four and a half billion years, while a form of radium called radium C, has a half-life of 0.0001 second. The half-life of most radioactive elements falls somewhere in between these two extremes.

As elements such as uranium, thorium, and radium that possess natural radioactivity disintegrate, there is an accompanying transmutation or transformation into other radioactive elements or isotopes. Each new radioactive isotope that is formed in this manner has its characteristic half-life and the property of disintegrating into another different radioactive isotope. The transmutation process stops only

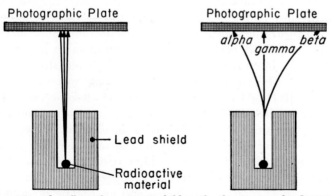

Figure 12.   The effect of a magnetic field on the three types of radiations given off by radioactive material. In the right-hand illustration the magnetic field is perpendicular to the plane of the paper.

Figure 13. Cyclotron installed at the University of Rochester. The upper and lower cylindrical objects are the magnetic poles, while the center part contains the semicircular metal electrodes. (Wide World Photo.)

when a stable isotope is formed, for example, when lead is formed from radium.

The natural transmutation of elements suggested the possibility of artificial transmutation or the conversion of one element into another by the chemist. The conversion of base metals into noble metals, i.e., lead into gold, had been a subject of considerable interest to the alchemist. As information accumulated on atomic structure it was realized that artificial transmutation of elements was a distinct possibility. To effect the transmutation of elements it is necessary to alter the charge on the nucleus, that is, to bring about a rearrangement of protons and neutrons in the nucleus of an element. Rutherford conceived the idea of bombarding the nucleus of an element with alpha particles from radium traveling at high velocities. He succeeded in knocking protons out of the nucleus of nitrogen atoms with the resultant formation of atoms of hydrogen and an isotope of oxygen. His experiments in 1919 were the first in which an element was transformed into another element artifically by the bombardment of the nucleus with atomic particles. Since 1919, other transmutations have been studied, and several radioactive isotopes have been produced by nuclear bombardment. The subatomic particles that were used to bombard the elements were (1) alpha particles, (2) protons, (3) electrons, (4) neutrons, and (5) deuterons (the nuclei of deuterium or heavy hydrogen). The common difficulty in the use of these subatomic particles for the production of radioactive isotopes was that of finding a means of imparting high velocity to the particles. There were many disadvantages in depending on natural radioactive elements as a source of alpha particles, neutrons, and others. For this reason, several instruments for the acceleration of subatomic particles were developed. Probably the most common particle accelerator is the cyclotron, which consists of a huge electromagnet whose poles inclose hollow semicircular metal electrodes (Fig. 13), in which charged particles are accelerated until they reach a velocity of several thousand miles a second. A combination of electrical and magnetic forces causes the charged particles to move in a circular path at gradually increasing speeds until they are finally directed at a target on the periphery of the electrodes containing atoms whose nucleus is to be bombarded (Fig. 14). In addition to the cyclotron, the betatron, synchroton and

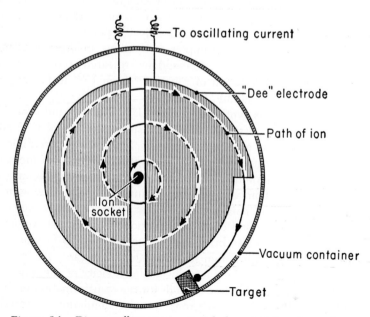

To oscillating current

"Dee" electrode

Path of ion

Ion socket

Vacuum container

Target

Figure 14.   Diagram illustrating essential characteristics of a cyclotron.

cosmotron, which are more powerful particle accelerators, have been built.

When neutrons were used in transmutation experiments it was observed that an element with a higher atomic weight than that of the original material often resulted. This suggested the formation of elements with higher atomic weights and atomic numbers than uranium. When the uranium isotope with an atomic weight of 238, designated U^{238}, was subjected to bombardment by slow-moving neutrons, two new elements were produced. The first, neptunium, atomic number 93, has a half-life of 2.3 days and is rapidly converted into plutonium with an atomic number of 94. Another isotope of uranium, U^{235}, was found to undergo splitting or fission into smaller atomic weight fragments when bombarded with neutrons. Apparently, 1 atom of U^{235} splits into two unequal fragments whose nuclei have atomic numbers between 30 and 60. The fission is accompanied by the release of several neutrons and a large amount of energy. The neutrons that are released strike other U^{235} atoms, causing more nuclear fission with a release of more neutrons and more energy, and thus start a chain reaction. If this fission process is not controlled an explosion results. This chain reaction fission process of the U^{235} isotope was the basis for the first atomic bomb. Since natural uranium contains 99.3 per cent of the U^{238} isotope and only 0.7 per cent of the U^{235} isotope, there is no danger of samples of uranium undergoing atomic explosions. During the war, tremendous research projects were directed toward the separation of pure U^{235} from U^{238} to hasten the construction of the first atomic bomb.

When plutonium was synthesized from U^{238}, it was found that this isotope also undergoes fission in a manner similar to that of U^{235} and is capable of producing an atomic explosion. Since it was very difficult and expensive to produce pure U^{235}, attempts were made to increase the production of plutonium. Under the pressure of wartime, an apparatus for the mass bombardment of uranium with slow-moving neutrons was constructed. This nuclear reactor was commonly called a *pile* because of the method of its construction (Fig. 15). It consisted of a huge cube of graphite bricks piled in a honeycomb fashion and interlaced with slugs of uranium sealed in aluminum cans. The graphite acted as a moderator since it reduced the velocity of the neutrons from U^{235} fission to a value low enough for the transformation of U^{238} into plutonium. To prevent neutrons from accumulating so rapidly that an explosion would result, rods of cadmium were inserted in slots in the pile. Cadmium is a material that absorbs neutrons and thus the rods acted as control rods to regulate the flow of neutrons through the pile to produce a maximum amount of plutonium with a minimum danger of explosion. After the uranium has been bombarded by neutrons in the pile the resulting plutonium is separated from the fission products and any unchanged uranium by a chemical process. The second atomic bomb used in Japan was said to be a plutonium bomb.

While working on the atomic bomb project with the cyclotron, Seaborg and his co-workers discovered two new elements. These were produced by the bombardment of uranium, U^{238}, and plutonium with high speed alpha particles. Elements 95 and 96 were named *americium* and *curium* respectively. Later, Seaborg announced the discovery of elements 97 and 98. In naming the new elements he continued the pattern followed for americium and curium by calling element 97 *berkelium* and element 98 *californium*. More recently, these investigators have reported the production of three new elements. Element 99 was named *einsteinium* for Einstein, element 100 *fermium* for Fermi, and element 101 *mendelevium* for Mendeleev. Element 102 has very recently been discovered at the Nobel Institute of Physics, and has been named *nobelium* after its birthplace.

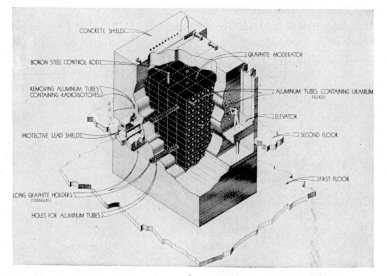

Figure 15. A cut away view of a nuclear reactor, more commonly known as a pile. (Isotopes Division, U. S. Atomic Energy Commission.)

Applications of Nuclear Energy

Atomic Power Plants

The enormous quantities of energy generated during the operation of a nuclear reactor or pile suggest its use as a source of power. Considerable research effort was required to develop new alloys and construction material capable of withstanding the high temperatures and providing protection from the intense radioactivity. In July 1955, the first atomic electric power generator, capable of supplying 10,000 kilowatts of power for public use, was placed in operation near Schenectady, N. Y. Since then, atomic power plants have been constructed in France, at Calder Hall, England, and in other locations in the United States.

Smaller power plants are already used to propel submarines, and are also being developed for aircraft and ocean-going vessels. Miniature power packs, or atomic batteries, have been produced and atomic powered flashlights are available commercially.

The Production of Radioisotopes

Even more important than the production of atomic power is the synthesis of many new radioactive isotopes by the neutrons in the pile. Elements other than uranium are often placed in the pile to be converted into useful radioactive isotopes. In fact, over four hundred radioactive isotopes have been produced by the atomic pile, the cyclotron and related apparatus. The following list includes some of the common and important artificially produced radioactive elements used in chemical, biological, and medical research.

ELEMENT	NAME	HALF-LIFE
H^3	Tritium	12.5 years
C^{14}	Carbon	5740 years
Ca^{45}	Calcium	180 days
Na^{24}	Sodium	14.9 hours
P^{32}	Phosphorus	14.3 days
S^{35}	Sulfur	87.1 days
Fe^{59}	Iron	46.3 days
Co^{60}	Cobalt	5.2 years
Br^{82}	Bromine	36 hours
I^{131}	Iodine	8 days
Au^{198}	Gold	2.7 days

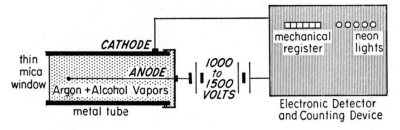

Figure 16. Diagram of Geiger tube in a typical Geiger-Müller counter circuit.

One of the most widely used devices for measurement of radiations from radioisotopes is the Geiger-Müller counter (Fig. 16). This instrument consists of a metal tube closed at one end with a thin mica window and filled with an ionizable gas, such as argon and alcohol vapors. As the tube is brought near a radioisotope, radiations enter the window, ionize the gas and cause a flow of electrons to move to the anode. This small surge of current is amplified and passes into the detector circuit causing a flash of light in a neon tube and a unit movement of a mechanical register.

Becquerel discovered radioactivity by its effect on photographic plates. It is now common practice to protect laboratory personnel by examination of frequently changed *film badges* containing dental x-ray film. The degree of darkening of the film is a measure of the total amount of radiation to which the badge wearer has been subjected in a given period.

Radioisotopes in Biological Research and Medicine

Since radioactive or stable isotopes of an element have the same chemical properties, biological systems in plants and animals treat the isotope in the same manner as the naturally occurring element. For example, the body is unable to distinguish between radioactive C^{14} and stable C^{12} thus allowing investigators to add tracer amounts of C^{14} to compounds to study the process of digestion, absorption and metabolism. By substituting a small amount of $C^{14}O_2$ for the natural $C^{12}O_2$ used in the process of photosynthesis, the resulting sugars and starch contain radioactive carbon. By tracing the C^{14} through the complex reactions of photosynthesis, considerable new information has been gained.

Radioactive sodium, Na^{24}, may be used to illustrate the use of a tracer element in medical research and diagnosis. The radioactive sodium is incorporated into the compound, sodium chloride, which is introduced into the blood stream of an animal or patient. Radiations from the isotope are then measured in different locations in the circulatory system. The extent of circulation in a crushed arm or leg in a patient can be used to determine whether the member should be amputated or whether the arm or leg can be saved. The short half-life of radioactive sodium permits its use in the human body, which may be damaged by the radiations released from a longer-lived isotope such as radium. A similar example of the use of an isotope in research, diagnosis, and treatment involves radioactive iodine, I^{131} (Fig. 17). Since it is known that the thyroid gland utilizes most of the iodine of the body, the rate of iodine uptake by the thyroid may be determined by the ingestion of small amounts of I^{131}. A normal individual exhibits a different rate from patients with thyroid disease. In hyperthyroidism, treatment with larger doses of I^{131} will effectively reduce the size of the thyroid gland by irradiation of thyroid tissue. Kidney function in

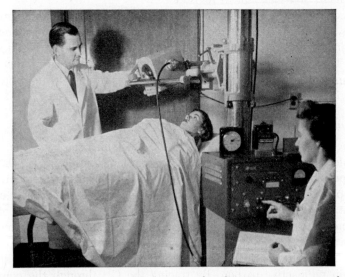

Figure 17. An illustration of the use of radioactive isotopes in therapy. (Courtesy of Dr. Titus Evans, Radiation Research Laboratory, State University of Iowa.)

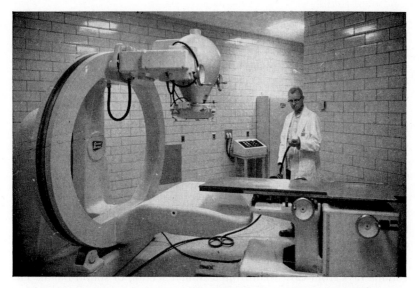

Figure 18.   A "cobalt bomb" installation for radiation therapy.

patients may be studied with Diodrast tagged with I^{131}. When diiodo-
fluorescein containing I^{131} is injected into a patient suspected of having
a brain tumor, the radioactive material will concentrate in the tumor,
if present, and aid the surgeon in its removal.

Radioactive phosphorus, P^{32}, has been used to study the formation
and deposition of bone and teeth. Since this isotope is taken up more
rapidly by developing red blood cells than mature cells, it is used to
treat polycythemia vera, a blood disorder involving an over-production
of red blood cells. The isotope has also been used to help locate breast
cancers and brain tumors. A radioisotope of sulfur, S^{35}, has been
incorporated into proteins and used to study the turnover rate of
plasma proteins and various aspects of protein metabolism in the
body. The study of the production of red blood cells and hemoglobin
in anemias has benefited from the application of radioactive iron, Fe^{59}.
Acetylsalicylic acid or aspirin has been tagged with C^{14} to study its
hydrolysis, absorption, and metabolism in the body.

When it was discovered that the radiations given off by the natural
radioactive element, radium, destroyed cancerous tissue more rapidly
than normal tissue, a new field of cancer therapy was initiated. In

recent years it has been found that an isotope of cobalt, Co^{60}, has many advantages over radium or x-ray as a source of radiation in cancer treatment. The cobalt metal can be fabricated in any shape and made intensely radioactive in a high neutron density nuclear reactor. It is much cheaper than radium and can be produced in quantities far beyond the total purified radium that exists in the world. The large applicators used in hospitals are called "cobalt bombs" and are capable of more effective treatment of deep-seated cancerous tissue (Fig. 18).

Radioisotopes in Industry

Since about 1947, the application of radioisotopes in industry has increased rapidly. The petroleum industry uses radioactive antimony to mark the boundary between various grades of oil and gasoline in the pipeline system used to transport petroleum products. In metallurgy flaws in metal castings are detected by the absorption of fewer gamma rays from Co^{60} than from a similar section of sound metal. The wear of piston rings and moving metal parts in a car's engine has been determined by irradiation of the metal and determination of the radioactivity in the crankcase oil. Similar studies have determined the wear of rubber tires, floor tiles and waxes. Thickness gauges for the measurement and control of the thickness of paper, plastic, and rubber sheets or films during manufacture employ beta emitting isotopes. By placing the isotope on one side of a moving film and a suitable detector and meter on the other side, the thickness can be measured and also controlled by electronic regulation of the position of the rollers. In the food industry, experiments on irradiation have indicated the superior keeping properties of food products exposed to radioactive rays. The polyethylene ware used in hospitals and laboratories retains its shape and usefulness at considerably higher temperatures after irradiation than before.

Just recently, the world's first private nuclear reactor for industrial research was placed in operation at the Armour Research Foundation in Chicago.

Review Questions

1. State the main assumptions of the atomic theory.
2. Why was it necessary to obtain relative weights of atoms of different elements when atomic weights were first determined?

3. What element is used as a standard reference element in calculating atomic weights? Why?
4. How would you explain the difference between an atom and a molecule?
5. A molecule of carbon monoxide consists of 1 atom of carbon and 1 atom of oxygen. What is the molecular weight of carbon monoxide?
6. Name three elements that exist as gases at room temperature.
7. Why can we speak of either an atom or a molecule of hydrogen, but only of an atom of carbon?
8. Carbonic acid molecules are made up of 2 hydrogen atoms, 1 carbon atom and 3 oxygen atoms. Calculate the molecular weight of carbonic acid.
9. Define electron, proton, and neutron.
10. How could you determine the atomic number and the atomic weight of an atom from a diagram of its atomic structure?
11. The nucleus of the sulfur atom contains 16 protons and 16 neutrons. How many planetary electrons revolve about the nucleus? What would be the atomic number of sulfur? The atomic weight?
12. Nitrogen has an atomic number of 7 and an atomic weight of 14. Draw a diagram of the nitrogen atom.
13. What is the essential difference between an isotope and an ordinary atom?
14. Name and describe the three types of rays given off by all radioactive elements.
15. What are radioactive isotopes? Can they be made artificially? Explain.
16. What is meant by the half-life of a radioactive element? Give an example.
17. Name the eight new elements that resulted from recent research in nuclear fission.
18. Describe a nuclear reactor or atomic pile. What part has the reactor or pile played in advancing medical research?
19. Name two radioactive isotopes that are used in the treatment of cancer and briefly describe their applications.
20. Describe the operation of a Geiger-Müller counter.
21. Give three examples of the use of radioactive isotopes in medicine.

Chapter 4

Valence and
Chemical Equations

Dalton's atomic theory described chemical reactions and the formation of compounds as the combination of atoms. As more information concerning the nature of the atom became available, chemists sought a solution to the fundamental question of why elements combine with each other. The simplest explanation for compound formation concerns the chemical affinity of one atom for another. The degree of affinity was expressed as the combining power of the atom, and, finally, as its *valence*.

Symbols

Since chemical compounds are usually represented by chemical formulas and the formulas are composed of symbols for the elements it would be helpful to consider symbols and formulas before studying valence. To avoid lengthy and awkward terminology the chemist has devised a system of symbols to represent chemical elements. Some elements are represented by the first letter of the name; thus C stands for carbon, O for oxygen, N for nitrogen, and H for hydrogen. Since the names of several elements have the same first letter we sometimes add another prominent letter in the name to distinguish them, as Ba for barium, Ca for calcium, Br for bromine, and Cl for chlorine. Some elements were known in ancient times and had Latin names given to them. The symbols for these elements are taken from the Latin instead of the English name. Ferrum is the Latin name for iron, and the symbol is Fe; mercury is represented by the symbol Hg from the Latin name, hydrargyrum.

The symbols for some of the important elements are given in the following table. When the symbol is derived from the Latin name of the element, the Latin name is given in parentheses:

ELEMENT	SYMBOL	ELEMENT	SYMBOL
Aluminum	Al	Magnesium	Mg
Barium	Ba	Mercury (hydrargyrum)	Hg
Bromine	Br	Nitrogen	N
Calcium	Ca	Oxygen	O
Carbon	C	Phosphorus	P
Chlorine	Cl	Platinum	Pt
Copper (cuprum)	Cu	Potassium (kalium)	K
Hydrogen	H	Silver (argentum)	Ag
Iodine	I	Sodium (natrium)	Na
Iron (ferrum)	Fe	Sulfur	S
Lead (plumbum)	Pb	Zinc	Zn

For our purposes, it is not necessary to study each of the 102 elements, since many of them are quite uncommon. The common elements, with many of their chemical and physiological properties, are listed in two tables in the Appendix.

These symbols or abbreviations for the elements are more accurately called *atomic symbols* in that they stand for one atom of an element. In chemical reactions, they are often used to designate an atomic weight of an element. When expressed in grams, the symbol O, for example, means a gram atomic weight of oxygen, or 16 gm. In this way, N stands for 1 atom of nitrogen, 1 atomic weight, or 14 gm. of nitrogen. To indicate more than one atom the proper numeral is placed before the symbol; thus 5N represents 5 atoms of nitrogen, 5 gram atomic weights, or $5 \times 14 = 70$ gm. of nitrogen.

Formulas

A *formula* expresses in symbols the composition of a molecule of a substance. Since molecules are composed of atoms combined in definite proportions, we can represent a molecule by a combination of the symbols of the atoms. A molecule of common salt is composed of 1 atom of sodium and 1 atom of chlorine, and can be represented by combining the symbols for these elements into the formula NaCl. Where there is more than one atom of the same kind in the molecule, we do not repeat the symbol but indicate the number as a *subscript to the symbol* for the element. For example, the formula for water is written H_2O, meaning that 1 molecule of water contains 2 atoms of hydrogen and 1 atom of oxygen. The small subscript 2 which follows the H indicates that 2 atoms are present in the molecule. A molecule of carbonic acid consists of 2 atoms of hydrogen, 1 atom of carbon and 3 atoms of oxygen. Its formula may be written as follows:

$$\underbrace{H + H}_{H_2} + \underbrace{C}_{C} + \underbrace{O + O + O}_{O_3}$$

$$[H_2CO_3]$$

The formula H_2CO_3 represents 1 molecule, 1 molecular weight, or 1 gram molecular weight of carbonic acid. The latter value equals the sum of the gram atomic weights of the atoms in the molecule, or 2 gram atomic weights of hydrogen plus 1 gram atomic weight of carbon plus 3 gram atomic weights of oxygen. Sodium sulfate is composed of 2 atoms of sodium, 1 atom of sulfur, and 4 atoms of oxygen; the formula may be illustrated as shown:

$$\underbrace{Na + Na}_{Na_2} + \underbrace{S}_{S} + \underbrace{O + O + O + O}_{O_4}$$

$$[Na_2SO_4]$$

Again observe that the subscript numbers are written after the atomic symbols to which they belong. As we have already seen, the atoms of most gases do not exist by themselves but unite to form a molecule of the gas. The molecule of hydrogen is written H_2, of nitrogen N_2, and of oxygen O_2.

To designate more than one molecule of a substance, we place the appropriate number in front of the formula. The term $3NaCl$ represents 3 molecules of sodium chloride, $2O_2$ represents 2 molecules of oxygen gas, and $4Na_2SO_4$ represents 4 molecules of sodium sulfate. To avoid confusion of the subscript numbers and the numbers written in front of the formulas, it would be wise, at first, to write the full meaning of the different terms. For example, $3H_2CO_3$ would read 3 molecules of carbonic acid, each molecule consisting of 2 atoms of hydrogen, 1 atom of carbon and 3 atoms of oxygen.

Electrovalence

If sodium atoms and chlorine atoms are allowed to react with each other, sodium chloride (common salt) is formed. This compound results from the transfer of an electron from the outer orbit of the sodium atom to the outer orbit of the chlorine atom with the resultant production of sodium and chloride ions. Sodium and other metallic atoms possess the property of giving up electrons from their outer electron orbits, whereas the non-metallic atoms such as chlorine have a tendency to accept extra electrons in their outer orbits. The loss of an electron would result in an atom whose charges were not balanced. In this case, there would be one extra proton in the nucleus not balanced by an electron and the atom would have one positive electrical charge. If an atom gained an electron it would have one negative electrical charge since there would be an electron in the outer orbit not balanced by a proton in the nucleus. These electrically charged atoms are called *ions*. The sodium ions and chloride ions formed by this electron transfer, having opposite electrical charges, attract each other to form the ionic compound sodium chloride as shown in Figure 19.

Another compound that is formed by electron transfer is magnesium sulfide, which is composed of the two elements, magnesium and sulfur. In this instance the magnesium atom transfers 2 electrons to the sulfur atom to form magnesium and sulfide ions which attract each other to form the ionic compound magnesium sulfide. This reaction is represented in Figure 19.

Using chemical symbols, one can readily distinguish between atoms and ions of the same element. Atoms of elements in the free or uncombined state are represented by the symbol alone, as metallic sodium, Na; metallic magnesium, Mg; and free sulfur, S. The ions or combined atoms are represented by the symbols with the positive or negative electrical charges added at the upper right of the symbol (as Na^+, Mg^{++} and S^{--}). Sodium chloride and magnesium sulfide are examples of ionic compounds; they consist of oppositely charged pairs of ions.

The electrical charge carried by an ion represents its valence or

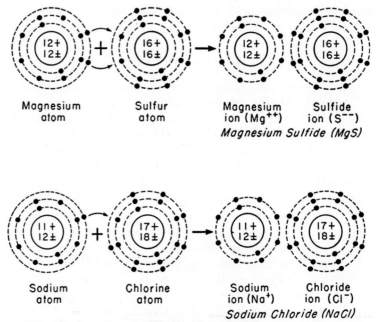

Figure 19. The formation of inorganic salts commonly occurs by the process of electron transfer.

combining capacity. The valence resulting from electron transfers is called *electrovalence* or *ionic valence*. It can readily be seen that the valence is equal to the number of electrons gained or lost by an atom when it is converted into an ion.

Covalence

Ionic compounds, in which the atoms are attracted to each other by electrical forces, are represented by inorganic acids, bases, and salts. Atoms can also combine to form compounds in other ways. For example, it is known that hydrogen atoms and oxygen atoms as well as other gaseous atoms combine in pairs to form molecules of a particular gas. Hydrogen gas consists of molecules of hydrogen which contain 2 hydrogen atoms held together by the force of a shared pair of electrons as shown in Figure 20.

Oxygen, chlorine, bromine, and other gaseous elements show a similar behavior. For example, chlorine atoms have 7 electrons in the outer shell. Two of these atoms are held together by the force of a shared pair of electrons which stabilize the molecule by furnishing 8 electrons in the outer shell of each atom (Fig. 20). When oxygen atoms form oxygen molecules, they are held together by the force of 2 shared pairs of electrons. This is necessary since there are only 6 electrons in the outer shell of the oxygen atoms, requiring 2 shared pairs to furnish 8 electrons for the outer shell of each atom. The process of joining atoms to form molecules by the sharing of electrons is called covalence. The combining number or valence in this type of combination is equal to the number of pairs of shared electrons involved.

A common covalent compound is water in which 1 oxygen atom is joined by 2 hydrogen atoms by the force of shared pairs of electrons as shown in Figure 21. This type of linkage is very important in organic chemistry where compounds of carbon are encountered. In the class of substances called hydrocarbons, carbon atoms are joined to hydrogen by the process of covalence. The carbon atom has 4 electrons in its outer shell and will combine with 4 hydrogen atoms forming 4 pairs of shared electrons.

Many of the compounds used by the chemist are neither completely electrovalent nor completely covalent compounds. The above ex-

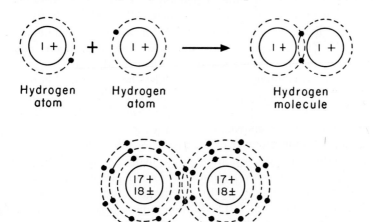

Hydrogen atom   Hydrogen atom   Hydrogen molecule

Chlorine Molecule

Figure 20. The formation of hydrogen and chlorine molecules illustrates the sharing of electrons, or covalence.

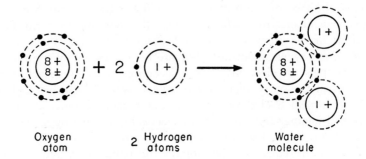

Oxygen   2 Hydrogen   Water
atom   atoms   molecule

Figure 21.   The water molecule composed of one oxygen atom and two hydrogen
atoms joined by the process of covalence.

amples were presented to illustrate the different types of linkage that
are involved in the formation of compounds.

Valence Number

In the theoretical consideration of valence, based on the electron
structure of the atoms and discussed in the foregoing paragraphs, it
was learned that atoms could combine with each other to form
molecules by the loss or gain of planetary electrons (electrovalence or
ionic valence) or by the sharing of pairs of planetary electrons (covalence). Since compounds are often formed by a combination of
valence factors, it may aid in the understanding of valence to consider
the valence number from a simple practical standpoint.

When atoms combine to form molecules they unite in different proportions in different compounds. The property which an atom has of
combining with other atoms is called its *valence*. Since hydrogen is
the lightest element known, the other elements are often compared
with it. The holding power of hydrogen for other atoms is 1 or, more
simply stated, the valence number of hydrogen is 1. One atom of
hydrogen combines with 1 atom of chlorine. The chlorine atom, and
any other atom that unites with a hydrogen atom in a 1:1 ratio, also
has a valence number of 1. The barium atom is able to hold 2 chlorine
atoms in combination, thus it has a valence number of 2. Aluminum
unites with 3 chlorine atoms, giving it a holding power three times
that of hydrogen, therefore its valence number is 3. Carbon tetrachloride is a compound in which 4 chlorine atoms are held in com-

bination with 1 carbon atom, hence the valence number of carbon is 4. The formulas of these compounds may be used to illustrate valence as follows:

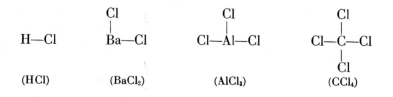

| H—Cl | Ba—Cl | Cl—Al—Cl | Cl—C—Cl |

(HCl)   (BaCl₂)   (AlCl₃)   (CCl₄)

Each bond represents a holding power, or valence, of 1. In the ordinary empirical formulas given in parentheses, the number of chlorine atoms that combine with H, Ba, Al, and C is given by the subscript following the Cl.

The elements are usually divided into two groups according to their valence. Any element that will combine with hydrogen, as chlorine, oxygen, and the like, is said to have a *negative valence number*; hydrogen and elements that do not combine with hydrogen, as barium, aluminum, and like elements, are said to have *positive valence numbers*. In general, all metals and hydrogen have a positive valence number; the other elements or nonmetals usually have a negative valence number. Each element with a positive valence number is often labeled with a $+$ over it for each positive valence or holding bond, as Na^+, Ba^{++}, and Al^{+++}. The negative elements are likewise marked with a $-$ sign for valences, as Cl^-, O^{--}, and S^{--}. A knowledge of the valence numbers of the elements is useful in writing the formula of a compound.

Some elements have more than one valence in different compounds. A study of the Periodic Table (inside back cover) will confirm the multivalent nature of many elements. In general, the valence of an element is related to the group number and as this group number increases, an element exhibits several valences in its various compounds. In writing the formulas of compounds likely encountered in medicine, a study of the valences of mercury, copper, and iron will be sufficient. Mercury, for example, has a valence of 1 in part of its compounds and 2 in the rest. Copper can also have a valence of 1 or 2. Iron has a valence of 2 in $FeCl_2$ and 3 in $FeCl_3$. In all cases where an element has more than one valence, the lower valence form is given the *ending -ous* and the higher valence form the *ending -ic*. The compound $FeCl_2$ is called ferrous chloride, while $FeCl_3$ is ferric chloride.

Radicals

In many chemical compounds we find groups of elements that act very much like a single element. In chemical reactions, these groups move from one compound to another without the individual elements separating from each other. Such groups of elements as the hydroxyl (OH) group in bases, the nitrate group (NO_3) in nitric acid, the sulfate group (SO_4) in sulfuric acid, and the ammonium group (NH_4) in ammonium compounds are called *radicals.* Compounds containing radicals are written with the radical elements grouped together as Na (OH) for sodium hydroxide, (NH_4) Cl for ammonium chloride and Ca (CO_3) for calcium carbonate.

Each radical has its own valence and if a radical is to be taken more than once in a formula, we enclose the group in parentheses and follow it by the proper subscript.

$$NH_4 + NH_4 + CO_3 \quad Ca + OH + OH \quad Mg + NO_3 + NO_3$$
$$(NH_4)_2 CO_3 \qquad\qquad Ca (OH)_2 \qquad\qquad Mg (NO_3)_2$$

Ammonium carbonate   *Calcium hydroxide*   *Magnesium nitrate*

The list of valence numbers of some of the common elements and radicals shown below will be found useful in writing the formulas for compounds:

VALENCE NUMBER OF SOME COMMON ELEMENTS AND RADICALS

VALENCE NUMBER OF 1:

Positive		Negative	
H+	hydrogen	Cl$^-$	chloride
Na+	sodium	OH$^-$	hydroxide
K+	potassium	NO_2^-	nitrite
Ag+	silver	NO_3^-	nitrate
Cu+	copper (cuprous)	Br$^-$	bromide
NH_4^+	ammonium	I$^-$	iodide
Hg+	mercury (mercurous)	HCO_3^-	bicarbonate

VALENCE NUMBER OF 2:

	Positive		Negative
Ca^{++}	........calcium	O^{--}	.........oxide
Cu^{++}	........copper (cupric)	S^{--}	.........sulfide
Ba^{++}	........barium	SO_3^{--}	.......sulfite
Hg^{++}	.......mercury (mercuric)	SO_4^{--}	.......sulfate
Pb^{++}	........lead	CO_3^{--}	.......carbonate
Zn^{++}	........zinc		
Mg^{++}	.......magnesium		
Fe^{++}	........iron (ferrous)		

VALENCE NUMBER OF 3:

	Positive		Negative
Al^{+++}	.......aluminum	PO_4^{---}	.....phosphate
Fe^{+++}	......iron (ferric)		

Application of Valence Numbers

Before we attempt to apply the information in the table to the writing of formulas, it may be of help to state two fundamental rules. Since compounds are made up of electrically neutral molecules, *the sum of the valence numbers of the positive elements or radicals must equal the sum of the valence numbers of the negative elements or radicals.* In the formula for a compound, *the element or radical with a positive valence number is always written first.*

When the positive element or radical has the same number of positive charges as the negative element or radical has negative charges, the formula is easy to write, as: H^+Cl^-; $Ba^{++}S^{--}$; $Al^{+++}PO_4^{---}$.

When a chemical formula is written incorrectly so that the positive and negative valences are not the same, it becomes a simple problem in arithmetic to make the charges balance. To write the formula for barium chloride, we may have begun by using one of each atom, $Ba^{++}Cl^-$. But to balance the charges, it will take 2 atoms of Cl^- (2 negative charges) to combine with 1 atom of Ba^{++} (2 positive charges) giving $Ba^{++}Cl_2^-$ as the correct formula. Aluminum hydroxide would be written $Al^{+++}(OH)_3^-$ in order to have 3 negative charges to balance the 3 positive charges. Ferric sulfate would require a little more effort to write correctly. The formula $Fe^{+++}SO_4^{--}$ is obviously incorrect as the charges do not balance. Two atoms of iron must combine with 3 sulfate radicals to form an electrically neutral molecule $Fe_2(SO_4)_3$ .To obtain the correct formula from $Fe^{+++}SO_4^{--}$ we determine the least common multiple of the opposite charges. In this case the number would be 6, then divide this number by the number of positive charges (3) to find the correct number of Fe atoms in the formula (2), and by the number of negative charges (2) to find the correct number of SO_4 radicals (3). The correct formula would then be $Fe_2^{+++}(SO_4)_3^{--}$ which could be checked by multiplying the positive and negative valences by their subscripts to compare the sum of the positive and negative charges. The correct formula for a compound such as calcium phosphate could be determined in a similar fashion. The positive and negative valences, $Ca^{++}PO_4^{---}$, would have a least common multiple of 6 giving $Ca_3^{++}(PO_4)_2^{---}$ for the proper formula.

Chemical Equations

The chemist makes use of symbols and formulas to state the facts of chemical changes or reactions. To represent the electrolysis of water we write the equation for the reaction as follows:

$$2\ H_2O \rightarrow 2\ H_2 + O_2$$

This shorthand form of expression tells us a great deal. At first glance, it merely states that water has been changed into hydrogen and oxygen. More completely, the equation tells us that 2 molecules of water decompose into 2 molecules of hydrogen gas and 1 molecule of oxygen. Quantitatively it states that 2 gram molecular weights of water (2×18.016 gm.) decompose to form 2 gram molecular weights of hydrogen (2×2.016 gm.) and 1 gram molecular weight of oxygen (32 gm.).

Any chemical reaction can be written in the form of an equation if we know the correct formulas for all the substances that react and all the products that are formed.

Balancing Chemical Equations

A chemical equation is significant only if it represents what actually takes place during a chemical reaction. It must signify the actual proportions of the reacting atoms. There are several ways by which we can tell whether an equation is correctly written or "balanced." Since atoms are neither created nor destroyed during a reaction, every atom that reacts must appear in the products of the reaction. Therefore, an equation must have the same number of atoms of each kind on both sides. The simple reaction for the union of magnesium and sulfur to form magnesium sulfide may be expressed as follows:

$$Mg + S \rightarrow MgS$$

If we check the numbers of each kind of atom, we find that there are the same number of atoms of each kind on each side of the equation, which means that it is *balanced*.

Since there are a great many chemical reactions that involve two compounds it may be well to consider the equations for such reactions. When a silver nitrate solution is added to a solution that contains sodium chloride, the two salts react to form insoluble silver chloride and sodium nitrate.

$$Ag^+NO_3^- + Na^+Cl^- \rightarrow Ag^+Cl^- + Na^+NO_3^-$$

Inspection of both sides of the equation will reveal that the equation is balanced. In a study of equations it will be found very helpful to write the valence charges of each atom or radical in a compound above the symbols. This practice will aid in writing correct formulas for the compounds and in balancing the equations.

An example of a more difficult equation to balance would be represented by the reaction of calcium sulfate and sodium phosphate to form calcium phosphate and sodium sulfate. We could start by writing the correct formula for the compounds involved.

$$Ca^{++}SO_4^{--} + Na_3^+PO_4^{---} \rightarrow Ca_3^{++}(PO_4)_2^{---} + Na_2^+SO_4^{--}$$

To balance the equation we begin by comparing the number of Ca atoms on both sides. Since there are 3 on the right and 1 on the left we must take 3 molecules of $CaSO_4$ to furnish 3 Ca atoms, thus

$$3Ca^{++}SO_4^{--} + Na_3^+PO_4^{---} \rightarrow Ca_3^{++}(PO_4)_2^{---} + Na_2^+SO_4^{--}$$

Comparing next the SO_4 radicals on each side, it will be found necessary to take 3 molecules of Na_2SO_4 to balance the 3 SO_4 radicals on the left side.

$$3Ca^{++}SO_4^{--} + Na_3^+PO_4^{---} \rightarrow Ca_3^{++}(PO_4)_2^{---} + 3Na_2^+SO_4^{--}$$

The next step would involve the Na atoms. By taking 2 molecules of Na_3PO_4 on the left we should have 6 atoms of Na on each side.

$$3Ca^{++}SO_4^{--} + 2Na_3^+PO_4^{---} \rightarrow Ca_3^{++}(PO_4)_2^{---} + 3Na_2^+SO_4^{--}$$

The 2 PO_4 radicals on the left side would balance the 2 on the right side. A recheck would reveal the same number of atoms and radicals of the same kind on each side of the equation; therefore it would be balanced.

When two compounds react to form two new compounds we are often able to predict the nature of the products that are formed. For example, if potassium sulfate were to react with barium chloride what new compounds would we expect to be formed?

$$K_2^+SO_4^{--} + Ba^{++}Cl_2^- \rightarrow ?$$

This common type of reaction is called a "metathetical" or "exchange of partners" equation. Since a reaction occurs and since every compound consists of an element or radical with a positive valence combined with an element or radical with a negative valence, there is only one possible combination of products that can be formed. The K^+ must combine with the Cl^- to form the new compound KCl, leaving Ba^{++} to combine with SO_4^{--} to form $BaSO_4$ as shown below:

$$K_2^+SO_4^{--} + Ba^{++}Cl_2^- \rightarrow K^+Cl^- + Ba^{++}SO_4^{--}$$

A little effort will show that 2 molecules of KCl must be formed to balance the equation.

$$K_2^+SO_4^{--} + Ba^{++}Cl_2^- \rightarrow 2K^+Cl^- + Ba^{++}SO_4^{--}$$

Applying this same principle to the equation for the reaction between silver nitrate and sodium chloride, we may reason as follows:

$$Ag^+NO_3^- + Na^+Cl^- \rightarrow Ag^+Cl^- + Na^+NO_3^-$$

The Ag^+ must find a new partner with a negative valence in order to form a silver salt other than $AgNO_3$. It therefore combines with Cl^-, leaving Na^+ and NO_3^- to form $NaNO_3$. In other words, the Ag^+ and Na^+ merely exchange partners to form two entirely new compounds. Similar reasoning may be applied to the majority of chemical reactions.

Types of Chemical Reactions

Three of the major types of chemical reactions have already been represented in this section on chemical equations. These three and two additional types may be described briefly as follows:

1. *Decomposition:* The breakdown of a compound into its component parts. Example: Water is decomposed into hydrogen and oxygen gases by an electric current.

2. *Synthesis:* The union of elements to form a compound. Example: The heating of magnesium and sulfur to form the compound magnesium sulfide.

3. *Metathetical or exchange of partners:* The reaction of the positive valence element of 1 compound with the negative valence element of another to form 2 new compounds. Example: Silver nitrate reacts with a solution of sodium chloride to form an insoluble white precipitate of silver chloride and the soluble compound sodium nitrate.

4. *Replacement:* The replacement of a component element in a compound by an uncombined element producing a new compound and a different uncombined element. Example: The reaction of metallic zinc and hydrochloric acid in which the hydrogen of the acid is replaced by the zinc, and the compound zinc chloride and hydrogen gas are formed.

$$Zn + 2H^+Cl^- \longrightarrow Zn^{++}Cl_2^- + H_2$$

5. *Oxidation-reduction reactions:* A reaction involving both an oxidation and a reduction. This type of reaction is discussed in Chapter 5.

General Rules and Summary

Rules for equation writing may be summarized as follows:

1. Write the correct formulas for the substances that are reacting by combining the symbols for the elements or radicals in each compound, then balancing the valence charges.

2. If possible, determine the products that are formed and write their correct formulas.

3. Balance the equation so that you have the same number of atoms of each kind on both sides.

In equation writing, it cannot be stressed too strongly that you can never change a formula to make the atoms balance. *If the formulas are written correctly, the equation can always be balanced.* When a given equation cannot be balanced, you should check the formulas to see if they are correct.

It is well to *practice writing formulas* until you thoroughly understand how the figures in the formulas and preceding the formulas apply to the different atoms. For example, $BaCO_3$ indicates 1 atom of barium, 1 atom of carbon and 3 atoms of oxygen; $Ca(NO_3)_2$, 1 atom of calcium, 2 atoms of nitrogen, and 6 (2×3) atoms of oxygen; and $Al_2(SO_4)_3$, 2 atoms of aluminum, 3 atoms of sulfur, and 12 (3×4) atoms of oxygen. When a number precedes the formula as in $2NaCl$, it means 2 molecules of sodium chloride; $3H_2O$ means 3 molecules of water; and $4H_2CO_3$, means 4 molecules of carbonic acid. The number that precedes a formula multiples every atom in it, therefore, $4H_2CO_3$ indicates 8 (4×2) hydrogen atoms, 4 carbon atoms, and 12 (4×3) oxygen atoms; and $2Al_2(SO_4)_3$ indicates 4 (2×2) aluminum atoms, 6 (2×3) sulfur atoms and 24 ($2 \times 3 \times 4$) oxygen atoms.

Review Questions

1. Why are the symbols for the elements often called atomic symbols?
2. The phosphoric acid molecule contains 3 atoms of hydrogen, 1 atom of phosphorus, and 4 atoms of oxygen. Write the formula for phosphoric acid.
3. Explain the different meanings of the following terms: $3N$, N_2, and $4N_2$.
4. How many atoms of each kind are there in the formula $K_2Cr_2O_7$?
5. What is meant by the term electrovalence and how is it related to the atomic structure of an element?
6. Define and illustrate covalence.
7. In what way is the element hydrogen useful in determining the valence of other elements?
8. Which type of elements usually have positive valence and which have negative valence?
9. Name three elements that have two valences, giving the valence in each case.
10. From the list of valences of common elements and radicals, pick out the radicals and give their valence.
11. What two fundamental rules are useful in writing formulas?
12. Write the correct formulas for the compounds that would result from the proper combination of the following pairs of elements:

    Al and Cl NH_4 and SO_4
    Ba and OH   Fe and O (ferric Fe)
    Ca and SO_4 Hg and Cl (mercuric Hg)

13. List and briefly describe the five major types of chemical reactions.
14. In writing a chemical equation, what three steps should be followed?
15. What should never be done in balancing a chemical equation?
16. If an equation will not balance, what should be checked first?
17. In writing most chemical equations, how can you predict the products of the reaction?
18. Write and balance the equations for the following reactions:
   (a) Aluminum chloride reacts with sodium hydroxide to form?
   (b) Potassium metal reacts with water to form potassium hydroxide and hydrogen gas.
   (c) Calcium chloride and sodium sulfate react to form?
   (d) Aluminum sulfate and potassium hydroxide react to form?

Chapter 5

Oxygen, Oxidation and Reduction

Historically the discovery of oxygen was a very important event which marked the beginning of modern chemistry. It was first prepared in 1772 by Scheele, a German chemist. Priestley, an English chemist, prepared oxygen in 1774, and is usually credited with its discovery since he published his findings that year, while Scheele delayed his report until 1777. The role of oxygen in combustion and respiration was studied by the French chemist Lavoisier in 1777. Further studies of its properties emphasized the now well-known essential nature of this element for plant and animal life.

Oxygen is essential for many processes other than the maintenance of life. Without it, we could have no fire to heat our homes, cook our food, or make possible our many industrial processes. The treatment of certain diseases, the purification of drinking water, and the disposal of sewage are dependent on an abundant supply of oxygen.

Occurrence

Of all the elements in the earth's surface, oxygen is the most abundant. One fifth of the volume of the air, eight ninths by weight of water, and approximately one half of the earth's crust is oxygen. In the air it exists as free molecular oxygen (O_2), elsewhere it is found combined with many other elements in the form of oxides. Oxygen is an important constituent of the major foodstuffs—carbohydrates, fats, and proteins—and makes up about two thirds of the human body.

Preparation

Oxygen is usually prepared commercially from air, which is essentially a mixture of this element and nitrogen. Air is liquefied by subjecting it to a high pressure at a low temperature. When the liquid air is allowed to evaporate, the more volatile nitrogen escapes first, leaving behind the fairly pure oxygen. Both the oxygen and nitrogen gases are then forced into steel cylinders under high pressure and stored for future use. Fortunately large quantities of nitrogen gas are used in the manufacture of ammonia; therefore the process is economically sound.

Another commercial source of pure oxygen is the electrolysis of water. When an electric current is passed through water, oxygen forms at the positive pole, or anode, and hydrogen forms at the negative pole, or cathode (Fig. 22). The oxygen and hydrogen gas thus formed are drawn off and stored under pressure.

In the laboratory, oxygen is usually prepared by heating potassium chlorate. The reaction may be represented as follows:

$$2KClO_3 \rightarrow 2KCl + 3O_2$$

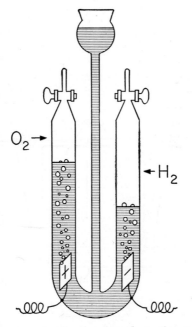

Figure 22. A simple apparatus for the electrolysis of water into hydrogen and oxygen gases.

This formation of oxygen proceeds slowly when a test tube containing potassium chlorate is heated by the flame of a bunsen burner. If some manganese dioxide (MnO₂) is mixed with the potassium chlorate before heating, the rate of formation of oxygen is increased considerably. Experimentally, it can be shown that the manganese dioxide is not changed in the reaction and can be recovered from the tube. A substance of this kind that can influence the speed of a chemical reaction without being altered itself is called a *catalyst*. The success of many commercial chemical processes depends upon the choice of a proper catalyst. The majority of the chemical reactions that occur in our bodies in the processes of digestion and metabolism are controlled by catalysts.

A visual illustration of the effect of the catalyst, manganese dioxide, is shown in Figure 23.

Properties

Oxygen is a colorless, odorless, tasteless gas which is slightly heavier than air. When subjected to a high pressure at a low temperature, the gas is converted to liquid oxygen. At a temperature of $-118°$ C. a pressure of 50 atmospheres is required for liquefaction.

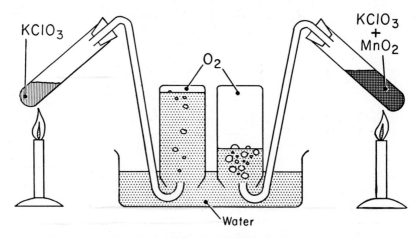

Figure 23. Catalytic action. When the tubes are heated under identical temperature conditions, the tube containing the catalyst liberates oxygen rapidly, whereas the tube containing potassium chlorate alone, liberates practically no oxygen.

This temperature ($-118°$ C.) is called the *critical temperature*, which is the particular temperature above which a gas cannot be liquefied no matter how much pressure is applied to it. Liquid oxygen is blue in color, slightly heavier than water and has a boiling temperature of $-183°$ C.

Approximately 3 cc. of oxygen will dissolve in 100 cc. of water at ordinary temperatures. This slight solubility insures a supply of the gas to aquatic plants and animals, and for the conversion of sewage and other contaminating substances in natural water into harmless material.

When oxygen takes up 2 electrons to complete its outer shell it assumes the stable configuration of an atom of inert gas. Its tendency to accept 2 electrons from both nonmetals and metals is responsible for its ability to form compounds with nearly all known elements. These compounds of oxygen with metals or nonmetals are called *oxides.* The formation of oxides can be readily demonstrated by the burning of such elements as sulfur, phosphorus, iron, and carbon in pure oxygen. For example, sulfur unites with oxygen to form sulfur dioxide:

$$S + O_2 \rightarrow SO_2 \uparrow$$

Carbon burns in oxygen to form carbon dioxide:

$$C + O_2 \rightarrow CO_2 \uparrow$$

The union of a substance with oxygen may be called *oxidation*. The burning of wood, the rusting of iron, and the decay of plant and animal matter are examples of oxidation. Oxygen is able to unite with food and tissue substances in the body at relatively low temperatures because these reactions are hastened by catalysts, called *enzymes*.

Combustion

When a substance unites with oxygen so rapidly that heat and light are produced in the reaction, we say the substance is burning. We commonly speak of rapid oxidation, or burning, as *combustion* although combustion may occur in the absence of oxygen.

Substances that will burn readily, such as paper, wood, candle, illuminating gas, and gasoline, are called *combustible;* those that will not burn, such as asbestos, stone, and clay, are called *incombustible*.

Since air is only one-fifth oxygen, substances burn less vigorously in it than in the pure gas, and many substances which are incombustible in air burn in oxygen. For example, powdered sulfur burns feebly in air but blazes up vigorously when thrust into oxygen, and iron wire is incombustible in air, yet burns brightly in the pure gas. It is often said that a substance is "burned" in the body to give energy. This merely means that the substance unites with oxygen in the tissues. Although burning commonly occurs with oxygen as one of the reacting substances, it can occur in the absence of this element. Hydrogen will "burn" in the presence of chlorine to form hydrogen chloride. If you sprinkle powdered antimony into chlorine gas, "burning" will start at ordinary temperatures.

Spontaneous Combustion

When a substance unites slowly with oxygen, heat is produced in the reaction. If the heat cannot escape, the temperature of the substance gradually rises, thus increasing the rate of oxidation. If the process is allowed to continue, the temperature is raised to a point at which the material bursts into flame. This temperature is called the *kindling temperature* and the process which causes the material to burst into flame is called *spontaneous combustion*. A burning match will set fire to a great many combustible substances because the reaction between the wood of the match and the oxygen of the air produces sufficient heat to raise the temperature of these substances to their kindling temperature. Substances with a low kindling temperature, as illuminating gas, ether, and gasoline, must be handled with care to prevent them from becoming fire hazards. Damp hay in a farmer's barn and oily rags left by painters often catch fire by spontaneous combustion.

Extinguishing Fires

There are two common ways to put out a fire: (1) by removing the source of oxygen from the burning material; (2) by lowering the temperature of the burning substance to below its kindling temperature. Chemical fire extinguishers contain a liquid which cools the burning substance below its kindling temperature and surrounds it with an incombustible gas. A common type of extinguisher contains water and chemicals that react to form carbon dioxide (CO_2) gas. In Figure 24, when the cylinder is inverted the acid is poured into the sodium bicarbonate solution, forming carbon dioxide gas as shown in the reaction:

Cools to below kindling temp.
Surrounds with incombustible gas

$$H_2SO_4 + NaHCO_3 \rightarrow NaHSO_4 + H_2O + CO_2 \uparrow$$

This gas is heavier than air and settles over the burning material, excluding its oxygen supply. This type of extinguisher has several disadvantages when used in the home or laboratory. The solution that spurts out of the hose can cause an unsightly mess and possible damage; the ions in the solution conduct electricity and increase the danger of fires of electrical origin; the capacity of the extinguisher is limited and it must be recharged periodically. For these reasons, a type of extinguisher with few of these disadvantages has gradually replaced the above extinguisher. This new type consists of a cylinder of carbon dioxide gas connected by a hose to a funnel-shaped nozzle for directing the gas at the base of the flame (Fig. 25). Obviously, the cylinders of gas have a greater capacity, cause less damage in use, and are safe to use on electrical fires and on burning gasoline or oil.

Oil or gasoline fires cannot be extinguished with water because these liquids are lighter than water and will float on the surface, thus spreading the fire. The water layer underneath the burning oil is unable to lower the temperature below the kindling temperature. An effective fire extinguisher for gasoline or oil fires contains foamite, a mixture of chemicals and licorice, which forms a thick foam of carbon

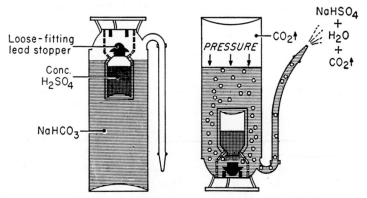

Figure 24. A representation of the changes occurring when the common type of fire extinguisher is inverted.

Figure 25.   Types of carbon dioxide gas fire extinguishers used in the laboratory.

dioxide bubbles on the surface of the burning oil and thus removes the oxygen (Fig. 26).

Another common extinguisher uses a heavy, incombustible liquid called carbon tetrachloride. When the liquid is sprayed on a fire, it

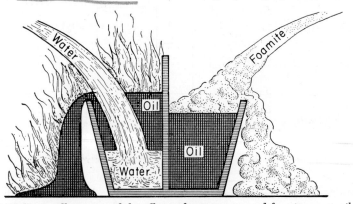

Figure 26.   An illustration of the effects of using water and foamite on an oil fire.

forms a blanket of incombustible gas over the burning substances, thus removing the oxygen supply. Carbon tetrachloride extinguishers should not be used in closed quarters because of the toxicity of the vapors. There is also the possibility that poison gases such as phosgene may be formed in the use of these extinguishers.

Uses of Oxygen

In Therapy

When oxygen is breathed into the lungs, it diffuses into the blood and loosely combines with the *hemoglobin* (red pigment of the blood). This unstable compound of oxygen and hemoglobin is called *oxyhemoglobin* and is responsible for the bright red color of arterial blood. The oxyhemoglobin is carried to the tissues where it releases its oxygen to react with food and waste products in the tissue cells. One of the waste products formed is carbon dioxide gas, which is carried back to the lungs and exhaled. When the oxyhemoglobin loses its oxygen, it changes from a bright red to deep purple color which accounts for the color of venous blood. Respiration and the role of oxygen in this process will be explained in greater detail in a later chapter on blood.

If the oxygen concentration in the air is diminished, it is often necessary to supply an additional source of the gas. Aviators flying at high altitudes, sailors in submarines, and men engaged in mine and fire rescue work find it necessary to carry oxygen for breathing. A person who has been exposed to smoke or gases other than oxygen, to oxygen-low atmospheres, or who has been under water for several minutes, usually becomes unconscious from the lack of oxygen. This oxygen lack is called *asphyxiation* and is treated by forcing the patient to breathe pure oxygen in an attempt to bring the oxygen content of the blood up to normal. Asphyxiation is also caused by breathing a gas such as carbon monoxide (CO), which unites with hemoglobin and thus prevents oxygen from combining with the hemoglobin. The administration of a high concentration of oxygen is an effective treatment in carbon monoxide poisoning.

In surgery, where a gas anesthetic such as nitrous oxide is used, oxygen is mixed with the gas to prevent asphyxiation (Fig. 27). Patients suffering from pneumonia and other lung diseases may have their normal lung capacity diminished by fluid to such an extent that they are unable to obtain an adequate supply of oxygen from the air.

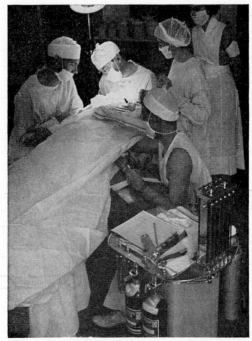

Figure 27.   When nitrous oxide is used as an anesthetic, oxygen is administered concurrently to prevent asphyxiation. (Courtesy of Dr. S. C. Cullen, University of Iowa Hospitals.)

The administration of oxygen (Figs. 28 and 29) may sustain the patient until the diseased lung is healed. Physicians have found that newborn babies who at birth experience difficulty in breathing or whose lungs do not readily expand can often be revived by a mixture of oxygen and a small amount of carbon dioxide (Fig. 30). The carbon dioxide acts as a respiratory stimulant.

In Industry

An important industrial use of oxygen is in the production of intense heat for cutting and welding iron and steel plates. When oxygen is mixed with hydrogen or acetylene gas and the mixture is ignited, the heat produced is sufficient to melt steel. The common type of welding torch uses an oxyacetylene flame. In recent years the iron and steel industry has found many important uses for oxygen in the production of metals. Liquid oxygen is being used as a concentrated source of

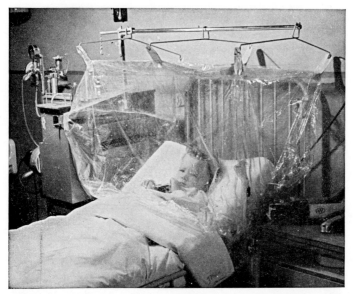

Figure 28. An oxygen tent in use. (Courtesy of Dr. S. C. Cullen, University of Iowa Hospitals.)

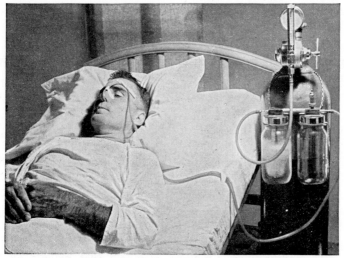

Figure 29. The administration of oxygen through a nasal catheter. (Courtesy of Dr. S. C. Cullen, University of Iowa Hospitals.)

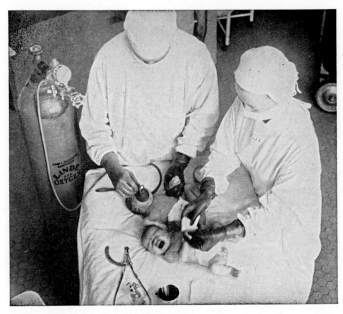

Figure 30. Oxygen administered to newborn babies. (Courtesy of Dr. S. C. Cullen, University of Iowa Hospitals.)

the gas for the burning of alcohol or other liquid fuels in modern military rockets.

Ozone

For many years it has been observed that the air in the neighborhood of an electrical discharge has a peculiar odor. The odor is caused by the formation of ozone which is a form of oxygen represented as O_3 compared to ordinary molecular oxygen, O_2. The characteristic odor of the atmosphere immediately following a thunderstorm is also probably due to the presence of ozone.

When an element exists in two or more different forms possessing different physical and chemical properties, the forms are known as allotropic modifications. Common elements that exhibit allotropic forms are oxygen, phosphorus, and sulfur.

Preparation

Ozone may be prepared by passing air or oxygen between two plates that are charged with several thousand volts of alternating current (Fig. 31). This so-called silent electrical discharge produces a low concentration of ozone, which emerges from the apparatus greatly diluted with air or oxygen. Since ordinary oxygen is in equilibrium with ozone, the reaction for the formation is reversible and prevents the accumulation of high concentrations of ozone.

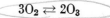

$$3O_2 \rightleftarrows 2O_3$$

The double arrow in the above equation indicates that oxygen may be changed into ozone and ozone may be changed back into oxygen. This equation therefore represents an equilibrium or balance between two chemical reactions each proceeding in the opposite direction.

Pure liquid ozone may be prepared by lowering the temperature of the mixture obtained by the above process to approximately −180° C.

Properties

Ozone is a colorless gas possessing a garlic-like odor and is more soluble and heavier than oxygen. Liquid ozone is dark blue in color and is capable of decomposing with explosive force, producing ordinary oxygen.

The most striking difference between ozone and oxygen is the increased chemical activity of ozone. For example, a noble metal such as silver will not combine with oxygen under ordinary conditions, but will form a film of brown silver oxide when exposed to a low concentration of ozone. Also turpentine reacts with ozone to form compounds called ozonides, which are very active oxidizing agents.

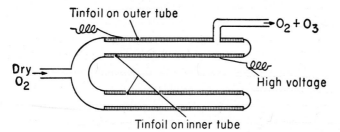

Figure 31. The apparatus used for the preparation of ozone.

Uses

Ozone, in the form of ozonized air produced by the silent electrical discharge, has been used to destroy objectionable odors, to sterilize bandages, to bleach delicate fabrics, and to disinfect water for drinking purposes. Because of its oxidizing properties, it is sometimes used to age tobacco artificially and to cause rapid drying of the oils used in the manufacture of linoleum.

A simple test for the presence of ozone depends on its ability to rapidly oxidize rubber. When a rubber band is stretched in ozonized air, it breaks within a few seconds because of the rapid oxidation.

— Oxidation and Reduction

loss of electrons — Oxidation and Reduction *-gain of electrons*

Oxidation

The word "oxidation" originally referred to the addition of oxygen to an element or compound. The present conception of oxidation involves a change in valence number or transfer of electrons. For example, the union of oxygen with an element always causes an increase in the valence number of the element. When metallic magnesium combines with oxygen its valence number is increased from 0 to $+2$. (Uncombined elements such as metals and gases are considered as having no valence, or a valence number of zero.) In a similar fashion, the combination of oxygen with a compound always produces a rise in the valence number of 1 or more of the elements in the compound. However, the valence number of an element in the free state or in a compound may be increased by combination with elements other than oxygen. In combining metallic magnesium with sulfur, magnesium sulfide (MgS) is formed and again the valence number of the magnesium is raised from 0 to $+2$. Whenever the valence number of an element is increased in a reaction, the process is called *oxidation*. The element that is oxidized may be in the free or combined form, and its valence number may be raised by combination with oxygen or some other element. The agent which causes the oxidation of an element or compound is called an *oxidizing agent*. Simple addition of oxygen to a substance always results in an oxidation reaction; there are also many oxidation reactions which do not involve oxygen and are therefore not oxygenation reactions.

Oxidation may also be considered as a loss of electrons by the element being oxidized. The metallic magnesium in its reaction with oxygen had its valence number increased from 0 to $+2$, or it may be said that the magnesium atom lost 2 electrons and became an ion with 2 positive charges (Fig. 32). The same electron loss occurs when magnesium combines with sulfur to form magnesium sulfide. Oxidation can, therefore, be defined as a reaction in which the element being oxidized loses electrons. The oxidizing agent gains the electrons lost by the element that is oxidized.

Reduction

Reduction is the opposite of oxidation and is the process in which the valence number of an element is decreased. Many reduction reactions also involve a loss of oxygen from a compound. For example, if mercuric oxide is decomposed by heating, oxygen and metallic mercury are formed. The mercury has been reduced in the reaction as its valence number decreased from $+2$ to 0 and it lost oxygen. In the reaction between magnesium and sulfur to form magnesium sulfide, the valence number of the sulfur was decreased from 0 to -2, indicating that the sulfur had been reduced. The agent which causes the reduction of an element is known as a *reducing agent*.

Reduction involves a gain of electrons by the element being reduced. In the reaction of magnesium and sulfur, the sulfur atom gains 2 electrons to form an ion with 2 negative charges. The sulfur is therefore reduced in the reaction since it has gained electrons. The reducing agent loses the electrons that are gained by the element being reduced.

Commonly, *oxidation-reduction reactions* are spoken of rather than separate oxidation or reduction reactions. In any reaction in which an

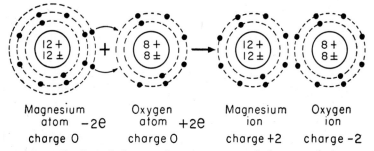

| Magnesium atom $-2e$ charge 0 | Oxygen atom $+2e$ charge 0 | Magnesium ion charge $+2$ | Oxygen ion charge -2 |

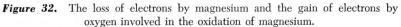

Figure 32. The loss of electrons by magnesium and the gain of electrons by oxygen involved in the oxidation of magnesium.

oxidation occurs, it is always accompanied by a reduction, and the oxidation and reduction always take place to an equal degree. In other words, there is a transfer of electrons which must balance since the electrons lost by the element being oxidized must be gained by the element being reduced. The oxidation-reduction reactions already discussed can be indicated as follows:

$$2\ Mg^0 + O_2^0 \rightarrow 2\ Mg^{++}O^{--}$$
$$Mg^0 + S^0 \rightarrow Mg^{++}S^{--}$$
$$2\ Hg^{++}O^{--} \rightarrow 2\ Hg^0 + O_2^0$$

(Since an element in the free state has zero valence, this valence number can be represented by a small zero above the symbol.) In the first reaction, magnesium is oxidized from a valence number of 0 to $+2$ while oxygen is reduced from 0 to -2. This confirms the statement that an oxidation is always accompanied by a reduction and that the oxidation and reduction occur to an equal degree (0 to $+2$ versus 0 to -2). The second reaction is similar to the first except that oxygen is not involved. In the third reaction, mercury is reduced from a valence number of $+2$ to 0 while oxygen is oxidized from a valence number of -2 to 0.

Another type of oxidation-reduction reaction that is often encountered is that between metal and a salt. For example, copper reacts with mercuric chloride to form cupric chloride and metallic mercury:

$$Cu^0 + Hg^{++}Cl_2^- \rightarrow Cu^{++}Cl_2^- + Hg^0$$

In this reaction, copper is oxidized from a valence number of 0 to $+2$, while mercury is reduced from $+2$ to 0. The oxidizing agent is mercuric chloride, since it causes copper to be oxidized. The metallic copper is the reducing agent because it brings about the reduction of the mercury. This oxidation reaction can readily be explained on the basis of electron transfer. The metallic copper would lose 2 electrons which are gained by the mercuric ions. Copper is converted to cupric ions, while the mercuric ions are converted to metallic mercury. Since the mercuric ions gained 2 electrons, they are the oxidizing agent and the metallic copper is the reducing agent.

The body requires a constant source of energy to carry on its manifold activities. Energy for muscular movement, for maintenance of body temperature, and so on, is obtained from the food by means of oxidation-reduction reactions. It requires a good many of these reactions to convert our meals into enough energy for a day's work.

Antiseptic Agents

Many of the common antiseptic agents owe their efficacy to the fact that they are oxidizing agents, since the oxygen destroys bacteria and the food on which they live. Hydrogen peroxide (H_2O_2) in a 3 per cent solution is a mild oxidizing agent and was once extensively used as an antiseptic. In contact with a wound, it effervesces and releases oxygen bubbles which aid in cleansing the wound. It also exerts a mild antiseptic action. Potassium permanganate ($KMnO_4$) is an antiseptic that releases oxygen when in contact with organic matter. In dilute solutions, it is effective in treating infections of the urethra and bladder. Iodine, in solution, is widely used as an antiseptic for minor cuts and wounds and for application to the skin in preparation for surgical procedures.

Stain Removal

The pigment of certain dyestuffs and stains is converted to a colorless compound by oxidation, while other pigments are decolorized by reduction. Therefore, bleaching agents usually consist of an oxidizing or a reducing agent and often have antiseptic properties. Hydrogen peroxide is used to remove blood stains from linen and to bleach organic matter such as hair, silk, and feathers. Potassium permanganate will remove stains from almost all white fabrics but should not be used on rayon. After the stain has been oxidized, the permanganate can be removed by an acid solution of hydrogen peroxide or by oxalic acid. A common bleaching solution is Javelle water, which is a solution of sodium hypochlorite. Hilex, Clorox, and many other household bleaching preparations contain sodium hypochlorite. It is very effective for removing the majority of the stains from cotton or linen encountered in the nursery and home.

Oxalic acid $(COOH)_2$ is a reducing agent that is used to remove iron stains, ink stains, and especially potassium permanganate stains. Another reducing agent that is useful is sodium thiosulfate ($Na_2S_2O_3$). It is very effective in removing iodine stains (Fig. 33) and is also used to remove stains caused by compounds that contain silver.

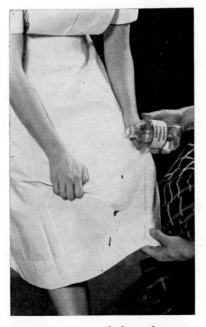

Figure 33. Removal of an iodine stain, using a solution of sodium thiosulfate.

Review Questions

1. Describe two methods for the preparation of oxygen.
2. What is a catalyst? What catalyst is used in the laboratory preparation of oxygen?
3. Why do substances burn more rapidly in oxygen than in air?
4. What conditions are necessary to cause spontaneous combustion?
5. Explain the two fundamental principles that are applied in extinguishing a fire.
6. Why are the majority of fires extinguished with water?
7. List several instances where an additional source of oxygen is necessary for normal respiration.
8. Why are small amounts of carbon dioxide often administered with oxygen in oxygen therapy?
9. How is oxygen carried from the lungs to the various tissues of the body?
10. How does ozone differ from oxygen? Describe several possible uses of ozone in the hospital.
11. Explain the terms "oxidation" and "reduction" on the basis of change in valence number and transfer of electrons.
12. What is an oxidizing agent? A reducing agent? Give examples of each.

13. Why do we always speak of an oxidation-reduction reaction rather than a separate oxidation or reduction reaction?

14. In the following oxidation-reduction reaction:

$$Fe + CuSO_4 \rightarrow FeSO_4 + Cu$$

What is oxidized? What is reduced? What is the oxidizing agent, the reducing agent?

15. Many of the common antiseptics are either oxidizing or reducing agents. How does this explain their antiseptic action?

16. Bleaching agents and stain removers are effective because they either oxidize or reduce dyestuffs or stains. Name two that are oxidizing agents and two that are reducing agents. List the stains that each of the four will remove.

Two types reactions.
1. Oxidation - reduction
2. double D (displacement / decomposition) → gas / precipitate etc.

Chapter 6

Water

Water is so abundant and so familiar to us that we tend to take for granted its properties and usefulness. Its importance to chemists through the centuries is emphasized by its early inclusion as one of the essential forms of matter: earth, air, fire, and water. The composition of water was first determined by Cavendish in 1781. He observed that water was formed when an electric spark was ignited in a mixture of one volume of oxygen and two volumes of hydrogen gas. The establishment of the composition of water ranks in importance with the discovery of oxygen in the development of the science of chemistry.

Occurrence

Water is the most abundant of all chemical compounds. About three fourths of the surface of the earth is covered with water, either as a liquid or, in the arctic regions, as ice. The soil contains large quantities of water essential for the growth of plants. Its presence in the atmosphere is readily recognized, because it often condenses into dew, fog, rain, or snow. As a substance essential to our existence, water ranks next to oxygen in importance. The body can survive several weeks without food but only a few days without water. The digestion of food, the circulation, and elimination of waste materials, the regulation of acid-base balance and body temperature: all depend upon an adequate supply of water. Approximately two thirds of the body weight is water, while most of the foods we eat have a water content of from 10 to 90 per cent. Bread, for example, is about 35 per cent, meat about 70 per cent, and most vegetables are over 75 per cent water.

Physical Properties

Pure water has no odor, taste, or color. The blue or green color of lakes and oceans is due to the presence of finely divided solid material. Water freezes at 0° C. (32° F.) and boils at 100° C. (212° F.).

When water freezes, it expands rapidly, increasing its volume by nearly one tenth in changing from water to ice. This property of expansion on freezing explains why pipes and other vessels containing water burst upon freezing. Since ice is lighter than water, the surface of a river or lake freezes first and the layer of ice protects the aquatic plants and animals from the cold.

As the temperature of water is raised, it vaporizes more and more rapidly until it reaches the boiling point. The temperature remains constant during the boiling process, and the vapor or steam given off is a colorless gas which condenses into a cloud of visible water particles in the cold air. The boiling point is 100° C. at sea level (an atmospheric pressure of 760 mm.). On high mountains, the atmospheric pressure is lower, causing a lowering in the boiling point. Cooking food at high altitudes may be difficult because the water boils before the temperature is high enough for cooking. This difficulty may be overcome by the use of a pressure cooker, where the steam that is formed in boiling is confined in a vessel to increase the pressure. The temperature may then be raised above the boiling point of water. For instance, a steam pressure of 15 pounds will raise the internal temperature about 20° C. above the boiling point of water. The increased temperature that can be obtained in a pressure cooker or in an autoclave is far more efficient than boiling water in cooking or in sterilization.

The universal distribution of water and its widespread use in the laboratory have caused many measurements to be based on its physical properties. For instance, the centigrade thermometer was based on the freezing and boiling points of water. The position of the mercury at the freezing point was marked as 0° C. and at the boiling point at 100° C. The length of the mercury column between these two marks was divided into 100 equal divisions called degrees. The name centigrade comes from the 100 divisions between these points.

The specific gravity of a solution is compared to water as a standard. The density of a liquid is called its *specific gravity* and is expressed as weight (in grams) per unit of volume (in cubic centimeters). The specific gravity of water is 1.000, since 1 cc. of water at 4° C. weighs 1.000 gm. If a specimen of urine weighed 1.030 gm. per cc. (gram per cubic centimeter) it would have a specific gravity of 1.030, and 1 cc. of the urine would be 1.030 times as heavy as 1 cc. of water.

Chemical Properties

In Chapter 4, we learned that water was a covalent compound whose structure could be represented as shown in Figure 21. The electronic formula in Figure 34 shows the electrons in the outer orbit of the oxygen atom and 2 pairs of shared electrons between the hydrogen atoms and the oxygen. Water is a polar molecule, i.e., a covalent compound in which the electronic charge is not uniformly distributed. Apparently the electrons including the shared pairs are closer to the oxygen, which results in that end of the molecule having a negative charge and the hydrogen end having a positive charge. This may be represented in several ways (Fig. 35). Since water is a polar compound, it has the property of attracting the ions of electrovalent compounds and disrupting their crystal structure. When solid crystals of sodium chloride are placed in water, the forces holding the sodium ions and chloride ions together are overcome by the attraction

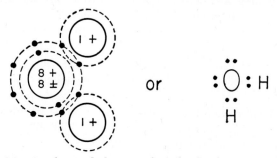

Figure 34.   Covalent and electronic formulas for the water molecule.

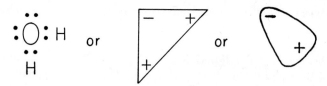

Figure 35.   Three ways to represent water as a polar molecule.

of the water molecules for the ions. This process results in the solution of the sodium chloride as represented in Figure 36. In a similiar fashion, water will also attract polar compounds. Since so many substances are either electrovalent or polar in nature, water has the property of dissolving a majority of common inorganic compounds. In the laboratory, the majority of chemical reactions will not take place unless the substances are in solution in water. In the living organism, the constituents of the cells are kept in solution by water, and most of the reactions that take place in the tissues will not take place in its absence.

Water is one of the most stable compounds known, and for many years it was thought to be an element. It may be heated to very high temperatures (2000° C.) without appreciable decomposition. However, if an electric current is passed through it, decomposition occurs; 2 volumes of hydrogen are produced for each volume of oxygen. The oxygen atom is approximately 16 times as heavy as the hydrogen atom, so that water is, by weight, eight ninths oxygen and one ninth hydrogen.

Another interesting chemical property of water is its action with certain metals. If a small piece of metallic sodium is placed in water, a violent reaction takes place with the formation of a hydroxide (any compound that contains the OH radical) and hydrogen gas:

$$2Na + 2H_2O \rightarrow 2NaOH + H_2 \uparrow$$

The compound that is formed is called sodium hydroxide. Hydrogen gas, like oxygen, exists as molecules, each containing 2 hydrogen atoms. (The small vertical arrow pointing upward, written after H_2 indicates that this product is a gas.)

Water will combine with the oxides of some metals to form a metallic hydroxide, which is also called a *base*.

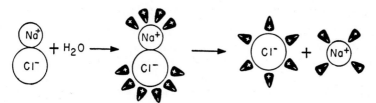

Figure 36. The effect of water on ionic compounds may be illustrated by sodium chloride going into solution.

$$CaO + H_2O \rightarrow Ca(OH)_2$$
Calcium oxide   *Calcium hydroxide*

Certain oxides of nonmetals react with water to form acids.

$$SO_3 + H_2O \rightarrow H_2SO_4$$
Sulfur trioxide   *Sulfuric acid*

An *acid* is a compound that contains hydrogen in a chemically reactive form.

One of the most important chemical properties of water is concerned with the process of hydrolysis. In *hydrolysis,* or breaking apart with water, the compounds are split into two parts, the hydrogen of the water uniting with one part to make an acid and the hydroxyl uniting with the other to make a hydroxide. An example of hydrolysis would be the reaction of water and a compound like ammonium sulfate.

$$(NH_4)_2SO_4 \quad + \quad 2HOH \rightleftarrows 2NH_4OH \quad + \quad H_2SO_4$$
Ammonium sulfate   *Ammonium*   *Sulfuric acid*
                                            hydroxide

The double arrow indicates that the reaction can go in both directions. Actually only a small amount of the ammonium sulfate reacts with water in this way.

The process of digestion in the body is mainly one of hydrolysis. For example, a complex molecule like fat is hydrolyzed as follows:

$$\text{fat} + HOH \rightarrow \text{fatty acid} + \text{glycerol}$$

The H of water goes into the fatty acid while the OH is an integral part of the glycerol molecule. Many examples of hydrolysis will be discussed later in the study of the chemistry of the reactions that occur in the body.

Heavy Water

Urey, in 1932, discovered that ordinary water contained a heavier variety in a proportion of about one part in 6000. He found that the heavy water was composed of deuterium (heavy hydrogen) combined with oxygen. The compound was called deuterium oxide with a formula of D_2O.

The physical properties of deuterium oxide are significantly different than those of ordinary water. It has a greater density and viscosity, a higher boiling point and lower freezing point than ordinary water.

When it was found that heavy water retarded the speed of fast neutrons in the atomic pile and could be used as a very efficient moderator in nuclear reactors, large quantities were produced commercially for this purpose. As heavy water became available many experiments were carried out to determine its effect on living organisms. It was found to retard the growth of seedlings and to kill certain bacteria, small fish, tadpoles, or mice when used as the sole source of water. Future experiments with heavy water may provide answers to metabolic problems that have long perplexed biochemists and physiologists.

Hydrates

Water molecules combine with the molecules of certain substances, forming loose chemical combinations called *hydrates*. These hydrates form well-defined crystals when their solutions are allowed to evaporate slowly. For example, copper sulfate forms blue crystals when a solution of this substance evaporates slowly. The formula for crystalline copper sulfate is $CuSO_4 \cdot 5H_2O$. The water held in combination is called *water of crystallization* and is written separately to indicate its loose chemical attachment. When this hydrate is heated, it loses its water of crystallization and changes into a white powder whose formula is $CuSO_4$. Examples of other common hydrates are washing soda, $Na_2CO_3 \cdot 10H_2O$; alum, $K_2Al_2(SO_4)_4 \cdot 24H_2O$; gypsum, $CaSO_4 \cdot 2H_2O$; and crystalline sodium sulfate, $Na_2SO_4 \cdot 10H_2O$.

When the water of crystallization has been removed from a hydrate, the resulting compound is said to be *anhydrous*. Substances which give up water of crystallization on exposure to air at ordinary temperatures are called *efflorescent*. Other substances take up water on exposure to atmospheric conditions and are said to be *hygroscopic*. If they take up so much water from the air that they form a solution, they are called deliquescent substances. Compounds like sodium hydroxide and calcium chloride are so deliquescent that they take up water from other materials. Calcium chloride is commonly used as a drying agent or desiccating agent by the chemist. It is also used on dirt roads to keep down the dust, because of its ability to take up water from the atmosphere.

A hydrate of special interest is gypsum, or calcium sulfate ($CaSO_4 \cdot 2H_2O$), which on heating gives up part of its water to form plaster of paris, ($CaSO_4)_2 \cdot H_2O$. When the plaster of paris is mixed with water

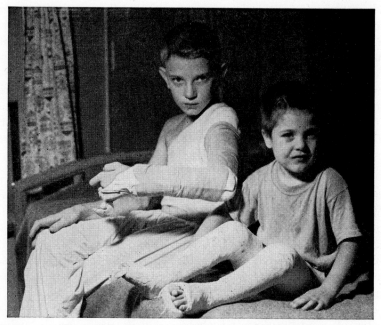

Figure 37. Typical examples of arm and leg casts.

it "sets" in a few minutes to re-form hard crystalline gypsum. In setting, it expands slightly to form a tight cast or mold. Plaster of paris is used extensively in making surgical casts, examples of which are shown in Figure 37. Chemically, the reaction may be represented as follows:

$$(CaSO_4)_2 \cdot H_2O + 3H_2O \rightarrow 2CaSO_4 \cdot 2H_2O$$
Plaster of paris   *Gypsum*

Purification of Water

Naturally occurring water contains impurities dissolved from the rocks and soil. Even rain water contains particles of dust and dissolved gases from the air. The impurities present in water may be classified as either mineral or organic matter.

The mineral matter found in natural water usually consists of common salt and various compounds of calcium, magnesium, and iron. Water that contains these dissolved salts does not readily form a lather with soap and is called *hard water*, while water with little or no mineral matter lathers easily and is called *soft water*.

The organic matter in water is derived from decaying animal and vegetable material. Bacteria utilize this type of material for food, and may cause diseases unless they are removed before the water is used for drinking purposes.

A source of pure drinking water is extremely important to the health of a community. For this reason, it would be appropriate to consider several of the methods for the purification of water.

Distillation

In the process of distillation, water is boiled and the resulting steam is cooled and condensed in a different container, as illustrated in Figure 38. The condensed steam is called the distillate, or distilled water. The chemist uses this method to produce water free from bacteria and dissolved mineral matter. Distilled water is used widely in the preparation of solutions in the laboratory and in the hospital. Distillation is the most effective method for the purification of water, but is too expensive to be employed by large towns or cities.

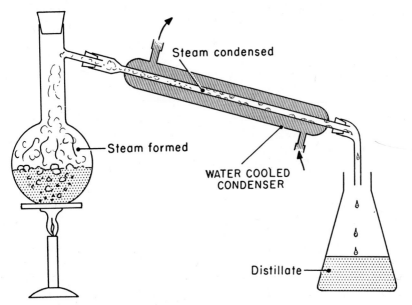

Figure 38. A simple apparatus for the distillation of water.

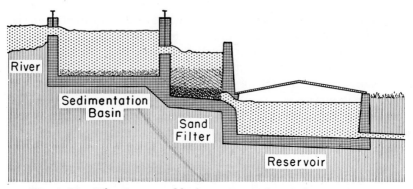

Figure 39.   Filtration as used by large cities in the purification of water.

Boiling

Water from natural sources may be made safe for drinking by boiling for ten to fifteen minutes. This process does not remove the impurities but does kill any pathogenic bacteria that might be present. The flat taste of boiled water is due to the loss of dissolved gases; it may be improved by aeration, such as pouring water from one vessel to another. This method of water purification is reliable in emergencies but is not generally employed for civilian water supplies.

Filtration

In the laboratory, suspended material is separated from water by passing the liquid through a porous material which has holes that are smaller than the suspended matter, thus holding it back. The dissolved impurities are not removed by this method. On a large scale, as in city water works, the water is filtered through beds of sand (Fig. 39). The bacteria are on the suspended organic matter and are largely removed by filtration. To destroy bacteria completely, it has become general practice to treat the water with chlorine, a substance which kills the remaining microorganisms.

Treatment with Ozone

Ozone is a more effective germicidal agent than chlorine, and does not produce the undesirable taste and odor associated with chlorine treatment. The expense of the electricity required to produce ozone from oxygen prohibits its widespread use in water purification, although beverage manufacturers often use ozone to purify the water in their products. Swimming pools filled with water purified by ozone have definite advantages over those using chlorine treated water.

Aeration

Water may be purified by exposure to air for long periods. The oxygen of the air dissolves in the water and oxidizes organic material, thus depriving bacteria of their source of food. It also kills bacteria by direct chemical reaction. Most cities do not depend on this process alone for water purification but use it to remove objectionable tastes and odors from the water. Aeration of water supplies is usually accomplished by spraying the water into the air from fountains, or by allowing it to flow in thin sheets over tiles.

Hard and Soft Water

Since the common methods of water purification do not remove the dissolved inorganic matter, many cities have hard water. There are many disadvantages to the use of hard water. It requires a large amount of soap to form a lather because the soap forms an insoluble compound or "curd" with the minerals in the water. This curd adheres to clothing and makes it rough and irritable to bedridden patients. Cooking with hard water has a toughening effect on foods, also the iron salts in hard water often discolor white fabrics, pottery, and enamelware. When hard water is boiled, the mineral salts deposit a scale on the sides of boilers, pipes, and utensils in which it is heated. This causes not only a waste of fuel but also a corrosion of the metal as well. Hard water should never be used in a sterilizer of surgical instruments because it dulls the cutting edges.

Methods for Softening Water

The inorganic matter which is present in hard water usually consists of bicarbonates, sulfates, or chlorides of calcium, magnesium, and iron. Water which contains only calcium or magnesium bicarbonate is called *temporary hard water,* because these salts can be removed by heating. When heated they are converted into the insoluble carbonates which form most of the scale on boilers and teakettles. Temporary hard water can therefore be softened by boiling:

$$Ca(HCO_3)_2 + \triangle \rightarrow CaCO_3 \downarrow + H_2O + CO_2$$

Calcium bicarbonate   **Calcium carbonate**
(soluble)   **(insoluble)**

(The small triangle is used by chemists as a symbol for heat, while the small vertical arrow pointing downward after the $CaCO_3$ indicates the formation of an insoluble substance or precipitate.)

Water which contains sulfates or chlorides of calcium, magnesium, or iron is called *permanent hard water* because it does not lose these salts on heating. Permanent hard water can be softened by adding a chemical compound which will convert the soluble calcium, magnesium, or iron salts into insoluble precipitates which may be removed by filtration. The following compounds are commonly used for water softening:

Sodium carbonate .... Na_2CO_3 (washing soda)
Sodium tetraborate .... $Na_2B_4O_7$ (borax)
Ammonium hydroxide .... NH_4OH (household ammonia)
Trisodium phosphate .... Na_3PO_4
Sodium hydroxide .... NaOH (caustic soda or lye)
Mixture of calcium hydroxide, $Ca(OH)_2$, and sodium carbonate, Na_2CO_3

The reaction between a soluble calcium salt and sodium carbonate may be used as a typical water softening reaction.

$$CaSO_4 + Na_2CO_3 \rightarrow CaCO_3 \downarrow + Na_2SO_4$$
Calcium   *Sodium*   *Calcium*   *Sodium*
sulfate   *carbonate*   *carbonate*   *sulfate*

Removal of the insoluble calcium carbonate leaves soft water.

Water softeners used in homes, hospitals, laundries, and small industries often employ synthetic *ion exchange resins* or *zeolite,* a material which is a natural sodium aluminum silicate ($Na_2Al_2Si_2O_8$). The sodium in zeolite is exchanged for the calcium, magnesium, or iron in the hard water as it filters through the softener, thus removing these objectionable impurities. After the zeolite has exchanged all its available sodium for calcium, magnesium, or iron, the original compound may be regenerated for further use by allowing sodium chloride to filter through the zeolite.

Since about 1940, many types of ion exchange resins have been produced and studied. The two major types are the cation (positive ion) and anion (negative ion) exchangers. The most common cation exchangers contain sulfonic acid groups, while the anion exchangers often contain quaternary ammonium groups. Water that is used in the hospital, in the laboratory, and in many industries must not only be softened, but must be free from inorganic ions. To produce this deionized or *demineralized water,* a bed of mixed resins is used. For example, a combination of a strongly acid cation exchanger and a strongly basic anion exchanger would remove sodium and chloride ions as represented in the following reactions:

$$Na^+ + Cl^- + H^+SO_3^- \text{ resin} \rightarrow Na^+SO_3^- \text{ resin} + H^+ + Cl^-$$
$$H^+ + Cl^- + NH_2 \text{ resin} \rightarrow Cl^-NH_3 \text{ resin}$$

Since ion exchange resins will not remove nonelectrolytes or organic matter from water, for intravenous fluids and strict analytical purposes, the water is first distilled and then passed through a mixed bed ion exchange resin.

Review Questions

1. List several functions of water in the body.
2. How would you describe dew, fog, frost, and snow from a chemical viewpoint?
3. Of what importance is the fact that ice is lighter than water?
4. Why are the water pipes in an unheated house drained during the winter?
5. For what reason are autoclaves more efficient than boiling water for sterilizing hospital supplies?
6. Why is the scientific thermometer called the centigrade thermometer?
7. Define and illustrate a polar compound.
8. Write equations for the reaction between:
    (a) Potassium and water.
    (b) Magnesium oxide and water.
    (c) Potassium carbonate and water.
9. How does heavy water differ from ordinary water?
10. Give three examples of hydrates.
11. What happens to a hydrate when it is heated? Illustrate with an example and name the product that is formed.
12. Would a deliquescent or an efflorescent compound make the best drying agent? Explain your reasoning.
13. What property of plaster of paris enables it to be used in the preparation of surgical casts?
14. What method of water purification would you use to prepare: (a) drinking water for a large city; (b) water for the preparation of solutions in the laboratory or hospital?
15. Why does recently boiled water have a flat taste? How can this be remedied?
16. Explain the difference between: (a) hard water and soft water; (b) temporary hard water and permanent hard water.
17. Write equations for the reactions that occur in the softening of (a) permanent hard water; (b) temporary hard water.
18. List several advantages for the use of soft water in the hospital, the home, and in industry.
19. Explain the difference between water softened by treatment with washing soda (Na_2CO_3) and by passing through a mixed-bed ion exchange resin.

Chapter 7

Solutions

We all recognize that it does not require a formal study of chemistry to observe that certain substances dissolve in water. The color, taste, and odor of some natural waters emphasize the ability of water to dissolve solids and gases. Early chemists were so impressed by the importance of solutions that they insisted substances did not react unless they were dissolved.

The common examples of sugar or salt dissolved in water illustrate a mixture which is called a solution. Here the sugar or salt molecules are uniformly distributed among the water molecules. A *solution,* then, is a uniform mixture of two or more substances whose particles are of atomic or molecular size. The particles dissolved in a salt solution are essentially sodium *ions* and chloride *ions*, while the particles dissolved in a sugar solution are sugar *molecules*. Since matter exists as a solid, liquid, or gas, many types of solutions are possible. For example, steel is a solution of carbon in iron, or a solid dissolved in a solid; household ammonia is a solution of ammonia gas in water, or a gas dissolved in a liquid. The air we breathe consists mainly of a solution of gases dissolved in a gas. The disinfectant, Lysol, is a solution of cresols in water, or a liquid dissolved in a liquid. In a solution, the substance which is dissolved is called the *solute,* while the substance in which the solute is dissolved is called the *solvent*. In a solution of common salt, the salt is the solute and the water is the solvent.

Importance of Solutions

The most common type of solutions are those in which a liquid is used as the solvent. By far the most important solvent is water; its solutions are called *aqueous solutions*. In the animal body, solutions are of great importance. The contents of living cells, and the food and waste material carried to and from the cells, exist in aqueous solutions. When food is digested in the body, it must be dissolved and carried into the blood stream in solution. The growth of plants depends on the circulation of solutions carrying food and waste material to and from the different parts of the plant. Since practically all chemical reactions take place in solution, it is essential to know their main properties. Many therapeutic agents are administered in the form of solutions to facilitate their absorption into the body, thereby assuring effective reaction.

Factors Affecting Solubility

Since we are concerned mainly with solutions that have solid solutes, the factors that influence their solubility will be considered first.

Nature of the Solute and Solvent

It is a well-known fact that our choice of solvent is important when we attempt to dissolve a solid substance. Water is a common solvent for many solutes such as sugar and salts but it is unsatisfactory for fat or paint. Iodine is only slightly soluble in water but will dissolve readily in alcohol. Ether, carbon tetrachloride, and gasoline are good solvents for fatty material, whereas turpentine is used to dissolve paint.

Surface

A finely powdered solute will dissolve more rapidly because more surface is exposed to the solvent.

Agitation

If the mixture is stirred, the rate of solubility of the solute is increased, since fresh solvent is continually coming into contact with the solute.

Temperature

The solubility of most solid solutes increases with a rise in temperature. However, there are some exceptions to this general rule. The following table illustrates the change in solubility of certain solutes at different temperatures:

SUBSTANCES	GRAMS DISSOLVED BY 100 CC. OF WATER AT		
	0° C.	20° C.	100° C.
Potassium nitrate	13.3	31.6	246.0
Copper sulfate	14.3	20.7	75.4
Sodium chloride	35.7	36.0	39.8
Calcium hydroxide	0.185	0.165	0.077

The first two substances show a definite increase in solubility as the temperature is raised, but the solubility of sodium chloride is only slightly affected by the change in temperature. The solubility of calcium hydroxide, on the other hand, decreases with a rise in temperature.

The solubility of gases is decreased by a rise in temperature and is increased by an increase in pressure. In the preparation of carbonated drinks, large amounts of carbon dioxide are forced into solution by pressure at a low temperature. If a cold bottle of soda water is opened, the pressure is released and the gas escapes slowly from the solution, forming bubbles in the water. If a warm bottle is opened, the carbon dioxide escapes rapidly, causing foam to spurt out of the bottle.

Types of Solution

Dilute and Concentrated Solution

Since solutions are mixtures, their concentration depends entirely upon the amount of solute dissolved in a definite quantity of solvent. When a solution contains a small percentage of the solute that could be dissolved in the solvent, it is said to be *dilute*; when it contains a large percentage, it is said to be *concentrated*.

Saturated Solution

If a solution is prepared by stirring an excess of solute until no more will dissolve it is said to be a *saturated* solution. At any given temperature a saturated solution will contain a definite quantity of solute in a given volume of solvent. For example, the addition of 40 gm. of sodium chloride to 100 gm. of water at 20° C. would result in a solution that contains 36 gm. of sodium chloride and 4 gm. of undissolved crystals. A state of equilibrium would exist between the dissolved and undissolved solute. Particles of the crystalline solute would be continually going into solution in a quantity that is exactly balanced by the amount of solute particles crystallizing out of the solution (Fig. 40). A saturated solution may be defined as a solution in which the dissolved solute exists in a state of equilibrium with the undissolved solute.

Supersaturated Solution

If a saturated solution is prepared at a higher temperature and is then allowed to cool, the extra solute that was dissolved at the higher temperature usually becomes insoluble and settles out of solution. If the hot solution is cooled slowly and is not disturbed, the excess solid may not settle out. In this case the solution will contain more solute than it can ordinarily dissolve at room temperature. Such a solution is called a *supersaturated solution.* If this solution 'is disturbed by the addition of a crystal of the solute, the material in excess of that required to saturate the solution at that temperaure will immediately crystallize out. Freshly prepared jams and jellies are common examples of supersaturated solutions. Upon standing, they may slowly form crystals of sugar.

Percentage Solutions

It is often important to have a more accurate knowledge of the concentration of a solution than merely being aware that it is dilute, concentrated, saturated, or supersaturated. A common method of expressing the concentration of an aqueous solution is to indicate the grams of solute in 100 cc. of a solution. This is the basis for the percentage solutions that are widely used in the laboratory and in medical

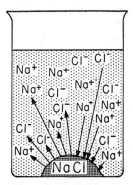

Figure 40. A state of equilibrium existing in a saturated solution of sodium chloride.

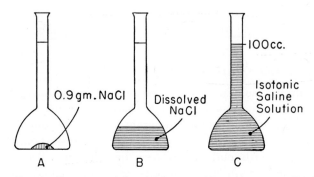

Figure 41.   An illustration of the preparation of a 0.9 per cent sodium chloride solution; A, 100 cc. volumetric flask containing 0.9 gm. sodium chloride; B, NaCl dissolved in water; C, solution diluted to the 100 cc. mark.

practice. A 10 per cent solution of sodium chloride, for example, would contain 10 gm. of sodium chloride dissolved in water and diluted until the solution had a final volume of 100 cc. Isotonic saline solution is a 0.9 per cent solution of sodium chloride; it contains 0.9 gm. of sodium chloride in 100 cc. of solution (Fig. 41).

To determine the amount of any substance required to prepare a definite volume of a percentage solution, one should start with the number of grams present in 100 cc. For example, to find the amount of glucose that must be used to prepare 300 cc. of a 5 per cent solution the following calculations would be made:

1. A 5 per cent solution contains 5 gm. in 100 cc.
2. Since 300 cc. is required:
    300/100 = 3 times the amount in 100 cc.
    3 × 5 gm. = 15 gm.
3. Therefore, 15 gm. of glucose are required to prepare 300 cc. of a 5 per cent solution.

When dealing with nonaqueous solutions, or using the precise technique of the physical chemist, percentage solutions are based on the grams of solute dissolved in 100 gm. of the solution. The preparation of solutions by weight is more time-consuming and in most laboratories is replaced by the weight per volume method described above. Where the solute is a liquid, the units used are cubic centimeters of solute in 100 cc. of solution. For example, a 5 per cent solution of alcohol is prepared by diluting 5 cc. of alcohol to a volume of 100 cc. with water. This type of solution is often expressed as per cent by volume.

Molar Solutions

A type of solution that is widely used by the chemist is the molar solution. This method of expressing the concentration is convenient because it bears a definite relationship to the molecular weight of the solute. A gram-molecular weight of a substance is known as a *mole* of the substance. A solution that contains one mole of the solute in one ·liter is called a *molar* solution. In calculating the amount of a compound that is used to prepare a given volume of a molar solution, the following scheme may be used:

FIRST STEP: Calculate the molecular weight of the compound and express it in grams.
Example: H_2SO_4 1 + 1 + 32 + 16 + 16 + 16 + 16 = 98
98 gm. equals 1 gram molecular weight.
SECOND STEP: A 1 molar (1M) solution contains the molecular weight in grams dissolved in 1 liter.
Example: 1M H_2SO_4 contains 98 gm. H_2SO_4 per 1000 cc.
THIRD STEP: To determine the amount of a compound present in a given volume of different molar solution.
Example: 1000 cc. of 0.5 M H_2SO_4
$$\frac{0.5M}{1.0M} = \tfrac{1}{2} \text{ times the amount in 1000 cc. of a 1M solution.}$$
$\tfrac{1}{2} \times 98$ gm. = 49 gm. H_2SO_4.
Therefore 1000 cc. of 0.5M H_2SO_4 contains 49 gm. H_2SO_4.
Example: 500 cc. of 3M H_2SO_4
$$\frac{3M}{1M} = 3 \text{ times the amount in 1000 cc. of a 1M solution.}$$
3×98 gm. = 294 gm. H_2SO_4 in 1000 cc. of 3M H_2SO_4.
$$500 \text{ cc. contains } \frac{500 \text{ cc.}}{1000 \text{ cc.}} = \tfrac{1}{2} \text{ the amount in 1000 cc. of 3M } H_2SO_4.$$
$\tfrac{1}{2} \times 294$ gm. = 147 gm. H_2SO_4.
Therefore 500 cc. of 3M H_2SO_4 contains 147 gm. H_2SO_4.

By the use of molar solutions, we can obtain any desired number of moles of a substance by merely measuring a volume of the solution.

Normal Solutions

Analytical laboratories often employ normal solutions. A *normal solution* contains one gram-equivalent weight of the solute in 1 liter of solution. A *gram-equivalent weight* is the quantity of a substance that will liberate or combine with 1.008 gm. of hydrogen. The gram-equivalent weight of any acid would be the weight equivalent to 1 (1.008) gm. of replaceable hydrogen. For example, HCl contains 1 gm. of replaceable hydrogen per mole; H_2SO_4, 2 gm. per mole; and H_3PO_4, 3 gm. per mole. One liter of 1M HCl would be equivalent to 1 liter of 1 normal (1N) HCl; 1 liter of IM H_2SO_4 equivalent to 1 liter of 2N H_2SO_4; and 1 liter of 1M H_3PO_4 equivalent to 1 liter of 3N H_3PO_4. An equivalent weight of any base is the weight that combines with 1 gm. of replaceable hydrogen. Since the hydroxyl ion (OH^-) of the base combines with the hydrogen ion (H^+) of the acid to form a water molecule, the gram-equivalent weight of a base would be the weight equivalent to 17 (17.008) gm. of OH^-. Sodium hydroxide contains 17 gm. OH^- per mole, $Ca(OH)_2$ contains 34 gm. OH^- per mole, and $Al(OH)_3$ contains 51 gm. OH^- per mole. One liter of a 1 molar solution of these bases would be equivalent to 1 liter of 1N NaOH, of 2N $Ca(OH)_2$, and of 3N $Al(OH)_3$. The gram-equivalent weights of salts may be determined by their relation to equivalent weights of acids or bases, and normal solutions of such salts may be prepared. To calculate the amount of a compound required to prepare a given volume of a normal solution, we may proceed as follows:

EXAMPLE: 1000 cc. of 0.5N NaOH
40.0 gm. equal 1 gram-molecular weight which is equivalent to 17 gm. OH^-; therefore 1000 cc. of 1N NaOH contains 40.0 gm., and 1000 cc. of 0.5N NaOH would contain $\frac{1}{2} \times 40$ or 20.0 gm. of NaOH.

EXAMPLE: 500 cc. of 2N HCl
36.5 gm. equals 1 gram-molecular weight which contains 1 gm. of replaceable hydrogen; therefore 1000 cc. of 1N HCl contains 36.5 gm. of HCl.
$$\frac{2N}{1N} = 2 \text{ times the amount in 1000 cc. of 1N HCl}$$
$36.5 \times 2 = 73.0$ gm. HCl in 1000 cc. of 2N HCl
$$\frac{500 \text{ cc.}}{1000 \text{ cc.}} = \tfrac{1}{2} \text{ the amount in 1000 cc. of 2N HCl}$$
$\frac{1}{2} \times 73.0 = 36.5$ gm. HCl
Therefore, 500 cc. of 2N HCl contains 36.5 gm. HCl.

Expressing the concentration in normality has a major advantage over expression as molar or percentage solution. Since the equivalent weight of an acid, base, or salt is involved, it follows that equal volumes of a 1N acid, base, or salt are chemically equivalent. For example 1 liter of a 1N HCl solution is chemically equivalent to 1 liter of a 1N NaOH solution. Therefore, if the normality of one solution is known, by measuring the volume of the two solutions that are chemically equivalent, one can calculate the normality of the other solution. This may be expressed in the simple equation:

cc. of A $\times$ N of A = cc. of B $\times$ N of B

A problem illustrating this point may be stated as follows:

A 20.0 cc. portion of 0.1N HCl required exactly 10.0 cc. of a NaOH solution to reach the chemical equivalent point. (This process is known as titration and involves the addition of the base to the acid in the presence of a suitable indicator until a color change of the indicator signifies the chemical equivalent point). What is the normality of the NaOH solution?

Substituting in the equation:

cc. of HCl $\times$ N of HCl = cc. of NaOH $\times$ N of NaOH
we have
$$20 \times 0.1 = 10 \times N$$
$$N = \frac{20 \times 0.1}{10} = 0.2$$
Therefore the NaOH solution is 0.2N.

Some Physical Properties of Solutions

Diffusion

If we drop a crystal of a colored solute such as potassium permanganate ($KMnO_4$) in a vessel of water, a purple color is soon observed in the water immediately surrounding the crystal. In a few hours, the purple color is scattered throughout the entire solution, showing that the molecules of the dissolved solute diffuse or move about freely in the solvent.

Freezing and Boiling Points of a Solution

A solution always has a lower freezing point and a higher boiling point than the pure solvent. Practical use is made of this lowering of the freezing point. For example, the brine or calcium chloride solutions used in refrigeration freeze at a much lower temperature than water. In the manufacture of ice, the circulating brine conducts heat away from the water, causing it to freeze while the brine remains liquid. A mixture of ice and common salt can lower the freezing temperature to $-21°$ C. and is often employed in making ice cream. The

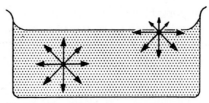

Figure 42.   The forces acting on water
molecules within a vessel of water.

so-called antifreeze compounds that are used in automobile radiators
are merely substances like alcohol and gycerol that lower the freezing point of the circulating water and prevent its freezing in the
winter.

Surface Tension

The molecules of a solution are constantly attracted to each other.
A molecule in the center of a solution is completely surrounded by
other molecules and is therefore equally attracted from all sides. A
molecule near the surface of the solution (Fig. 42) is attracted downward more strongly because there are more molecules in the solution
below it than in the air above the surface. This downward pull on
the surface molecules causes them to pack tightly together to form a
surface film. *Surface tension* is the force or tension required to break
this film. Water has a higher surface tension than most liquids, in
fact the parlor trick of floating a steel needle on water is made possible by the strength of its surface film.

Osmosis

Many plant or animal membranes are semipermeable in that they
allow one component of a solution to pass through, while they hold
back another component. The roots of a plant are covered with a
semipermeable membrane that allows the passage of water into the
plant but will not allow the substances in the sap to pass out into the
ground. If the solutions on either side of a semipermeable membrane
are unequal in concentration, there is a tendency to equalize the concentration. The diffusible component, usually water, will tend to flow
from the more dilute solution into the concentrated solution. This
selective flow of a diffusible component through a membrane is called
osmosis (Fig. 43); the pressure exerted by the movement of the com-

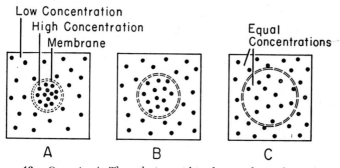

Figure 43. Osmosis. *A*, The solution within the membrane has a higher concentration of salts than the solution on the outside. *B*, In the process of osmosis, water flows into the solution of high concentration until the concentrations are equalized, *C*.

ponent is called the *osmotic pressure.* The osmotic pressure of a solution is proportional to the amount of solute dissolved in the solution. When the solutions on each side of a semipermeable membrane have established equilibrium and have an equal concentration of components, they are said to be *isotonic.*

Isotonic Salt Solution

The normal concentration of salts in the blood is approximately equivalent to a 0.9 per cent sodium chloride solution. Very little osmosis occurs when living tissues are in contact with a salt solution of this strength. A 0.9 per cent solution of sodium chloride is therefore called an *isotonic salt solution.* When blood is mixed with an isotonic salt solution, there is an equilibrium between the 0.9 per cent salt solution on one side of the red cell membrane and the cell contents on the other side. Therefore, no osmosis occurs, the red corpuscles do not change in size or shape, and the isotonic salt solution is isotonic with respect to the red blood cell (Fig. 44).

If a solution contains a lower concentration of salt than the blood, it is said to be *hypotonic.* Distilled water is an example of a hypotonic solution. When blood is mixed with a hypotonic solution, the corpuscles begin to swell and finally rupture. Since the two solutions on either side of the cell membrane are of unequal concentration, osmosis occurs and water flows into the cell from the lower to the higher concentration. This causes dilution of the cell contents and the cell in-

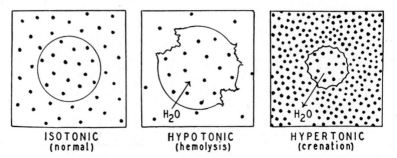

ISOTONIC   HYPOTONIC   HYPERTONIC
(normal)   (hemolysis)   (crenation)

Figure 44. A simple representation of the changes that occur in the red blood cell when it is suspended in an isotonic, a hypotonic, and a hypertonic solution.

creases in size until it bursts. This disintegration of corpuscles in a hypotonic solution is called *hemolysis* (Fig. 44) and the blood is said to be *laked*.

A solution that contains a higher percentage of salt than the blood is called a *hypertonic* solution. A 5 per cent solution of sodium chloride would be an example of a hypertonic solution. When blood is mixed with a hypertonic solution, the water in the cell contents flows out through the cell membrane into the solution of higher concentration. This causes the cell to decrease in size; this shrinking of corpuscles in a hypertonic solution is called *crenation* (Fig. 44).

It is evident from the previous discussion that solutions cannot be safely introduced into the blood stream unless they are practically isotonic with respect to the corpuscles. When drugs are administered intravenously, they are often dissolved in isotonic salt solution. A sterile isotonic salt solution is commonly used to cleanse wounds to prevent changes in the tissues by osmosis. After hemorrhage, the fluid content of the circulatory system is often increased by the injection of sterile isotonic salt solution.

True Solutions, Collodial Solutions, and Suspensions

In a *true solution*, the solute dissolves in the solvent to form a homogeneous mixture of individual molecules. As has already been stated, the particles of the dissolved substance are too small to be seen and will never settle out of the solution. When a solid solute does not dissolve in the solvent and the particles are so large that they can be seen with the naked eye, the mixture is called a *suspension*. The solid substance usually settles to the bottom of the solvent on standing. Many finely divided solutes which do not dissolve in the solvent have particles so small that they will not settle out of the mixture on standing and cannot be seen with the naked eye. These substances whose particles are intermediate in size between those in true solutions and in suspensions, are called colloids; when mixed with a solvent they form *colloidal solutions*. Such solutions are more accurately called colloidal dispersions since the solute does not dissolve in the solvent.

The particles in the three types of solutions would, therefore, vary from molecular size in the true solution to a large visible particle in the suspensions. The size of the particles in a colloidal solution are usually considered to vary from 1 to 100 millimicrons ($m\mu$) in diameter. A millimicron is one-millionth of a millimeter ($1 \mu = 1/1000$ mm. and $1 m\mu = 1/1000 \mu$). The relationship of these types of solutions and some of their properties is shown in the following tabulation:

TRUE SOLUTIONS	COLLOIDAL SOLUTIONS	SUSPENSIONS
1. Particle size less than 1 mμ	1 mμ to 100 mμ	100 mμ or more
2. Invisible	Visible only in ultra- or electron microscope	Visible to naked eye
3. Will pass through filters and membranes	Will pass through filters but not membranes	Will not pass through filters
4. Possess molecular movement	Exhibit brownian movement	Move only by force of gravity

The electron microscope that is used to make colloidal particles visible is shown in Figure 45, while its powers of magnification are illustrated in Figure 46.

In colloid chemistry, the particles are called the dispersed phase, and the fluid in which they are dispersed is called the dispersion medium. The correct term for a colloidal solution is therefore a colloidal dispersion, although the term "solution" is commonly used. Many substances of biological interest such as proteins, starch, and soap form *colloidal solutions* when added to water. When such a colloidal solution is a liquid it is called a *sol*, when a solid it is known as a *gel*.

Substances may be transformed into colloidal size either by the gathering of particles of atomic or molecular size into particles with colloidal dimensions or by the subdivision of a mass into colloidal size particles. The first process is called *condensation* or *precipitation*, while the second is known as *dispersion or peptization*. An example

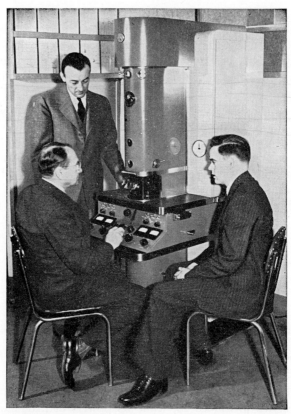

Figure 45. The electron microscope, 50 to 100 times more powerful than the best light microscope, includes a diffraction camera. Seated are Dr. V. K. Zworykin (left) and Dr. James Hillier and standing is P. C. Smith, the men largely responsible for the development of the electron microscope in this country. (Courtesy of R.C.A., Camden, N. J.)

of the condensation or precipitation method is the formation of arsenic sulfide solution by precipitation of arsenic oxide with hydrogen sulfide.

$$As_2O_3 + 3H_2S \rightarrow As_2S_3 + 3H_2O$$

The dispersion process can be most easily achieved by the mechanical grinding of material into particles of colloidal size. A device that is used for this purpose is called a *colloid mill*.

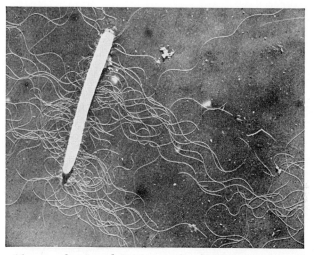

Figure 46. An electron photomicrograph of a common bacteria, *Proteus,* showing flagella. (Magnification 20,000 times.) (Courtesy of C. F. Robinow and W. Van Iterson.)

Properties of Colloids

Size

As has been stated, any substance that is subdivided into particles ranging in size from 1 to 100 mμ is a colloid. Particles of this size have a relatively large surface compared with their small weight. For example, if we subdivided a tennis ball into pieces the size of colloidal particles and spread them in a layer, they would cover a surface equal to 20 tennis courts. Powdered charcoal is an example of a colloid whose particles have an extremely large surface in comparison to their weight.

Electric Charge

When colloidal particles are dispersed in water they carry a characteristic electrical charge on their surface. The nature of the charge may be determined by placing the colloidal solution in a U-tube fitted with electrodes. As an electric current is passed through the colloid, it will migrate to the anode if it is negatively charged, as

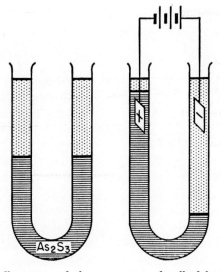

Figure 47. An illustration of the movement of colloidal particles under the
influence of an electric current. This process is known as electrophoresis.

shown in Figure 47, and to the cathode if it is positively charged.
This process is called *electrophoresis*. The particles of any one colloid
all have the same electrical charge. For example, arsenic sulfide, As_2S_3,
has negatively charged particles.

Movement

The molecules in a true solution are in a state of constant rapid
motion. Both solute and solvent molecules exhibit this *molecular
motion*. Since colloidal particles are composed of an aggregate of
many molecules, the movement of the particle is very slow compared
to that of an individual molecule. Apparently the major motion in a
colloidal dispersion is caused by the bombardment of the particles by
the molecules of the dispersion medium. This erratic movement of
colloidal particles was first observed under an ultramicroscope by
Robert Brown and is known as *brownian movement.*

If a strong beam of light is passed through a colloidal solution, the
path of the beam is clearly outlined because of the reflection of the
light from the surfaces of the moving colloidal particles (Fig. 48).
This phenomenon is called the *Tyndall effect;* it may be used as a

simple test to distinguish between true solutions and colloidal
solutions.

Adsorption

A characteristic property of colloids is their ability to adsorb or take
up other substances on their surfaces. This process is called *adsorption*
and has many practical applications. For instance, charcoal is used in
gas masks to adsorb poisonous gases, and in tablets to aid in the
treatment of indigestion. Some cities use charcoal to remove gases
and offensive odors from their water supply. A medical preparation
such as argyrol contains colloidal silver adsorbed on a protein.

Dialysis

Substances that dissolve to form true solutions are often called
crystalloids to distinguish them from colloids. Crystalloids will readily
pass through membranes that hold back the colloidal particles. In

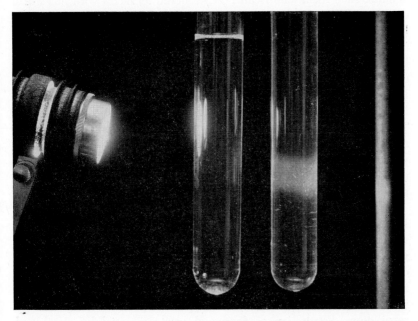

Figure 48. A demonstration of the Tyndall effect. The colloidal particles in the
tube on the right reflect the beam of light and make its path visible.

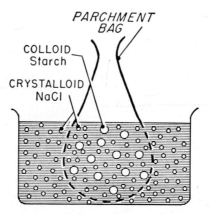

Figure 49. The process of dialysis. The crystalloid particles, NaCl, readily pass through the holes in the membrane, while the colloidal particles of starch are held back.

general, such membranes can be considered as sieves with holes of a definite size. If the substance to be diffused through the membrane has particles smaller than the holes, as in the case of a crystalloid, it will readily pass through, but colloidal particles larger than the holes are withheld. If a solution containing both crystalloids and colloids is placed in a parchment bag and the bag is suspended in a beaker of distilled water, the crystalloids will pass through the membrane into the distilled water while the colloids will remain in the bag. The membrane is called a *dialyzing membrane* and the process of separation of the crystalloids from the colloids is called *dialysis*. This process is represented in Figure 49, in which sodium chloride is used as an example of a crystalloid and starch as a colloid. A commercial application of dialysis is shown in Figure 50.

Most animal membranes may be regarded as dialyzing membranes. In the human body, the process of absorption of the digested food material takes place through the mucous membrane of the intestinal wall. As long as the food remains in a colloidal solution, it cannot dialyze through the membrane. The process of digestion converts the food into crystalloid material that can pass through the intestinal wall into the blood stream. Many other processes in the body such as respiration, distribution of food and waste material by the blood, formation of urine by the kidneys, and the proper distribution of fluid in the tissues depend upon the passage of substances through membranes.

Gels

Certain colloidal solutions as gelatin and agar are liquid when freshly made but solidify on standing to form a jelly-like material. This semisolid substance retains the water that was used to prepare the solution and is called a *gel*. Common examples of gels in the home are fruit jellies, gelatin desserts, custards, and cornstarch puddings.

Emulsions

If we shake together two liquids that do not mix, as oil and water, the result is a milky appearing solution called an *emulsion*. Small globules of oil remain suspended in the water for a short time but the two liquids soon separate. For this reason, a mixture of oil and water is called a *temporary emulsion*. Milk and cream are examples of *permanent emulsions*. If a certain type of colloid is added to a temporary emulsion, it coats the globules of the fat or oil and prevents them from running together, thus making a more permanent emulsion. A small amount of a soap solution will make a permanent emulsion of

Figure 50. Large scale dialysis in the manufacture of antitoxin. (Courtesy of Parke Davis & Company, Detroit.)

oil and water. Colloids that act in this fashion are called *emulsifying agents*. Milk is an emulsion of butter fat in water with casein acting as an emulsifying agent. Mayonnaise is an emulsion of oils and vinegar to which the colloids of egg yolks are added as emulsifying agents.

Importance of Colloids

A knowledge of colloids is important from both a chemical and physiological standpoint. Colloidal chemistry is essential for an understanding of oils, greases, soaps, starch, paints, lacquers, rubber, textiles, leather, cream, milk, and many pharmaceutical products used as medications. Such processes as cooking, washing, dyeing of fabrics, water purification, and sewage disposal are more readily explained by the use of colloidal chemistry.

It is difficult to estimate the extent of the influence of colloids on physiological processes. The tissues of the body are colloidal in nature; therefore many of the reactions that occur in the tissues involve colloidal chemistry. For example, the digestion of food begins as a colloidal process, the food first forming a colloidal solution before it is completely digested into small molecules. The contraction of muscle tissue during movement of the body is governed by colloidal phenomena. Abnormal conditions such as edema, pain, headaches, and certain diseases are closely related to colloidal chemistry.

Colloidal chemistry, therefore, is an important division of chemistry and a more thorough understanding of its principles will aid in the intelligent treatment of the ills of the human body.

Review Questions

1. Name four types of solutions. For each type give an example not mentioned in the book.
2. Define solution, solute, and solvent.
3. Given a dry solid that is soluble in water, what factors influence the solubility of the solid? How would you proceed to prepare a solution of the substance in the shortest possible time?
4. Why are bottles of carbonated beverages cooled before removing the caps?
5. Distinguish between the following terms: (a) dilute and concentrated, (b) saturated and supersaturated.
6. How many grams of cane sugar would be required to prepare 500 cc. of a 10 per cent solution?
7. A physiological salt solution contains 0.9 per cent sodium chloride. Three liters (3000 cc.) would contain how many grams of sodium chloride?

8. One liter (1000 cc.) of 2M sodium hydroxide contains how many grams of sodium hydroxide?

9. How many grams of sulfuric acid (H_2SO_4) are there in 400 cc. of a 0.5N solution?

10. Compare the preparation of a normal solution with that of a molar solution.

11. A 20.0 cc. portion of 0.5N HCl required exactly 10.0 cc. of a sodium hydroxide solution to reach the chemical equivalent point. What is the normality of the NaOH solution?

12. Explain your conception of surface tension, osmosis, and osmotic pressure.

13. Why is physiological salt solution said to be isotonic with respect to the red blood cell?

15. Outline the main differences between true solutions, colloids, and suspensions.

16. What is meant by electrophoresis and why do colloid particles exhibit this phenomenon?

17. Of what physiological importance is the process of dialysis? Can you suggest a practical application of dialysis in the field of medicine?

18. List several examples of emulsions that are encountered in the home and in the hospital. What type of pharmaceutical products are usually permanent emulsions?

19. What is the Tyndall effect? Why does a true solution fail to exhibit this phenomenon?

Chapter 8

Acids, Bases, and Salts

As increased knowledge concerning atoms, molecules, elements and compounds became available, it soon became apparent that a classification system would be desirable. Elements were classified by a system based on increasing atomic numbers and similar physical and chemical properties. This resulted in the periodic table, a detailed discussion of which is beyond the scope of this text. Compounds are not as readily classified; but, in the main, may be divided into three major groups: acids, bases, and salts.

Acids

Acids are most commonly encountered in aqueous solution although they may exist as solids, liquids, or gas. Boric acid, for example, is a solid; sulfuric acid is a liquid; and hydrochloric acid is a solution of the gas, hydrogen chloride. As a rule, acids are not very reactive unless they are in solution. The following list will help us to understand the composition of some of the common acids:

ACID	FORMULA
Hydrochloric acid	HCl
Hydrobromic acid	HBr
Nitric acid	HNO_3
Carbonic acid	H_2CO_3
Sulfuric acid	H_2SO_4
Phosphoric acid	H_3PO_4
Boric acid	H_3BO_3

From the above formulas, it can be seen that acids consist of hydrogen combined with another element or with a radical. The element or radical that is combined with hydrogen in an acid is called the *acid radical.*

Hydrogen is usually attached to the acid radical by covalent bonds as shown in the acid, hydrogen chloride (Fig. 51). Acids are polar compounds since the acid radical attracts the electrons and exhibits a negative charge, leaving the hydrogen end of the molecule with a positive charge. When acids are dissolved in water their polar nature favors a split into positively charged hydrogen ions and a negatively charged acid radical.

Properties of Acids

1. All acids in solution have a sour taste. Citrus fruits, for example, taste sour because of the presence of the organic acid, citric acid. The sour taste of vinegar is due to acetic acid.

2. Acids change the blue color of litmus dye to red. This is one of the simplest tests for the presence of an acid. A substance like litmus that has one color in an acid solution and another color in a basic solution is called an *indicator.*

3. Acids react with many metals to form hydrogen gas. The metal replaces the hydrogen of the acid, liberating hydrogen gas. For example, in the following reaction zinc replaces the hydrogen of sulfuric acid to form zinc sulfate and gaseous hydrogen:

$$Zn + H_2SO_4 \rightarrow ZnSO_4 + H_2 \uparrow$$

Not all of the metals possess enough chemical activity to replace the hydrogen of an acid. There are some metals that produce only a few bubbles of hydrogen from acids, while still others show no reaction. A list of metals arranged in order of their activity in replacing the hydrogen of acids is shown in the following tabulation.

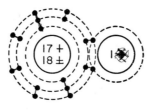

Hydrochloric acid

Figure 51.   A molecule of hydrochloric acid illustrating covalent bonding between the hydrogen and the chlorine atoms.

```
Potassium ..................K
Sodium .....................Na
Calcium ....................Ca
Magnesium ................Mg
Aluminum .................Al
Zinc .......................Zn
Iron .......................Fe
Nickel .....................Ni
Tin ........................Sn
Lead .......................Pb
HYDROGEN ...............H
Copper ....................Cu
Mercury ...................Hg
Silver .....................Ag
Platinum ..................Pt
Gold ......................Au
```

In this list the most active metals are located at the top, and the most inactive metals at the bottom. *All metals above hydrogen in the tabulation have the property of replacing hydrogen from an acid, while those listed under hydrogen will not replace it from an acid.* This series is commonly known as the *electromotive series*. Since the hydrogen of an acid may be replaced by most metals we can enlarge our definition of an acid to include the fact that the hydrogen of an acid is *replaceable hydrogen.*

Acids react with all of the common industrial metals and should not be allowed to come in contact with surgical instruments or metal containers. All laboratory reactions that involve acids are carried out in glass vessels.

4. Acids react with oxides and hydroxides to form water and a salt. The action of an acid on an oxide or hydroxide of a metal may be represented as follows:

$$MgO + 2HNO_3 \rightarrow Mg(NO_3)_2 + H_2O$$

$$NaOH + HCl \rightarrow NaCl + H_2O$$

In the reaction between an acid and a metallic hydroxide, or base, both the acid and the base are neutralized. A reaction of an acid and a base to form water and a salt is therefore called a *neutralization reaction.* To obtain an accurate measure of the concentration of an acid in solution, a sample of the solution is titrated with a base of known concentration, as illustrated in Figure 52. An indicator is used to mark the point of neutralization. The basic solution contained in a burette is slowly added to the acid solution and indicator in a flask until the indicator changes color. At the neutralization point, the volume of the acid and base used are known, as is the normality of the base. Using the simple equation:

$$\text{cc. of NaOH} \times \text{N of NaOH} = \text{cc. of HCl} \times \text{N of HCl}$$

the normality of the acid may be calculated.

5. Acids react with carbonates and bicarbonates to form carbon dioxide gas. Sodium carbonate (Na_2CO_3) or washing soda, and sodium bicarbonate ($NaHCO_3$) or baking soda, react with acids to form carbon dioxide gas, water, and a salt.

$$Na_2CO_3 + H_2SO_4 \rightarrow CO_2 \uparrow + H_2O + Na_2SO_4$$

$$NaHCO_3 + HCl \rightarrow CO_2 \uparrow + H_2O + NaCl$$

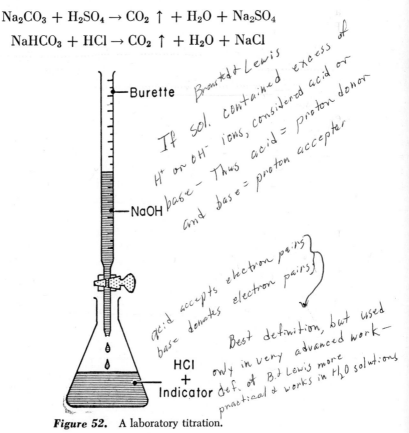

Burette

Bronsted & Lewis

If sol. contained excess of
H^+ or OH^- ions, considered acid or
base — Thus acid = proton donor
and base = proton accepter

NaOH

acid accepts electron pairs
base donates electron pairs

HCl
+
Indicator

Best definition, but used
only in very advanced work —
def. of B.& Lewis more
practical & works in H_2O solutions

Figure 52. A laboratory titration.

Baking soda is widely used for the neutralization of acid and for the production of carbon dioxide gas. A great many patent medicines for the relief of pain, indigestion, and constipation contain bicarbonates that neutralize the acid in the stomach. Neutralization of the acid in the stomach by frequent use of sodium bicarbonate interferes with gastric digestion and may result in more serious disturbances. Baking powders contain a bicarbonate and some acid-forming substance, which, when moisture is added, release gaseous carbon dioxide throughout the cake batter, making it light. The lactic acid of sour milk produces the same effect when mixed with baking soda. The action of a common type of fire extinguisher depends upon the reaction between sulfuric acid and sodium bicarbonate.

The Naming of Acids

Acids composed of hydrogen and one other element are called *binary* or *hydro-acids*. They are named from the second element and always begin with the prefix *hydro-* and end with the suffix *-ic*. Examples:

H   Cl   H   Br   H   F
Hydro-chlor-ic   *Hydro-brom-ic*   *Hydro-fluor-ic*

Many acids contain oxygen in addition to hydrogen and another element and are called *ternary* or *oxy-acids*. Such acids are named after the element other than hydrogen or oxygen and end with the suffix *-ic*. Examples:

H_2SO_4 H_3PO_4 H_2CO_3
Sulfur-ic   *Phosphor-ic*   *Carbon-ic*

If the same three elements unite to form more than one ternary acid, the acid with the greatest number of oxygen atoms ends in *-ic*, while the acid with the lowest number of oxygen atoms ends in *-ous*. Examples:

HNO_3 H_2SO_4
Nitr-ic   *Sulfur-ic*

HNO_2 H_2SO_3
Nitr-ous   *Sulfur-ous*

Bases

Most of us are familiar with such common bases as lye, used in opening clogged drains, and household ammonia, used in cleaning. These compounds and others which contain the hydroxyl radical combined with a metal or with the ammonium radical are considered bases or alkalies by the chemist. Oxides of metals probably should be classed as bases since they react with water to form hydroxides.

$$MgO + H_2O \rightarrow Mg(OH)_2$$

The following list contains examples of the common bases:

BASE	FORMULA
Sodium hydroxide	NaOH
Potassium hydroxide	KOH
Magnesium hydroxide	$Mg(OH)_2$
Calcium hydroxide	$Ca(OH)_2$
Ammonium hydroxide	NH_4OH

The metallic hydroxides and oxides all exist as solids while ammonium hydroxide consists of a gas dissolved in water. The hydroxyl radical is formed from hydrogen and oxygen by a covalent linkage, whereas the metal is combined with the hydroxide in an electrovalent linkage (Fig. 53). This combination may be illustrated with the base, sodium hydroxide.

Properties of Bases

1. When a base is dissolved in water, the solution has a slippery feeling.

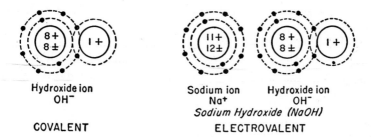

Hydroxide ion
OH⁻

COVALENT

Sodium ion   Hydroxide ion
Na⁺   OH⁻
Sodium Hydroxide (NaOH)

ELECTROVALENT

Figure 53. The hydroxide ion is formed by covalent linkage whereas the sodium ion and hydroxide ion are joined by electrovalent forces to form sodium hydroxide.

2. Solutions of bases have a bitter, metallic taste. (*Caution:* They should be tasted only in dilute solutions.)

3. Bases change the red color of litmus to a blue. In general, bases reverse the color change that was produced by an acid in an indicator.

4. Bases react with acids to form water and a salt:

$$2KOH + H_2SO_4 \rightarrow 2H_2O + K_2SO_4$$

This is another example of a neutralization reaction.

The Naming of Bases

Since bases consist of a metal combined with the hydroxyl radical, they are named by starting with the name of the metal and ending with the word *hydroxide*. For example, NaOH is sodium hydroxide, KOH is potassium hydroxide, and $Ca(OH)_2$ is calcium hydroxide. (The only exception to this rule concerns the base that does not contain a metal; this is named ammonium hydroxide in a similar fashion.)

Action of Acids and Bases on Tissues

Strong acids (sulfuric, nitric, and hydrochloric) and strong bases (sodium and potassium hydroxide) will destroy tissues by dissolving their protein material and extracting their water. Concentrated sulfuric acid is an extremely effective dehydrating agent that rapidly burns tissue on contact. Concentrated nitric acid combines with tissue staining it yellow in addition to its destructive action. Basic solutions will also combine with the tissue fats and cause more extensive destruction than that produced by acids. Household lye (crude NaOH) is a common example of a strong base. This substance is very caustic and must be handled carefully to prevent damage to the skin.

If strong acids or bases are spilled on the skin, a serious burn may result. In either case, the area should be flooded with water to remove quickly any of the acid or base that has not combined with the tissue. In the case of acid burns, a weak alkaline solution should then be applied to neutralize any acid that remains on the skin. Dilute ammonia water (NH_4OH), limewater [$Ca(OH)_2$] or baking soda ($NaHCO_3$) are effective weak bases that may be applied without injury to the skin. In the treatment of alkali burns, the excess alkali remaining on the skin should be neutralized with a dilute acid. The acetic acid in vinegar or a boric acid solution may be safely used. A very dilute solution of a strong acid may be used, but care should be taken to prevent further injury to the tissues from a solution that is too concentrated.

Animal fibers, such as wool, or silk, are also proteins and are attacked by acids or bases. Silk or woolen materials cannot be washed in strong laundry soaps because the soap contains some free base; this may cause them to shrink and may also partially dissolve the fabrics. Basic substances such as lye, washing soda, and ammonia are often used as cleaning agents because of their ability to dissolve protein and fats.

Salts

When an acid and a base react with each other they form water and a salt.

$$HCl + KOH \rightarrow H_2O + KCl$$

Salts may also be formed by the displacement of hydrogen from an acid with a metal.

$$Mg + 2HNO_3 \rightarrow Mg(NO_3)_2 + H_2 \uparrow$$

We may define salts either as compounds formed by replacing the hydrogen of an acid with a metal, or as the compound other than water formed when an acid and a base react with each other. Salts may be considered also as the combination of a metal or a metallic ion with the acid radical of an acid. Inorganic salts, acids, and bases ordinarily consist of ions combined by electrovalence even in the solid or crystalline state. On the basis of advanced physical chemistry, we cannot accurately refer to a molecule of sodium chloride, sulfuric acid, or sodium hydroxide, although it is extremely difficult to gain a clear understanding of all the properties of these compounds without reference to molecules.

Reactions of Salts

1. Salts react with each other to form new salts.

$$NaCl + AgNO_3 \rightarrow NaNO_3 + AgCl \downarrow$$

This is a common reaction in chemistry and is used as a test for the presence of a chloride. When silver nitrate is added to a solution that contains chlorides, a positive test is indicated by the formation of a

Salt = gen. definition = any formula
with no H+ or OH present, brings things
whether dissolved/salt will self together
or does not.

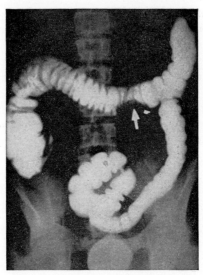

Figure 54. Carcinoma of the colon diagnosed from an x-ray photograph of the large intestine filled with barium sulfate solution. (From Farrell, J. T., Jr.: Roentgen Diagnosis of Diseases of the Gastrointestinal Tract, Springfield, Ill., Charles C. Thomas, Publisher.)

white precipitate (insoluble AgCl). Silver nitrate solutions are used therapeutically as germicides. One drop of a 1 per cent solution of silver nitrate is placed in the eyes of newborn babies to prevent gonorrheal infections. It is also often used in bladder infections, but its germicidal activity is stopped when it reacts with the sodium chloride in the urine to form the insoluble silver chloride.

2. Salts react with acids to form other salts and other acids.

$$BaCl_2 + H_2SO_4 \rightarrow BaSO_4 \downarrow + 2HCl$$

The insoluble barium sulfate formed in this reaction is opaque to x-rays. When given patients by mouth, it coats the stomach and intestine, outlining them on the x-ray photograph. It is commonly used as a diagnostic aid in the detection of ulcers and cancer in the gastrointestinal tract (Fig. 54).

3. Salts react with bases to form other salts and other bases.

$$MgSO_4 + 2KOH \rightarrow K_2SO_4 + Mg(OH)_2 \downarrow$$

Magnesium hydroxide, the insoluble base formed in this reaction, is often used in medicine. When mixed with water, it forms a suspension known as milk of magnesia. Since it is a weak base, milk of magnesia is often used to neutralize excess acid in the stomach.

Normal and Acid Salts

A *normal* salt is one in which all the hydrogen of an acid has been replaced by a metal. For instance, all the salts in the three reactions just discussed are normal salts. Salts formed from acids that contain more than one replaceable hydrogen atom may retain one or more hydrogen atoms in their molecule and are called *acid salts*. For example, sulfuric acid may react with sodium hydroxide to form sodium acid sulfate, which is commonly called sodium bisulfate or sodium hydrogen sulfate.

$$H_2SO_4 + NaOH \rightarrow NaHSO_4 + H_2O$$

If both hydrogen atoms are replaced by sodium, the normal salt sodium sulfate is formed.

$$H_2SO_4 + 2NaOH \rightarrow Na_2SO_4 + 2H_2O$$

Other examples of acid salts are sodium bicarbonate ($NaHCO_3$), sodium dihydrogen phosphate (NaH_2PO_4), and disodium hydrogen phosphate (Na_2HPO_4). The latter two compounds are made from phosphoric acid, which has three replaceable hydrogen atoms; therefore two acid salts are possible.

The Naming of Salts

Normal salts that are formed from binary acids are named by starting with the name of the metal or ammonium radical and ending the name of the nonmetal with the suffix *-ide*, for example, sodium chloride for NaCl, ammonium chloride for NH_4Cl, potassium bromide for KBr, and potassium iodide for KI. If the metal has more than one valence, the endings -ous and -ic are used after the name of the metal. A salt in which the metal has the lower valence contains the suffix -ous, while the salt of the metal with the higher valence uses the suffix -ic. Mercury has a valence of $+1$ or $+2$ and its salts are named mercurous chloride for Hg_2Cl_2 and mercuric chloride for $HgCl_2$. In a similar fashion, iron salts in which the iron has a valence of $+2$ or $+3$ are named ferrous chloride for $FeCl_2$ and ferric chloride for $FeCl_3$.

The names of salts derived from ternary acids depend on the name of the acid. If the name of the acid ends in -ic, the name of the salt ends in *ate:*

> HNO_3, nitric acid ....$NaNO_3$, sodium nitrate
> H_2CO_3, carbonic acid ....K_2CO_3, potassium carbonate
> H_2SO_4, sulfuric acid ....$BaSO_4$, barium sulfate

If the name of the acid ends in -ous, the name of the salt ends in *-ite:*

> HNO_2, nitrous acid ....$NaNO_2$, sodium nitrite
> H_2SO_3, sulfurous acid ....$BaSO_3$, barium sulfite

This type of salt may also be named from the acid radical in the acid from which the salt was formed. The following radicals would form salts named as follows:

> SO_4, sulfate radical ....Na_2SO_4, sodium sulfate
> CO_3, carbonate radical ....$CaCO_3$, calcium carbonate
> NO_2, nitrite radical ....KNO_2, potassium nitrite
> PO_4, phosphate radical ....$AlPO_4$, aluminum phosphate
> SO_3, sulfite radical ....K_2SO_3, potassium sulfite
> NO_3, nitrate radical ....$Ba(NO_3)_2$, barium nitrate

When the metal has more than one valence, these salts are named in a similar fashion to those derived from binary acids. For example, $HgNO_3$ would be named mercurous nitrate, $Hg(NO_3)_2$ would be named mercuric nitrate, and Hg_2SO_3 would be named mercurous sulfite.

Acid salts are named like normal salts except that the name of the radical is preceded by the prefix bi-, the word hydrogen, or the word acid. The acid salt $NaHSO_4$ is named sodium bisulfate, sodium hydrogen sulfate, or sodium acid sulfate. The common prefix is bi- as in sodium bicarbonate $NaHCO_3$, and potassium bisulfite $KHSO_3$.

Importance of Salts

Many salts are essential for the proper functioning of the body. Calcium and phosphorus salts are necessary for the normal deposition of bones and teeth, while iodides are required for correct function of the thyroid gland. Iron salts are used in the formation of hemoglobin, the respiratory pigment of the blood. To achieve a normal electrolyte balance in body fluids and tissues an adequate supply of sodium, potassium and magnesium salts as chlorides, bicarbonates and phosphates are required. The acid-base balance of the body is dependent on the correct proportion of many inorganic salts.

Since excesses or deficiencies of certain salts occur in various disease conditions the physician often administers inorganic salts for their therapeutic value. The following table lists some common salts and their use in medicine.

SALT	FORMULA	COMMON NAME	USES
Aluminum sulfate	$Al_2(SO_4)_3$		Deodorant, anti-perspirant
Ammonium chloride	NH_4Cl		Expectorant, acid-forming agent
Barium sulfate	$BaSO_4$	"Barium"	Coats the intestinal tract with a compound opaque to x-rays
Calcium carbonate	$CaCO_3$	Precipitated chalk	Antacid, in gastric ulcers
Calcium sulfate	$(CaSO_4)_2H_2O$	Plaster of paris	Casts and molds
Ferric hydroxide	$Fe(OH)_3$	Dialyzed iron	In anemias
Magnesium carbonate	$MgCO_3$		Antacid, cosmetic
Magnesium sulfate	$MgSO_4$	Epsom salts	Cathartic
Mercuric chloride	$HgCl_2$	Bichloride of mercury	Disinfectant
Mercurous chloride	Hg_2Cl_2	Calomel	Cathartic
Potassium iodide	KI		Expectorant
Potassium nitrate	KNO_3	Saltpeter	Diuretic
Silver nitrate	$AgNO_3$	Lunar caustic	Antiseptic; astringent
Sodium bicarbonate	$NaHCO_3$	Baking soda	Antacid in hyperacidity
Sodium chloride	$NaCl$	Table salt	Saline solution
Sodium iodide	NaI		Iodized salt

[handwritten marginal notes: "agent facilitating in removal of secretions of bronchopulmonary mucus membrane"; "agent increasing secretion of urine"]

Review Questions

1. Into what three fundamental groups are most inorganic compounds divided?
2. Define the terms: acid radical, indicator, and replaceable hydrogen.
3. List the outstanding characteristics of an acid.
4. Why should surgical instruments not be allowed to stand in acid solutions or in a solution of copper sulfate? Write the equations for the reaction between iron and hydrochloric acid, and iron and copper sulfate.
5. Write the equation for a typical neutralization reaction.
6. If 1 gram molecular weight of sodium bicarbonate will neutralize 1 gram molecular weight of hydrochloric acid as shown in the following equa-

tion, how many grams of hydrochloric acid would be neutralized by 10 gm. of sodium bicarbonate?

$$NaHCO_3 + HCl \rightarrow CO_2 \uparrow + H_2O + NaCl$$

7. List the four outstanding characteristics of a base.

8. Explain why acids and bases would be classed as polar compounds.

9. How would you proceed with an emergency treatment of a burn caused by household lye?

10. Why is laundry soap not used to wash the face?

11. What is the difference between an acid salt and a normal salt?

12. List four common salts that may be encountered in the hospital, and describe their uses.

13. Write the equations for the reaction of potassium hydroxide with phosphoric acid to form three different salts.

14. Name the following acids and bases:

H_2SO_4	HCl	HNO_3
$Ca(OH)_2$	NH_4OH	H_2SO_3
HNO_2	H_2CO_3	H_3PO_4

15. Name the following salts:

$HgNO_3$	$Fe(NO_2)_3$	$KHSO_3$
$AgCl$	$HgSO_4$	$CuCl$
$CuSO_4$	$AlPO_4$	Na_2HPO_4
Na_2SO_3	K_2CO_3	$Al_2(SO_4)_3$
$MgBr_2$	$Ca(HCO_3)_2$	$Ba(HSO_4)_2$

16. Write the formulas for the following compounds:

Hydrobromic acid	Ferric sulfate
Ammonium carbonate	Potassium bicarbonate
Cuprous sulfite	Calcium hydroxide
Sodium dihydrogen phosphate	Aluminum nitrite
Mercuric nitrate	Barium phosphate

Amphoteric (or amphiprotic) sub. acts as base in presence of acid and acts as acid in presence of base. Some buffers use amphoteric substances

Chapter **9**

Electrolytes and Ionization

The development of the electric battery in 1800 led to its use in many chemical experiments. It was used to decompose water into its elements, and assisted in the discovery of several new elements in the 19th century. The fundamental charges of electricity are closely related to the structure of an atom, since the proton carries a positive electrical charge in the nucleus, while the planetary electrons carry negative charges. In the practical application of an electric current, we seldom speak of the charge of the proton or the electron; instead, we refer to a positive or negative charge of electricity. The metal in the wire that carries an electric current is called a *conductor*, while substances that prevent the flow of electricity are called *nonconductors or insulators*. Copper, aluminum, and silver are examples of good conductors; glass, porcelain, and rubber are good insulators.

Electrolytes

In the 1830's, Michael Faraday studied the effect of an electric current on solutions of chemical compounds. He observed that certain compounds when in solution will conduct an electric current while others will not.

A simple apparatus for demonstrating the conductivity of a solution is shown in Figure 55. It consists of a source of current connected to a light bulb in such a way that the bulb will not burn until a conductor is placed between the two electrodes. If the solution being tested will conduct the electric current, the open circuit between the two electrodes is completed and the light bulb will glow. Solutions of acids, bases, and salts are found to conduct an electric current readily and cause the bulb to burn brilliantly. The bulb will not light when the electrodes are placed in distilled water or solutions of sugar,

115

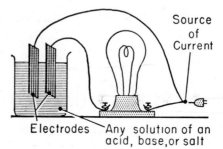

Figure 55. Diagram of a simple conductivity apparatus.

alcohol, or glycerol. Substances whose solutions will conduct an electric current are called *electrolytes*. A compound whose solution will not conduct the current is called a *nonelectrolyte*. In general, compounds other than acids, bases, and salts are classified as nonelectrolytes.

Theory of Ionization

In 1887, Arrhenius, a Swedish chemist, proposed a theory to explain how an electrolyte in solution conducts an electric current. The main points of his theory are as follows: (1) When an electrolyte dissolves in water some of its molecules split or dissociate into positively charged particles and negatively charged particles called *ions*. (2) The sum of the positive charges that result from the dissociation of the electrolyte is equal to the sum of the negative charges. (3) Nonelectrolytes that fail to conduct an electric current when in solution do not dissociate to form ions. (4) Ions possess different properties than the corresponding uncharged atoms or molecules and are responsible not only for the electrical properties but also for the chemical properties of a solution. (5) In an extremely dilute solution, electrolytes are completely dissociated into ions; however, in ordinary concentration, an equilibrium exists between the ions and the undissociated molecules.

The ionization of an electrolyte like sodium chloride would be represented as an equilibrium between sodium chloride molecules and sodium and chloride ions in solution. As discussed earlier under valence, the electrical charge on the ions is numerically equal to their valence:

$$NaCl \rightleftarrows Na^+ + Cl^-$$

Sodium chloride   *Sodium*   *Chloride*
molecules   *ion*   *ion*

The major modification of the Arrhenius theory resulting from later experimental work involves the fifth point. We now know that this assumption does not hold for strong electrolytes like sodium chloride, but the theory is still valid for weak electrolytes in solution. Debye and Huckel in 1923 proposed a theory to account for the behavior of the ions of a strong electrolyte in solution. They stated that strong electrolytes were 100 per cent dissociated in solutions of 0.1M concentration or less, but that attraction between the positive and negative ions in stronger solutions hindered their movement and decreased the conductivity of the solution. The correct equation for an ionic compound such as sodium chloride and most salts should then be written as a nonreversible reaction:

$$NaCl \rightarrow Na^+ + Cl^-$$

Sodium ions Chloride ions

In general the dissociation of ionic compounds and dilute solutions of covalent strong electrolytes such as hydrochloric acid would be written as nonreversible reactions, while weak electrolytes and more concentrated solutions of covalent strong electrolytes would be represented as equilibrium reactions as shown in the first equation.

It is important to stress the fact that the properties of an ion are different from those of an uncharged atom. The hydrogen ion (H^+) has a sour taste, while the hydrogen atom has no taste. The cupric ion (Cu^{++}) is blue, whereas the copper atom is copper colored. When an atom takes on an electric charge and exists as an ion, it always assumes new properties.

The Ionization of Electrolytes

The modern theory of ionization is built on a more complete foundation of knowledge than that proposed by Arrhenius. Many compounds, especially salts, are formed by electron transfer and consist of ions even when they exist in the crystalline state. When they are dissolved in water, the forces holding them in the tightly packed crystalline state are broken and they gain freedom of movement. They then behave like ions in solution; for example, they will migrate under the influence of an electrical current and are classified as electrolytes. Covalent polar compounds, while not consisting of ions in the solid state, will form ions when dissolved in water and are also classed as electrolytes.

Strong electrolytes are solutions of ionic compounds and covalent polar compounds that dissociate completely into ions when in dilute solutions. Weak electrolytes are substances that dissociate only slightly into ions when in solution and exist essentially as undissociated molecules. Most salts, bases, and acids, such as HCl, HNO_3 and H_2SO_4, are classed as strong electrolytes. Examples of weak electrolytes are the base NH_4OH, and acids such as H_2CO_3, H_3BO_3, and acetic acid.

Acids

As described in Chapter 8, hydrogen chloride exists as a gas and is a covalent polar compound. When dissolved in water, the hydrogen chloride dissociates into hydrogen ions and chloride ions. The hydrogen ions apparently unite with water molecules and become hydrated. These hydrated hydrogen ions which are formed when acids are dissolved in water are called hydronium ions.

$$H^+ + H_2O \rightarrow H_3^+O$$

The ionization of an acid such as hydrogen chloride in an aqueous solution would be represented as the reaction between hydrogen chloride and water.

$$HCl + H_2O \rightarrow H_3^+O + Cl^-$$

The chemist recognizes the existence of hydrated hydrogen ions, and is also aware that other ions exist in solution in a hydrated state. For uniformity and convenience, hydrogen and other ions are commonly written without their attached water molecules. The ionization of two strong acids and a weak acid may thus be written as follows:

$$HCl \rightarrow H^+ + Cl^-$$
$$H_2SO_4 \rightarrow H^+ + H^+ + SO_4^{--}$$
$$HOOCCH_3 \rightleftarrows H^+ + OOCCH_3^-$$

The weak acid, acetic acid, is represented as a reversible reaction to indicate the existence of undissociated acetic acid molecules. From these equations, we can see that the hydrogen ion is always formed when acids ionize. The hydrogen ion then is common to all acids and must be responsible for the acid properties. Therefore we can further define acids as compounds that form hydrogen ions in water solutions.

Bases

Bases are usually metallic hydroxides in which the hydrogen and oxygen of the hydroxyl group are linked to the hydroxyl radical by electrovalence (Chap. 8). When dissolved in water a base acts as an electrolyte, dissociating into freely migrating hydroxyl and metallic ions. The ionization of two strong bases and a weak base is shown in the following equations:

$$NaOH \rightarrow Na^+ + OH^-$$
$$KOH \rightarrow K^+ + OH^-$$
$$NH_4OH \rightleftarrows NH_4^+ + OH^-$$

Ammonium hydroxide is a weak base that is incompletely ionized in solution, and is therefore written as a reversible reaction between undissociated molecules and ions. The hydroxyl ion is shown to be common to all bases; therefore the properties of a basic solution are due to this ion. Bases may be defined as compounds whose solutions form hydroxyl ions.

Neutralization

A neutralization reaction between an acid and a base can be represented by an ionic equation.

$$Na^+ + OH^- + H^+ + Cl^- \rightarrow Na^+ + Cl^- + H_2O$$

The hydrogen ions of the acids unite with the hydroxyl ions of the base to form water molecules, which are not ionized. The neutralized solution has neither acidic nor basic properties, since hydrogen ions and hydroxyl ions are no longer present but are held in combination in the undissociated water molecules.

Strength of Acids and Bases

As discussed previously, covalent strong electrolytes, such as hydrochloric acid, are completely dissociated in very dilute solution, but, in more concentrated solutions, as a result of interionic attraction, they may not appear to be 100 per cent ionized in many situations. In general acids that ionize to a large extent in ordinary dilutions are called strong acids, while those that ionize to a small extent are called weak acids. Strong bases are highly ionized and furnish many hydroxyl ions, while weak bases are slightly ionized and furnish only a small number.

of hydroxyl ions. Nearly all salts ionize to a large degree and are not usually spoken of as strong or weak. The degree of dissociation into ions of some typical electrolytes in dilute solutions is shown in the following table:

	DISSOCIATION INTO IONS (PER CENT)		DISSOCIATION INTO IONS (PER CENT)
Hydrochloric acid	95.0	Sodium hydroxide	91.0
Nitric acid	92.0	Potassium hydroxide	91.0
Sulfuric acid	61.0	Ammonium hydroxide ...	1.3
Acetic acid	1.3	Potassium chloride	86.0
Carbonic acid	0.17	Sodium chloride	84.0
Boric acid	0.01	Most salts	70–86

As we have just seen, strong and weak electrolytes refer to the degree of ionization. The terms *concentrated* and *dilute* have a meaning different from strong and weak. A concentrated acid or base is one whose solution contains a large amount of the electrolyte compared to the water, while a dilute solution contains a small amount of electrolyte compared to the water. A strong acid or base would cause injury to the tissues if taken internally; however, a weak acid such as acetic, in vinegar, is often used in food, and boric acid may be safely introduced into the tissues of the eye. A weak base such as magnesium hydroxide can be administered to neutralize excess acidity in the stomach.

Salts

Ordinary salts are electrovalent compounds composed of any positively charged ion, or cation, except hydrogen and any negatively charged ion, or anion, except the hydroxyl ion. In an aqueous solution, the forces holding the tightly packed ions together are weakened with the resultant dissociation into freely moving anions and cations. The ionization of some typical salts is shown in the following equations:

$$NaCl \rightarrow Na^+ + Cl^-$$
$$KNO_3 \rightarrow K^+ + NO_3^-$$
$$MgSO_4 \rightarrow Mg^{++} + SO_4^{--}$$
$$CaCl_2 \rightarrow Ca^{++} + Cl^- + Cl^-$$
$$AlBr_3 \rightarrow Al^{+++} + Br^- + Br^- + Br^-$$

It may readily be seen that no one ion is common to all salts. Since acids, bases, and salts are the only electrolytes, salts may be defined as electrolytes that form neither hydrogen ions nor hydroxyl ions in solution.

Salts with an Acid or Basic Reaction

It might be expected that solutions of normal salts should be neutral, since they do not contain hydrogen ions or hydroxyl ions. However, certain salts such as sodium carbonate and sodium acetate form solutions that are alkaline, while others such as ammonium sulfate, ammonium chloride, and copper sulfate form acid solutions. The basic reaction of a solution of sodium acetate may be understood if we consider what happens when this salt is dissolved in water. Although water is usually considered a nonelectrolyte, a few of its molecules will ionize, forming some hydrogen ions and hydroxyl ions.

$$H_2O \rightleftarrows H^+ + OH^-$$

When a salt is dissolved in water, the ions of the salt may react with H^+ and OH^- of water, a process called hydrolysis. The hydrolysis of sodium acetate may be represented as follows:

$$NaC_2H_3O_2 \rightarrow Na^+ + C_2H_3O_2^-$$
$$H_2O \rightleftarrows OH^- + H^+$$
$$\Updownarrow$$
$$HC_2H_3O_2$$

In the aqueous solution, the sodium ions and the hydroxyl ions remain dissociated since they are the ions of the strong base sodium hydroxide. The acetate ion combines with the hydrogen ion to form the slightly ionized weak acid, acetic acid. The hydrogen ions that might exist in solution are effectively tied up in the undissociated acetic acid molecules, leaving an excess of hydroxyl ions to explain the basic behavior of the solution.

The acidity of an ammonium chloride solution may be explained in a similar fashion. The reaction for the hydrolysis of the salt may be written as follows:

$$NH_4Cl \rightarrow Cl^- + NH_4^+$$
$$H_2O \rightleftarrows H^+ + OH^-$$
$$\Updownarrow$$
$$NH_4OH$$

In the aqueous solution, the hydrogen ions and chloride ions remain dissociated since they are the ions of the strong acid, hydrochloric acid. The ammonium ion combines with the hydroxyl ion to form the slightly ionized weak base, ammonium hydroxide. The available hydroxyl ions in solution are thus tied up in the undissociated molecules of ammonium hydroxide, leaving an excess of hydrogen ions to account for the acidity of the solution. It may readily be seen that these hydrolysis reactions are just the reverse of neutralization reactions. Viewed in this manner, a salt with a basic reaction in solution is one that is formed from a strong base and a weak acid. Conversely, a salt with an acidic reaction in solution is one that is formed from a strong acid and a weak base. Salts formed from a strong acid and a strong base, such as sodium chloride, would form a neutral aqueous solution.

Importance of Ions

The majority of chemical reactions are between ions rather than between molecules. Electrolytes that ionize in solution react rapidly, nonelectrolytes react slowly in solution, and dry substances usually fail to react with each other. The specific properties of acids, bases, and salts depend upon the ions that are formed when these substances are in solution.

Ions are of fundamental importance in the body. The formation of bones and teeth depends upon the combination of calcium, magnesium, phosphate, and carbonate ions in the proper proportions. Ions in the body fluids produce an osmotic pressure that is responsible for the passage of food and waste material into and out of the tissue cells. Digestion of food in the body is controlled by the ratio of hydrogen ions and hydroxyl ions in the gastric and intestinal fluids. Calcium ions are necessary for the clotting of blood and for the formation of the milk curd in the stomach; ferrous ions are essential in the formation of hemoglobin (the red pigment of the blood). The contraction of muscles and the conveying of impulses by nerves require the presence of certain ions.

Hydrogen Ion Concentration

It has already been stated that water ionizes to a very slight extent:

$$H_2O \rightleftarrows H^+ + OH^-$$

It has been determined that one molecule out of every 550,000,000 molecules of water is ionized. From this fact, it can be calculated that *log = power or exponent of 10 which, when the indicated procedure is carried out will give the number.*

1 gm. of hydrogen ions is present in 10,000,000 liters of water, or a liter of water contains only $\frac{1}{10,000,000}$ of a gram of hydrogen ions. Since numbers like 10,000,000 are unwieldy, they are often expressed as powers of ten. The powers of ten are usually written as follows:

$10^1 = 10$

$10^2 = 100$

$10^3 = 1000$

$10^4 = 10,000$

$10^5 = 100,000$

$10^6 = 1,000,000$

etc.

Fractions that contain such large numbers may be expressed as 1 over 10 to a power; or the fraction may be eliminated entirely by taking 10 to the minus power. Examples:

$$\frac{1}{1000} = \frac{1}{10^3} = 10^{-3} \text{ and } \frac{1}{100,000} = \frac{1}{10^5} = 10^{-5}$$

Since a liter of water contains $\frac{1}{10,000,000}$ of a gram of hydrogen ions, the hydrogen ion concentration of water may be expressed as $\frac{1}{10^7}$ or more conveniently as 10^{-7} gm. of hydrogen ions per liter.

As the negative power of 10 increases, the hydrogen ion concentration decreases, since the fraction of a gram of hydrogen ions in a liter decreases. There are more hydrogen ions per liter in a solution whose hydrogen ion concentration is 10^{-5} than in one whose concentration is 10^{-6}.

A neutral solution like water has as many hydrogen ions as hydroxyl ions. Since water has a hydrogen ion concentration (abbreviated H^+ conc.) of 10^{-7}, it follows that any solution with a H^+ conc. of 10^{-7} is neutral. A solution is acid when it contains more hydrogen ions than hydroxyl ions. The H^+ conc. of an acid solution would thus be greater than 10^{-7}, or have more than $\frac{1}{10,000,000}$ of a gram of hydrogen ions per liter. For example, a solution with a H^+ conc. of 10^{-3} would have $\frac{1}{1000}$ of a gram of H^+ per liter, or 1 gram of H^+ in 1000 liters. If there are more hydroxyl ions than hydrogen ions in a solution, it is alkaline or basic. Similarly, an alkaline solution would have a H^+ conc. of less than 10^{-7}.

.·. The use of such large fractions or powers is unwieldly, so a simplified method of expressing H^+ conc. was suggested by Sørensen. Since

brackets = concentration per mole

pH = 7

[H₃O]

(-?)

exponent or (-?)

[1×10⁻⁷]

pH = - log [H₃O]

= - log

pH = pH of 1 - 7

acid = pH of 1 - 7

base = pH of 7-14

H$^+$ conc. is usually expressed as 10$^-$ some power, he suggested leaving out the 10$^-$ and using only the numerical value of the negative power. He called this the *pH value*, meaning the power of the H$^+$ conc. A neutral solution has a *pH* of 7 since its H$^+$ conc. is 10^{-7}. The *pH* of alkaline solutions is greater than 7, while the *pH* of acid solutions is less than 7. The relationship between the H$^+$ conc. of a solution and its *pH* is shown in the following diagram:

	Acid							Neutral					Base		
H$^+$ conc.	10^0	10^{-1}	10^{-2}	10^{-3}	10^{-4}	10^{-5}	10^{-6}	10^{-7}	10^{-8}	10^{-9}	10^{-10}	10^{-11}	10^{-12}	10^{-13}	10^{-14}
pH	0	1	2	3	4	5	6	7	8	9	10	11	12	13	14

0.1 M HCl   0.1 M Acetic Acid   0.1 M H$_3$BO$_3$ Neutral Solution   0.1 M NH$_4$OH   0.1 M NaOH

The methods for determining the *pH* of a solution may be classified as electrometric or colorimetric. The electrometric method employs an electrically operated electrometer or "pH meter" which indicates the pH of a solution on a special dial. Several types of these *pH* meters are available and are widely used in industry and in research laboratories (Fig. 56). The colorimetric method does not require such expensive equipment, but is not as accurate as the electrometric method. A set of indicators is available that shows definite color shades for each *pH* value. A series of tubes is prepared containing solutions whose *pH* values vary at regular intervals from *pH* 0 to *pH* 14. When the proper indicator is added to each tube the result is a standard series of *pH* values for use in the colorimetric method. The *pH* of a solution may be determined by adding one of the indicators to the solution and matching the color that is produced with the color of one of the tubes in the set of permanent color standards.

Importance of pH Values

All body fluids have definite *pH* values that must be maintained within fairly narrow ranges for proper physiological functions. The *pH* of the blood is normally between 7.35 and 7.45. Gastric juice has a *pH* of 1.6 to 1.8 and the urine has a range of *pH* from 5.5 to 7.0. The saliva is nearly neutral (*pH* 7), while the bile (*pH* 7.8–8.6) and the pancreatic juice (*pH* 8) are more alkaline fluids.

Many biological processes depend on the *pH* of their environment. The enzymes that digest our food have their optimum activity at

$k_w = [H_3O^+][OH^-]$

$k_w = 1\times10^{-14}$

$k = \dfrac{[H_3O^+][OH^-]}{[H_2O]^2}$

i.e., $k = \dfrac{[C][D]}{[A]^n[B]^n}$

$k = \dfrac{[C][D]}{[A]^n[B]^n}$

$A + B \rightleftharpoons C + D$

definite pH values. Bacteria are best grown on culture media that have had their pH carefully adjusted. The stains that are used to prepare bacteria and tissues for microscopic examination must have the pH of their solutions at a certain value for proper staining technic.

If the pH of the blood falls below 7.0 or goes above 7.8, death occurs. Since many of the reactions that take place in our tissues form acid substances, the blood must have a mechanism to prevent such changes in pH. Certain salts such as bicarbonates, phosphates and salts of proteins have the special function of maintaining the pH of blood and other body fluids within narrow limits. These substances, which are salts of weak acids and are able to withstand additions of acid or alkali without appreciable change in pH, are called *buffers*. The specific role they play in maintaining a constant pH in the blood will be discussed under acid-base balance in the chapter on blood (see Chap. 20).

Buffer salts have many important applications in physiological studies and are often used to maintain the pH of biological solutions.

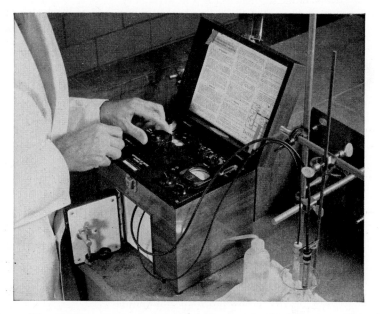

Figure 56. A pH meter is an essential instrument in the laboratory. This pH meter is shown with external electrodes.

Review Questions

1. Define and give examples of conductors, insulators, electrolytes, and non-electrolytes.
2. How does a solution of an electrolyte conduct an electric current between the electrodes in Figure 55?
3. Outline the important points of Arrhenius' theory of ionization.
4. Give definitions of acids, bases, and salts from the standpoint of ionization.
5. Why are some acids and bases referred to as strong acids or bases, whereas others are termed weak acids or bases? Give an example of a strong acid, a strong base, a weak acid and a weak base.
6. Write the equation for the ionization of : (a) a strong acid; (b) a weak base.
7. Write the equations for the ionization of the following salts in aqueous solutions: (a) sodium sulfate, (b) ammonium phosphate, and (c) aluminum carbonate. How can the ionization of salts be readily distinguished from the ionization of acids or bases?
8. Why is the ionization equation of most salts represented as a nonreversible reaction?
9. Would a solution of $(NH_4)_2SO_4$ be acidic or basic? Explain.
10. A certain acid solution contains $\frac{1}{10,000}$ of a gram of hydrogen ions in a liter. In what other ways could you express the hydrogen ion concentration of the solution? What is its pH?
11. Construct a diagram of the pH scale similar to that on page 124 in which the acids and bases below the scale are replaced by physiological fluids at their proper pH positions.
12. Why are pH values widely used to designate the acidity or alkalinity of biological fluids?
13. How do you explain the fact that water is a neutral solution?
14. What is a buffer? What would happen to the body if no buffers were present in the blood or tissues?

Chapter 10

Introduction to Organic Chemistry

Prior to the nineteenth century, the study of chemistry was confined mainly to inorganic substances such as metals, nonmetals, acids, bases and salts. Laws and theories were based on the behavior of inorganic compounds and gases. Although chemical compounds had been isolated from plants and animals, chemists believed that a "vital force" connected with living matter was necessary for the production of these organic compounds. The first experimental evidence disproving the vital force theory resulted from the accidental production of urea by the German chemist Wöhler in 1828. He prepared urea by heating the inorganic compound ammonium cyanate. Urea was considered an organic compound because it was produced by the body and found in the blood and urine.

Since many chemists championed the vital force theory, they attempted to prove errors in Wöhler's experiment. Such efforts stimulated others to attempt organic synthesis in the laboratory, and their success marked the beginning of modern organic chemistry.

After it had been shown that organic compounds could be made without the assistance of living cells, a new classification of chemical compounds was necessary. Analyses of organic compounds revealed that they all contained the element carbon. We now classify organic compounds as those that contain carbon as one of their elements. Therefore, *organic chemistry* is a study of the compounds of carbon, regardless of their relation to the living cell. Compounds that do not contain carbon are considered as inorganic compounds and are studied in inorganic chemistry. A few carbon compounds had previously been classed as inorganic, such as carbon dioxide, carbon monoxide, carbonic acid, and the carbonates. For convenience, their classification has remained the same and they are studied as part of inorganic chemistry.

Figure 57.   A prescription department in a modern drug shop. The majority of
prescriptions compounded are organic in nature.

Importance of Organic Compounds

Organic substances are found in all types of plant and animal tissue.
Food containing carbohydrates, fats, and proteins are organic in
nature and are obtained from edible plant and animal tissue. To maintain health of the body, we require an adequate supply of food, vitamins, hormones, enzymes, and many other organic compounds. The
majority of drugs that are used for their beneficial physiological effects
are organic in nature (Fig. 57).

Coal, coke, natural gas, and petroleum and its derivatives (gasoline,
lubricating oil, kerosene, petroleum jelly, etc.) have as their source
products of plants and animals that lived many thousand years ago.
The textile fabrics that are commonly used are either naturally occurring organic materials like wool, cotton, silk, and linen, or synthetic
organic compounds like rayon, Orlon, Dacron, and many others. Per-

fumes, dyes, cellophane, aviation gasoline, lacquers, Bakelite, synthetic vitamins, plastics, and the sulfa drugs are but a few of the organic chemists' contributions to our welfare.

Comparison of Organic and Inorganic Compounds

Organic compounds are much more numerous than are inorganic compounds. There are over 500,000 known organic compounds compared to about 30,000 inorganic. Any of the 102 elements may combine to form inorganic substances while organic compounds are composed mainly of carbon, hydrogen, and oxygen, with occasional nitrogen, sulfur, and phosphorus. Organic molecules are usually more complex and therefore possess a higher molecular weight than inorganic molecules. Proteins, for example, are organic molecules with molecular weights that range from several thousand to over a million.

Inorganic compounds are composed of ions held together by strong electrovalent forces. In the crystalline form, their molecules are held together either by ionic forces or by strong electrostatic forces. High temperatures are required to break these bonds. Therefore, these compounds are nonvolatile and possess high melting points. They are readily soluble in water since water is a polar compound that breaks the bonds between the ions causing hydration of the individual ions. These hydrated ions conduct an electric current, classifying inorganic compounds as electrolytes. Organic compounds are usually polar or nonpolar covalent compounds consisting of molecules held together by relatively weak covalent forces. Since this molecular attraction is weak, organic compounds are usually volatile and possess low melting points. They are not usually soluble in water because there is no tendency for water to separate their molecules into ions. They will mix freely with other organic compounds and are often soluble in organic solvents. Since they do not form ions in solution, organic compounds are classed as nonelectrolytes, and will not usually conduct an electric current when in solution. Inorganic compounds exhibit rapid rates of reaction, while organic reactions are relatively slow, since they represent the activity of molecules rather than ions. The body produces many types of catalysts that increase the rates of organic reactions occurring in digestive and metabolic processes.

Inorganic compounds whose molecules have the same composition usually have the same properties. The molecular or *empirical* formula

NaOH represents only sodium hydroxide and all molecules of NaOH have the same properties. However, organic compounds that possess different properties may often have the same empirical formula. The formula for glucose, the sugar present in the blood, is $C_6H_{12}O_6$. Fifteen other sugars including fructose and galactose have this empirical formula; yet they vary in solubility, degree of sweetness, and utilization by the animal body. These compounds are called *isomers* and the different properties of each one is due to the arrangement of the atoms within the molecule.

The Properties of Carbon

Before attempting a study of even the most elementary organic compounds, it is absolutely necessary to understand the properties of the carbon atom. In the discussion of valence it was stated that metallic elements had a tendency to lose electrons, whereas non-metallic elements tend to gain electrons. Inorganic compounds such as sodium chloride and magnesium sulfide are formed by the loss or gain of electrons from the outer orbits of the atoms. The ions that are formed in these compounds give rise to the terms ionic bond and electrovalence. Since the carbon atom contains 4 electrons in its outer shell (Fig. 58) it would be necessary for carbon to gain 4 more electrons to obtain a stable outer shell of 8 electrons. For this reason, carbon compounds are practically never formed by the transfer of electrons from the outer shell of the reacting atoms. Instead, the carbon atom becomes more stable by sharing its electrons with atoms of other elements—or with other carbon atoms. For example, hydrogen will readily share its 1 electron with 1 electron from carbon to achieve the stable arrangement of the helium atom.

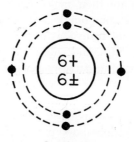

Carbon

Figure 58.   Diagram illustrating electron arrangement in the carbon atom.

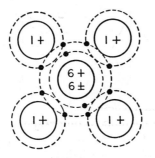

Methane

Figure 59. The methane molecule illustrates the covalent linkage between carbon and hydrogen atoms.

Four hydrogen atoms will combine with 1 carbon atom—to form the simple organic compound methane (Fig. 59). This involves the co-operation of four pairs of shared electrons. In methane as well as in thousands of other organic compounds, the hydrogen is joined to the carbon by covalence, producing a covalent compound. For conveni-ence, the carbon, hydrogen, and oxygen atoms which make up the majority of organic compounds are often represented with dots around the atomic symbol representing the number of electrons in the outer orbit of the atom.

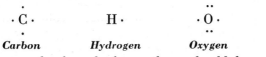

$\cdot \overset{\displaystyle \cdot}{\underset{\displaystyle \cdot}{C}} \cdot$	$H \cdot$	$\cdot \overset{\displaystyle \cdot\cdot}{\underset{\displaystyle \cdot\cdot}{O}} \cdot$
Carbon	*Hydrogen*	*Oxygen*

Using this scheme, the formula for methane should be written as illustrated:

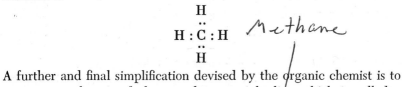

$$H : \overset{\displaystyle H}{\underset{\displaystyle H}{\overset{\cdot\cdot}{\underset{\cdot\cdot}{C}}}} : H \qquad Methane$$

A further and final simplification devised by the organic chemist is to represent each pair of electrons by a straight line which is called a single bond and is shown in the following formula for methane:

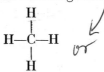

$$H - \overset{\displaystyle H}{\underset{\displaystyle H}{C}} - H \qquad \textit{or}$$

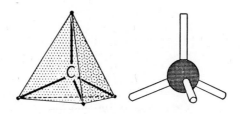

Carbon Atom

Figure 60.　The valence bonds of the carbon atom extend in space to form a tetrahedron.

This single bond is similar to the valence bonds shown earlier, although it should always be kept in mind that this single bond represents a pair of shared electrons in a covalent compound. It is extremely helpful in writing the formulas of organic compounds to remember that carbon always has a valence of 4. Carbon may be considered as an atom that has 4 electrons that it is able to share with other atoms, or more simply, as an atom with 4 valence bonds ready to combine with any combination of 4 valence bonds possessed by other atoms.

The valence bonds of carbon do not exist in a single plane although they are usually represented in that fashion for convenience. Structurally, the carbon atom should be represented as a tetrahedron with the valence bonds extending from the center to each corner as shown in Figure 60. Or, using a more practical method, the carbon atom can be represented as a sphere containing four holes into which small wooden pegs can be fitted at the proper angles. This is the basis of the molecular models of organic compounds and is also shown in Figure 60. Kits containing different colored spheres to represent carbon, hydrogen, oxygen, and other atoms as well as requisite wooden pegs are available for the construction of accurate models of organic compounds. The space relationships of the carbon and hydrogen atoms of methane are shown as the molecular model in Figure 61.

It may readily be reasoned that if a carbon atom was only able to combine with dissimilar atoms, only a few thousand organic compounds would be produced. One of the outstanding properties of the carbon atom is its ability to share its electrons with other carbon atoms. When 2 carbon atoms are joined by the sharing of one pair of electrons, they are connected by a single bond and may be represented in the following fashion:

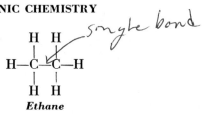

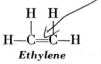

Ethane

If the 2 carbon atoms are joined by the sharing of two pairs of electrons, they are said to be connected by a double bond which may be represented thus:

Ethylene

Finally the carbon atoms may be joined by the sharing of three pairs of electrons, and are said to be connected by a triple bond and may be represented as follows:

H—C≡C—H

Acetylene

There are not many important organic compounds containing triple bonds between the carbons, although several examples will be studied in which double or single bonds connect the carbon atoms.

In addition to hydrogen, other atoms will also share electrons with carbon atoms to form simple organic compounds. For example, an atom of the halogens, chlorine, bromine, or iodine will readily share an electron with the carbon atom to obtain a stable configuration of

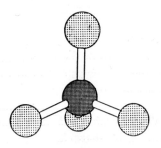

Methane

Figure 61. The space relationships of hydrogen and carbon atoms are shown in this molecular model of methane.

8 electrons in its outer shell. The common compound carbon tetrachloride would result if 1 carbon atom combined with 4 chlorine atoms
as illustrated:

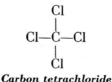

Carbon tetrachloride

In this compound, the chlorine atoms are joined to the carbon by a
shared pair of electrons or a single bond. This single bond indicates
that chlorine needs to gain but 1 electron to produce a stable configuration in its outer shell, or that chlorine has a valence of 1, or 1
valence bond. If hydrogen and halogen atoms are combined in different proportions with the carbon atom, several new organic compounds
may be produced. The following three compounds represent the addition of 1, 2, and 3 halogen atoms to the hydrocarbon methane.

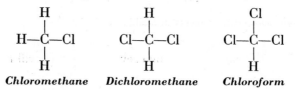

Chloromethane   *Dichloromethane*   *Chloroform*

There are thousands of organic compounds containing only carbon,
hydrogen, and oxygen. Since oxygen has 6 electrons in its outer orbit,
it must share 2 pairs of electrons to reach a stable arrangement. Oxygen may share 2 pairs of electrons with carbon and be connected to it
by a double bond or it may share 1 pair with carbon and 1 pair with
hydrogen as shown in the following:

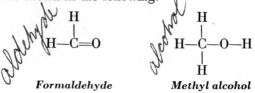

Formaldehyde   *Methyl alcohol*

The manner in which oxygen is combined with carbon or hydrogen
determines the type of organic compound that will be produced. For
example, the first compound in which the oxygen is combined with
carbon by a double bond is called an aldehyde, while the second

compound in which oxygen is combined with carbon and hydrogen by a single bond is called an alcohol. Other types of organic compounds formed by the combination of oxygen with carbon and hydrogen will be discussed in later chapters.

Review Questions

1. Why was Wöhler's production of urea so important to the progress of organic chemistry?
2. Of what importance is organic chemistry in the practice of medicine?
3. List several of the outstanding differences between organic and inorganic compounds.
4. What method of classification is used to distinguish inorganic from organic chemical compounds?
5. Explain why the linkage of carbon with other elements is covalent rather than electrovalent.
6. How does the organic chemist represent the electrons in the outer orbit of carbon, hydrogen, oxygen in a simplified manner?
7. Write the formula for methane in four different ways and explain the relationship between them.
8. Give two examples of compounds with formulas that illustrate the linkage of carbon with other elements in addition to hydrogen.

Chapter 11

Aliphatic Compounds

Organic compounds are divided into two major classes, *aliphatic* and *cyclic* compounds. Aliphatic compounds consist of chains of carbon atoms, and possess a more simple structure than the cyclic compounds. The simplest aliphatic compounds consist of only two elements, carbon and hydrogen, and are called hydrocarbons. The addition of a third element, oxygen, greatly increases the number and complexity of organic compounds. In addition to hydrocarbons, aliphatic compounds are classified in a few fundamental classes, or series, whose members possess similar properties. Each class is characterized by the presence of an active group or radical that determines its chemical behavior. Knowledge of the characteristic group or radical associated with each class of aliphatic compound is essential to the understanding of the properties and reactions of each type of organic compound. Formulas for these compounds are usually written in a manner to emphasize the active group or radical. Examples of each important class of aliphatic compound will be considered in this chapter.

Hydrocarbons

Organic compounds composed of only carbon and hydrogen are called *hydrocarbons*. They are not only the most simple organic compounds but are also the most fundamental since the majority of the complex organic compounds are derived from them. The family of hydrocarbons made up of compounds in which the atoms of carbon are joined to each other by a single pair of shared electrons or by single bonds is known as the *alkanes*. These compounds are often called the *methane series* since methane is the simplest member of the family. This series of hydrocarbons shows little chemical activity and

usually require high temp. & cat

136

alkanes = substitution reactions

alkenes + alkynes = addition reactions

its members are sometimes called *paraffin* hydrocarbons from the
Latin *parvum affinis* meaning little affinity.

From an inspection of the formulas for the first three members of
the series, it can be seen that each successive member contains one
more carbon atom and two more hydrogen atoms than the one preceding it.

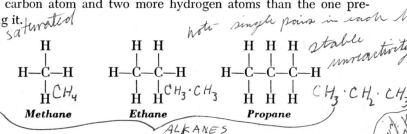

Methane   *Ethane*   *Propane*

Molecular models showing the space relationships between the carbon
and hydrogen atoms in ethane and propane are illustrated in Figure 62.
A series of this type is known as a *homologous series* and the members
of the series are known as *homologs*. As the series progresses, the
number of carbon atoms increases and the chain of carbon atoms becomes longer. However, alkanes with 4 or more carbon atoms intro-
duce new complications. For example, two compounds having the
same molecular formula C_4H_{10} are known to exist. These compounds
exhibit different properties, having different melting points and boiling
points. Such compounds are called *isomers* and the phenomenon is
known as *isomerism*. The existence of isomers depends on the arrangement of the carbon atoms in the carbon chain. When more than 3

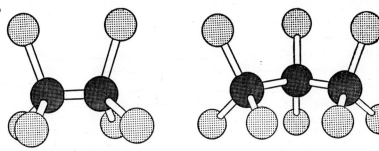

Ethane   Propane

Figure 62. Molecular models of ethane and propane.

[handwritten margin notes:]
empirical formula
butane $CH_3 \cdot CH_2 \cdot CH_2 \cdot CH_3$ C_4H_{10}
C_4H_{10}
isobutane $CH_3 \cdot CH \cdot CH_3$
             CH_3

carbon atoms are present, 1 carbon atom can form a branched chain by joining a central carbon atom in the chain. This is illustrated in the four-carbon compound, butane, and its isomer, isobutane.

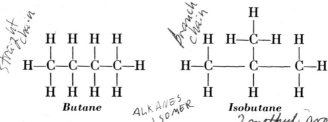

Butane   ALKANES ISOMER   *Isobutane*

[handwritten: straight chain; branch chain; 2 methyl propane]

Application of this line of reasoning will show the existence of three isomers of pentane, five isomers of hexane, and an increasing number of isomers of hydrocarbons with longer carbon chains.

The naming of the first four alkane hydrocarbons follows no set rule. However, once it is learned that methane, ethane, propane, and butane contain from 1 to 4 carbon atoms respectively, it will be easier to recognize more complex compounds derived from these simple hydrocarbons. Starting with alkanes having 5 or more carbon atoms, the Latin root is used. For example, pentane, hexane, heptane, and octane contain 5 to 8 carbon atoms respectively.

Saturated and Unsaturated Aliphatic Compounds

The hydrocarbons of the methane series are said to be *saturated* because the carbon atoms have combined with all the hydrogen atoms they are capable of holding. Saturated hydrocarbons have only *single bonds between the carbon atoms,* therefore, each two carbon atoms are joined by the sharing of one pair of electrons.

An organic compound is called *unsaturated* when its carbon atoms are not completely saturated with hydrogen atoms. In these compounds two carbons are joined by two or three pairs of shared electrons. Unsaturated compounds, therefore, have *double or triple bonds between the carbon atoms*. A series of hydrocarbons similar to the methane series is formed by these unsaturated compounds. Hydrocarbons that have a double bond between the first two carbon atoms form the *ethylene series,* those with a triple bond between the first two carbon atoms compose the *acetylene series*. The first member of each series is shown below:

[handwritten left margin notes:]
4-ethyl-6-methyl-octane
if another methyl is added
to 6 c (above) call 66-dimethyl

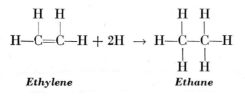

$$\underset{\textbf{\textit{Ethylene}}}{\text{H}-\overset{\displaystyle \text{H}}{\underset{\displaystyle |}{\text{C}}}=\overset{\displaystyle \text{H}}{\underset{\displaystyle |}{\text{C}}}-\text{H}} \qquad \underset{\textbf{\textit{Acetylene}}}{\text{H}-\text{C}\equiv\text{C}-\text{H}}$$

This type of compound is more active chemically than the saturated compounds because they are able to unite with other atoms or radicals. If 2 atoms of hydrogen combined with ethylene, the saturated compound, ethane, would be formed.

$$\underset{\textbf{\textit{Ethylene}}}{\text{H}-\overset{\displaystyle \text{H}}{\underset{\displaystyle |}{\text{C}}}=\overset{\displaystyle \text{H}}{\underset{\displaystyle |}{\text{C}}}-\text{H}} + 2\text{H} \rightarrow \underset{\textbf{\textit{Ethane}}}{\text{H}-\overset{\displaystyle \text{H}}{\underset{\displaystyle \text{H}}{\text{C}}}-\overset{\displaystyle \text{H}}{\underset{\displaystyle \text{H}}{\text{C}}}-\text{H}}$$

In a similar fashion, the addition of 4 atoms of hydrogen would "saturate" the acetylene molecule to form ethane.

Ethylene exists as a gas, and is used in medicine as an anesthetic. Acetylene gas is widely used in industry in combination with oxygen in oxyacetylene torches. The intense heat produced by the oxyacetylene flame will melt iron and steel, therefore it is used in cutting and welding processes.

Sources of Hydrocarbons

Natural gas and petroleum are the most important natural sources of hydrocarbons. Large deposits of these substances have been formed over the years by the gradual decomposition of marine life and other biological materials. These deposits usually accumulate under a dome-shaped layer of rock several thousand feet under the earth's surface. When a hole is drilled through the rock layer, the pressure under the dome forces the gas or oil to the surface. After the pressure is released from a deposit of oil, pumps are used to bring the remaining oil to the surface.

Natural Gas

Natural gas is an excellent source of low molecular weight hydrocarbons. Natural gas occurs in most parts of the United States, but the majority is produced in the southwest. In recent years, a vast network of pipelines has been installed to carry natural gas from Texas to other parts of the United States.

The typical composition of natural gas is shown in the following table:

TYPICAL COMPOSITION

HYDROCARBON	TYPICAL COMPOSITION (PER CENT)	USES
Methane	82	Fuel, carbon black
Ethane	10	Fuel, carbon black
Propane	4	Bottled gas
Butane	2	Bottled gas
Higher hydrocarbons	2	Low-boiling gasoline

The propane and butane are removed by liquefaction before the gaseous fuel is introduced into the pipelines for distribution. The liquid propane and butane are stored under pressure in steel cylinders from which they are released as a gaseous fuel to be used in rural areas and in locations that are not supplied by natural gas mains. Large quantities of *carbon black,* also called gas black or lamp black, are produced from natural gas. A large proportion of the carbon black produced by this process is used in the manufacture of rubber tires. Natural gas is also used for the production of hydrogen and for the preparation of many organic compounds, including alcohols and acids.

Petroleum

The crude oil or petroleum obtained from oil wells is another rich source of hydrocarbons. In contrast to natural gas, the hydrocarbons in petroleum are of higher molecular weight. Petroleum has been known for several centuries and has been used for many purposes, most particularly as a fuel. It was not until recent years, however, that petroleum was separated into its hydrocarbon components. It is a very complex mixture of hydrocarbons and its composition varies with the location of the oil field from which it is obtained. It contains mainly a mixture of paraffins, cycloparaffins, and aromatic hydrocarbons. In addition to the hydrocarbons, petroleum contains about 10 per cent by weight of sulfur, nitrogen, and oxygen compounds.

Petroleum is separated into its hydrocarbon fractions by the process of distillation. The distillation fractions from a typical petroleum are shown as follows:

Distillation Fractions from a Typical Petroleum

NAME	COMPO-SITION (PER CENT)	MOLECULAR SIZE	BOILING RANGE (° C.)	USES
Gases	2	C^1–C^5	0	Fuel
Petroleum ethers	2	C^5–C^7	30–110	Solvents
Gasoline	32	C^6–C^{12}	30–200	Motor fuel
Kerosene	18	C^{12}–C^{15}	175–275	Diesel and jet fuel
Gas oil (fuel oil)	20	C^{15} . . .	250–400	Fuel
Lubricating oils and residue		C^{19} . . .	300 . . .	Lubricants, paraffin wax, petrolatum and asphalt

The gases from petroleum contain both saturated and unsaturated hydrocarbons. The unsaturated gases are used in the production of aviation gasoline, synthetic rubber, and other organic compounds. The saturated hydrocarbons, especially propane and butane, are liquefied and sold as bottled gas. The petroleum ether fraction consists mainly of pentanes, hexanes, and heptanes, and is used as fat solvents; paint, varnish, and enamel thinner; and dry cleaning agents.

The gasoline obtained from the original distillation of petroleum is called straight-run gasoline. As the demand for larger quantities and better quality gasolines increased, new processes of manufacture were developed. Modern gasoline is produced by a combination of a fractional distillation process, high temperature processes involving catalysts, and the addition of compounds such as tetraethyl lead and ethylene bromide as antiknock agents.

In the early days of the petroleum industry, kerosene was used for lighting, cooking, and heating. As the demand for gasoline increased and that for kerosene decreased, a catalytic process was developed to convert kerosene into gasoline. At present, kerosene is finding increased usage as a fuel for gas turbines and jet engines.

The gas oil and fuel oil fraction is used as a source of fuel for oil burning furnaces and diesel oil for diesel engines. Lubricating oils of varying grades, viscosities, and properties are separated from the petroleum fraction containing hydrocarbons with 20 or more carbon atoms. The residual material contains paraffin wax, petrolatum or petroleum jelly, and asphalt.

Halogen Derivatives of Hydrocarbons

The ability of halogen atoms to join with carbon by a shared pair of electrons or a single bond has already been discussed. Halogens are also able to react with hydrocarbons, replacing hydrogen atoms from their molecules. Some important halogen derivatives of methane are shown below:

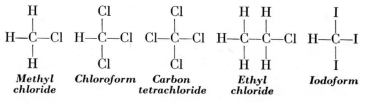

| Methyl chloride | Chloroform | Carbon tetrachloride | Ethyl chloride | Iodoform |

The halogen derivatives illustrated above are frequently used in medicine and industry. Methyl and ethyl chlorides exist as liquids at high pressures. They are refrigerants since they vaporize readily and draw heat from other objects. When sprayed on the skin, they produce local anesthesia by freezing the nerve endings. Chloroform is a volatile liquid that was once widely used as an anesthetic. It sometimes produces harmful effects, however, and has been replaced by other anesthetics. Carbon tetrachloride is used in medicine to kill or stupefy hookworms in the intestinal tract so they can be removed by the use of a cathartic. Both chloroform and carbon tetrachloride are noninflammable and are good solvents for fats and greases. Large quantities of carbon tetrachloride are used in dry cleaning and in the "pyrene" type of fire extinguisher. Iodoform has some anesthetic properties but it is seldom used; its chief use being as an antiseptic.

Halogens will also react with unsaturated hydrocarbons as shown in the reaction:

$$\begin{array}{ccc} \text{H} \quad \text{H} & & \text{H} \quad \text{H} \\ | \quad\; | & & | \quad\; | \\ \text{H—C}{=}\text{C—H} + \text{Br}_2 \;\rightarrow\; & & \text{H—C—C—H} \\ & & | \quad\; | \\ & & \text{Br} \; \text{Br} \end{array}$$

Ethylene   *Ethylene dibromide*

Large quantities of ethylene dibromide and ethylene dichloride are used in the preparation of ethyl fluid for ethyl gasoline.

Halogen derivatives of the hydrocarbons are often called *alkyl halides.*

Alkyl Radicals

Inorganic radicals such as the OH, CO_3, and SO_4 groups were defined as groups of elements that behaved as a unit in chemical reactions. Organic radicals are similar in that their composition is not changed when they undergo chemical reactions. For example, methyl iodide, CH_3I, undergoes many reactions in which the iodide is changed while the $CH_3—$ group remains intact.

Organic radicals are named from the hydrocarbon from which they are derived by substituting the suffix -*yl* for -*ane.* The $CH_3—$ group would thus be named methyl from methane. The general term alkyl radicals is derived from the alkanes. Common alkyl radicals may be represented as follows:

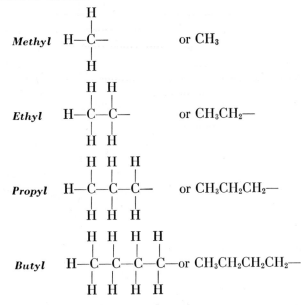

Methyl   H—C—   or CH_3

Ethyl   H—C—C—   or $CH_3CH_2—$

Propyl   H—C—C—C—   or $CH_3CH_2CH_2—$

Butyl   H—C—C—C—C—or $CH_3CH_2CH_2CH_2—$

Alcohols

As has been stated previously, there are thousands of organic compounds that contain the three elements carbon, hydrogen, and oxygen. The addition of oxygen to hydrocarbons produces derivatives

Denatured alcohol

such as alcohols, ethers and aldehydes which will be considered later in this chapter.

Oxygen, with six electrons in its outer orbit, must share two pairs of electrons to attain a stable arrangement. When oxygen shares one pair of electrons with carbon and the other pair with hydrogen an alcohol results, whereas if each pair of electrons is shared with a separate carbon atom an ether is produced. The sharing of both pairs of electrons with a single carbon atom results in an aldehyde.

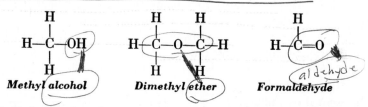

Methyl alcohol   **Dimethyl ether**   **Formaldehyde**

Of all the classes of organic compounds, alcohols are probably the best known. For centuries it has been recognized that alcoholic beverages contain ethyl or grain alcohol. Also it is common knowledge that most temporary antifreeze preparations for automobile radiators contain methyl or wood alcohol. The simplest hydrocarbon derivative that would result from oxygen sharing electrons with carbon and hydrogen is methyl alcohol shown with its molecular model as follows:

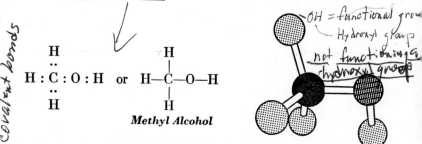

Methyl Alcohol

This combination of oxygen and hydrogen attached to a carbon is called a *hydroxyl group* and the compound is known as an *alcohol*. Alcohols may also be considered hydrocarbons in which one hydrogen is replaced by a hydroxyl group. A homologous series of alcohols would result from the addition of a hydroxyl group to each succeeding member of the alkane hydrocarbons. Methyl, ethyl, and propyl alcohols would be the first three members of the series.

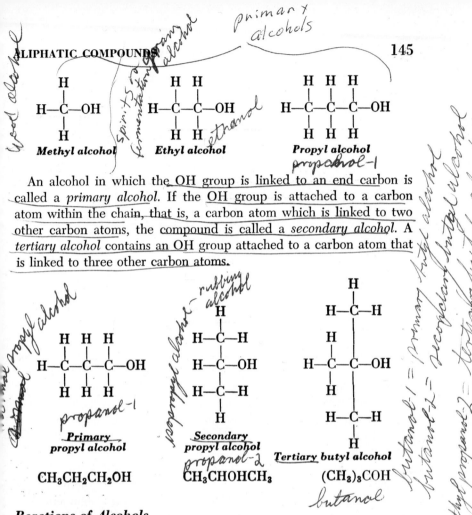

Methyl alcohol *Ethyl alcohol* *Propyl alcohol*

An alcohol in which the OH group is linked to an end carbon is called a *primary alcohol*. If the OH group is attached to a carbon atom within the chain, that is, a carbon atom which is linked to two other carbon atoms, the compound is called a *secondary alcohol*. A *tertiary alcohol* contains an OH group attached to a carbon atom that is linked to three other carbon atoms.

Primary
propyl alcohol

$CH_3CH_2CH_2OH$

Secondary
propyl alcohol

$CH_3CHOHCH_3$

Tertiary butyl alcohol

$(CH_3)_3COH$

Reactions of Alcohols

The oxidation of alcohols to form new compounds is one of their most important reactions. The rapid oxidation or burning of alcohols results in complete oxidation to form carbon dioxide and water. When methyl or ethyl alcohol are burned, they yield considerable amounts of energy (heat). If alcohols are treated with oxidizing agents at lower temperatures, they form several intermediate compounds (aldehydes, ketones, organic acids, etc.) before being completely oxidized to carbon dioxide and water. Mild oxidation of a primary alcohol results in the formation of an *aldehyde*, while a similar oxidation of a secondary alcohol produces a *ketone*.

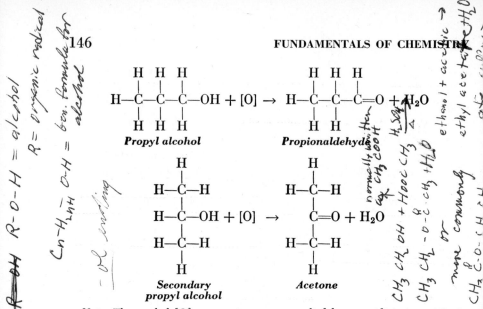

Propyl alcohol → **Propionaldehyde**

Secondary propyl alcohol → **Acetone**

Note: The symbol [O] represents oxygen supplied by an oxidizing agent in an oxidation reaction.

Another common reaction of alcohols is their reaction with acids, in which they behave in a manner similar to inorganic hydroxides. When an acid reacts with an alcohol, water and an organic ester are formed; when an acid reacts with an inorganic hydroxide, water and a salt are formed. Alcohols do not ionize and therefore do not contain the hydroxyl ions which are responsible for many of the properties of inorganic hydroxides.

METHYL ALCOHOL. Methyl alcohol is commonly called wood alcohol because it was once exclusively produced by the destructive distillation of wood. When hard wood is heated in a retort at temperatures up to 400° C., the vapors that are given off contain methyl alcohol, acetic acid, acetone, and other organic compounds. A synthetic process for the production of methyl alcohol from carbon monoxide and hydrogen was developed in 1923 and has largely supplanted the wood distillation method. In this process, carbon monoxide and hydrogen react under a high pressure and a temperature of 350° C. in the presence of zinc and chromium oxide catalysts.

$$CO + 2H_2 \xrightarrow[\text{Cr}_2\text{O}_3]{\text{ZnO}} CH_3OH$$

Carbon monoxide   Methyl alcohol

Recently a method has been developed for the production of methyl alcohol by the controlled oxidation of natural gas. Since ethyl and propyl alcohols and other important organic compounds are produced by this same reaction, this method is becoming increasingly important.

Methyl alcohol is a colorless, volatile liquid with a characteristic odor. It is used as a denaturant for ethyl alcohol, as a solvent for shellac in the varnish industry, as an antifreeze for automobile radiators, and as the raw material for the synthesis of other organic compounds. When taken internally, methyl alcohol is poisonous, small doses producing blindness by degeneration of the optic nerve, while large doses are fatal. The taste, odor, and poisonous properties of wood alcohol make it a desirable denaturing agent to be added to ethyl alcohol to prevent its use in beverages. During the prohibition era in the United States, several persons were blinded and others killed after drinking ethyl alcohol denatured in this fashion. An individual who was blinded temporarily after drinking a small amount of methyl alcohol was said to be "blind drunk."

ETHYL ALCOHOL. Ethyl alcohol is commonly known as alcohol, or as grain alcohol since it may be made by fermentation of various grains. It is prepared commercially by two major methods. One involves the fermentation of the sugars and starch of common grains, potatoes, or blackstrap molasses. The yeast used in fermentation contains enzymes that catalyze the transformation of sugars into alcohol and carbon dioxide, as shown in the following equation:

$$C_6H_{12}O_6 \xrightarrow[\text{enzymes}]{\text{yeast}} 2C_2H_5OH + 2CO_2$$

	Glucose	Ethyl alcohol	Carbon dioxide

ethyl alcohol is depressant — performance of simple tests falls off — also depresses repressions

Enzymes and fermentation will be studied more completely in the section on biochemistry. The other method is a synthetic method which makes use of the reaction of the unsaturated hydrocarbon ethylene with sulfuric acid, followed by a hydrolysis reaction. This reaction is illustrated using semistructural formulas for the organic compounds involved:

$$H_2C{=}CH_2 + H_2SO_4 \rightarrow CH_3CH_2OSO_3H$$

Ethylene   *Ethyl sulfate*

$$CH_3CH_2OSO_3H + H_2O \rightarrow CH_3CH_2OH + H_2SO_4$$

Ethyl sulfate   *Ethyl alcohol*

The ethylene used in this process is produced by the cracking of petroleum hydrocarbons.

Ethyl alcohol is a colorless, volatile liquid with a characteristic pleasant odor. Industrial ethyl alcohol contains approximately 95 per cent alcohol and 5 per cent water. It is difficult to remove all the water from alcohol since in simple distillation processes a constant boiling mixture of 95 per cent alcohol and 5 per cent water is formed. Methods for removing this water have been developed since the solvent properties of pure, absolute alcohol are considerably different than those of industrial alcohol. A large proportion of the industrial ethyl alcohol produced each year is used as an antifreeze in automobile radiators. It is an excellent solvent for many substances and is used in the preparation of medicines, flavoring extracts, and perfumes. Large quantities of ethyl alcohol are used in the manufacture of acetaldehyde, ether, and chloroform, and for the synthesis of butadiene for the manufacture of synthetic rubber.

The process of fermentation has been used for centuries to produce the alcohol found in intoxicating beverages such as beers, wines, and liquors. Many countries levy a high tax on alcohol when used for beverage purposes. This practice has resulted in the production and consumption of large quantities of illegal or "bootleg" liquors. A comparison of the price of denatured industrial alcohol with that of taxed grain alcohol will readily show why most of the alcohol produced in the United States is denatured before use. Denatured industrial alcohol costs approximately sixty cents a gallon, while tax paid ethyl alcohol costs in excess of eighteen dollars a gallon. The concentration of alcohol in beverages is usually expressed as per cent or "proof." For example, beers and wines contain from 3 to 20 per cent alcohol while liquors such as whiskey, rum, and gin contain from 80 to 100 proof alcohol. The standard 95 per cent alcohol is 190 proof while 100 proof alcohol is 42.5 per cent. When ethyl alcohol is taken internally, it is rapidly absorbed and oxidized. It may therefore be used as a readily available source of energy and is often employed to overcome shock or collapse. If large quantities are taken, it causes a depression of the higher nerve centers, mental confusion, lack of muscular coordination, lowering of normal inhibitions, and eventually stupor.

ETHYLENE GLYCOL. All of the alcohols so far considered have been monohydroxy alcohols. Since it is possible to replace a hydrogen atom on more than 1 carbon atom in a hydrocarbon with a hydroxyl group, it is possible to have polyhydroxy (polyhydric) alcohols. The simplest polyhydric alcohol would be one formed by replacing a hydrogen on each of the two carbons of ethane by a hydroxyl group. This compound is called *ethylene glycol.* It is prepared by oxidizing ethylene to ethylene oxide and subsequently hydrolyzing the oxide to ethylene glycol as shown in the following equations:

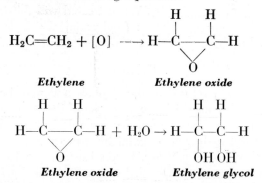

Ethylene   *Ethylene oxide*

      Ethylene oxide   *Ethylene glycol*

Ethylene glycol is water-soluble and has a very high boiling point compared to methyl and ethyl alcohols. These properties make it an excellent, permanent, or nonvolatile type of antifreeze for automobile radiators. Antifreeze preparations such as Prestone and Zerex consist of ethylene glycol plus a small amount of dye. Large quantities of ethylene glycol are used in the preparation of solvents, paint removers, and plasticizers (softeners) used in the paint, varnish, and lacquer industry. Propylene glycol is one of the constituents of suntan lotion.

GLYCEROL. The most important trihydric alcohol is glycerol which is sometimes called glycerin. It is an essential constituent of fat (an ester of glycerol and fatty acids) and may be prepared by the hydrolysis of fat as represented in the following equation:

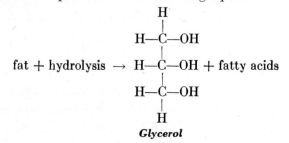

Glycerol

Glycerol is a syrupy, sweet-tasting substance that is soluble in all proportions of water and alcohol. It is nontoxic and is often used for the preparation of liquid medications. Since it has the ability to take up moisture from the air, it tends to keep the skin soft and moist when applied in the form of cosmetics and lotions. This property is also used to help maintain the moisture content of products made of tobacco. Large quantities of glycerol are also used in the manufacture of resins and photographic film. When treated with nitric acid, glycerol is readily converted into nitroglycerin, which is a common explosive used in the manufacture of dynamite and smokeless powder.

Ethers

Ethers are closely related to the alcohols and may be considered as a primary alcohol in which the hydrogen of the hydroxyl group has been replaced by an alkyl group. For example, methyl alcohol could have its hydroxyl hydrogen replaced by a methyl group to produce the simple ether, *dimethyl ether*. Ethers can also be described as an oxygen atom connected to two alkyl groups. The alkyl groups may be the same or may be different, resulting in such compounds as *methyl ethyl ether* or *diethyl ether*. The most common and most important ether is diethyl ether.

Diethyl ether is prepared by the reaction of ethyl alcohol and concentrated sulfuric acid. This reaction takes place in two steps as follows:

$$CH_3CH_2OH + H_2SO_4 \rightarrow CH_3CH_2OSO_3H + H_2O$$
Ethyl alcohol   *Ethyl hydrogen sulfate*

$$CH_3CH_2OSO_3H + CH_3CH_2OH \rightarrow CH_3CH_2-O-CH_2CH_3 + H_2SO_4$$
Ethyl hydrogen   ethyl   *Diethyl ether*
sulfate   alcohol

The over-all reaction may be represented very simply by the removal of 1 molecule of H_2O from 2 molecules of ethyl alcohol.

$$C_2H_5 \boxed{OH} + \boxed{H} OC_2H_5 \longrightarrow C_2H_5-O-C_2H_5 + H_2O$$
Ethyl   *Ethyl*   *Diethyl ether*
alcohol   *alcohol*

Diethyl ether, which is often called ethyl ether or ether, is extensively used as a general anesthetic. It is easy to administer, and causes excellent relaxation of the muscles. Blood pressure, the pulse rate, and the rate of respiration as a rule are only slightly affected. Its main disadvantages are its irritating effect on the respiratory passages and its after-effect of nausea. Since ether is extremely volatile and inflammable, care must be taken in its use as an anesthetic to prevent serious fires and explosions.

Another ether, *divinyl ether*, called Vinethene (Fig. 63), is often used as a rapid-acting, short-term anesthetic. When properly administered, this ether does not produce the after-effect of nausea. Recently, methyl propyl ether has been used as a general anesthetic. It has been claimed that this substance, called *metopryl*, is less irritating and more potent than ethyl ether.

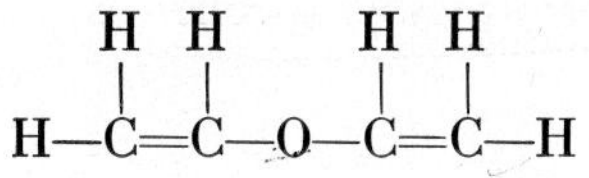

$$H-\underset{\underset{H}{|}}{\overset{\overset{H}{|}}{C}}=\underset{\underset{H}{|}}{\overset{\overset{H}{|}}{C}}-O-\underset{\underset{H}{|}}{\overset{\overset{H}{|}}{C}}=\underset{\underset{H}{|}}{\overset{\overset{H}{|}}{C}}-H \qquad H-\underset{\underset{H}{|}}{\overset{\overset{H}{|}}{C}}-\underset{\underset{H}{|}}{\overset{\overset{H}{|}}{C}}-\underset{\underset{H}{|}}{\overset{\overset{H}{|}}{C}}-O-\underset{\underset{H}{|}}{\overset{\overset{H}{|}}{C}}-H$$

Divinyl ether 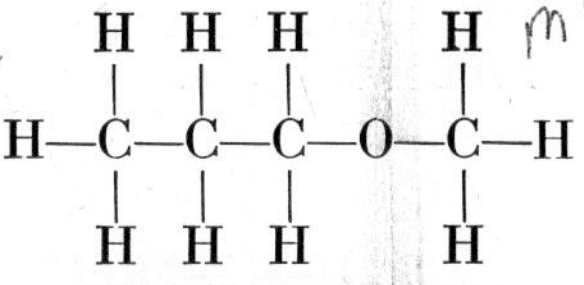   **Methyl propyl ether**

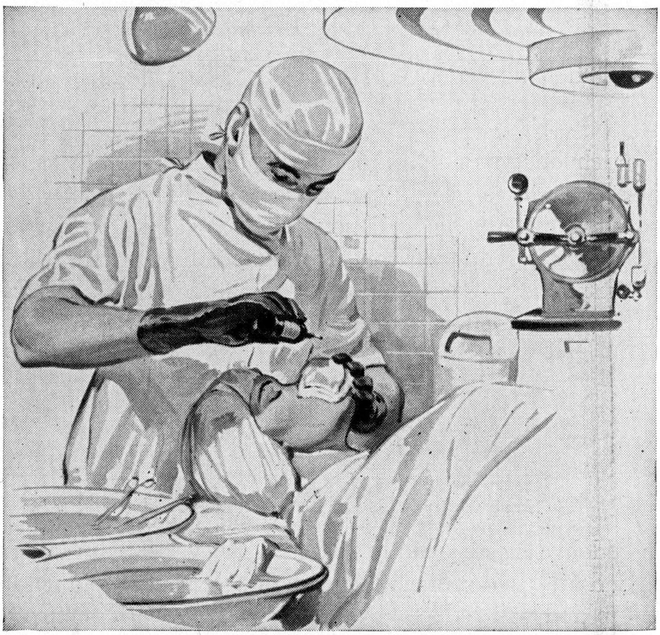

Figure 63.   The use of Vinethene as an anesthetic. (Merck & Co., Inc.)

$CH_3\overset{O}{\underset{}{C}}-$ = acetyl radical

Methyl ether is used as a solvent and as a propellant for aerosol sprays. Diethyl ether is an excellent solvent for fats and is often used in the laboratory for the extraction of fat from foods and animal tissues. In general, ethers are good solvents for fats, oils, gums, and resins.

Aldehydes

Aldehydes are another type of aliphatic compound closely related to alcohols. Primary alcohols are readily oxidized to aldehydes in the presence of a suitable catalyst. Since two hydrogens are removed in this oxidation process, aldehydes may be described as primary alcohols from which 2 hydrogen atoms have been removed. The simplest aldehyde, formaldehyde, is prepared from methyl alcohol as shown in the following equation:

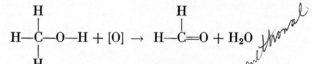

$$\underset{\text{Methyl alcohol}}{H-\overset{\displaystyle H}{\underset{\displaystyle H}{C}}-O-H} + [O] \rightarrow \underset{\text{Formaldehyde}}{H-\overset{\displaystyle H}{C}=O} + H_2O$$

methanal

found in ants – Latin name

The name aldehyde is derived from alcohol dehydrogenation and the typical aldehyde group may be represented as $-\overset{\displaystyle H}{C}=O$ or $-CHO$.

Aldehydes undergo many types of chemical reactions. Oxidation of aldehydes to form organic acids may be achieved by ordinary oxidizing agents, while reduction to the corresponding primary alcohol is carried out in the presence of hydrogen and a suitable catalyst. The reaction for the oxidation of acetaldehyde may be written as follows:

$$\underset{\text{Acetaldehyde}}{H-\overset{\displaystyle H}{\underset{\displaystyle H}{C}}-\overset{\displaystyle H}{C}=O} + O \rightarrow \underset{\text{Acetic acid}}{H-\overset{\displaystyle H}{\underset{\displaystyle H}{C}}-\overset{\displaystyle O}{C}-OH}$$

ethanal

most common name

found in fermentation

Since aldehydes are readily oxidized, they have an affinity for oxygen, and are good reducing agents. Simple sugars contain an aldehyde group and will reduce cupric ions (Cu^{++}) to cuprous (Cu^+).

aldehydes & ketones = carbonyl groups

alcohol (2) → aldehyde

ETHANAL AL suffix = aldehyde

$R-\overset{\displaystyle H}{C}=O$ or $R-CHO$

AL →[O] *ACID*

The cuprous ions then form cuprous oxide which settles out of the solution as an insoluble red precipitate. This reaction is the basis of Benedict's test, a clinical method of determining the presence of sugar in the urine.

Formaldehyde is a colorless gas with a sharp, penetrating odor. The gas dissolves readily in water, and a 40 per cent solution is known as *formalin*. Formalin is widely used as a disinfectant and as a preservative of tissues. Formaldehyde may be converted into a solid known as *paraformaldehyde* which is formed by the union or polymerization of several molecules of formaldehyde. This process is common to most aldehydes. Paraformaldehyde is used as an antiseptic. The most extensive use of formaldehyde is in the manufacture of synthetic resins. A more recent application of formaldehyde is in the manufacture of the high explosive trimethylene trinitramine which was developed during World War II.

Acetaldehyde is produced commercially, either by oxidation of ethyl alcohol as discussed earlier or by the hydration of acetylene. It is a colorless liquid with a characteristic, sharp odor. It is used industrially in the synthesis of such important compounds as acetic acid, ethyl acetate, and butyl alcohol. Three molecules of acetaldehyde polymerize to form *paraldehyde* which is a more stable liquid than acetaldehyde. Paraldehyde is an effective hypnotic, or sleep producer, and is relatively nontoxic. This compound has an irritating odor and an unpleasant taste. It is not used as widely as it was formerly. Paraldehyde is readily depolymerized by heating and is a convenient source of acetaldehyde.

Ketones

Ketones are very closely related to aldehydes and to alcohols. The oxidation of a secondary alcohol produces a ketone. The functional group of a ketone consists of a carbon atom connected by a double bond to an oxygen atom. This is called a *carbonyl group* and in a ketone must be connected to two alkyl groups. An aldehyde differs from a ketone in that its carbonyl group is on the end of the hydrocarbon chain and is connected to a hydrogen atom and to an alkyl group. The typical ketone, acetone, may be formed by the oxidation of secondary propyl alcohol as shown.

$$CH_3 - \overset{O}{\underset{\|}{C}} - CH_3$$

dimethyl ketone

may also be named by radical + ketone

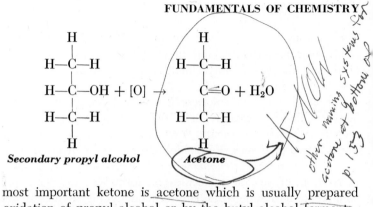

$$
\begin{array}{ccc}
& H & \\
& | & \\
H-C-H & & \\
& | & \\
H-C-OH + [O] & \rightarrow &
\end{array}
\qquad
\begin{array}{c}
H \\
| \\
H-C-H \\
| \\
C=O + H_2O \\
| \\
H-C-H \\
| \\
H
\end{array}
$$

Secondary propyl alcohol   *Acetone*

The most important ketone is acetone which is usually prepared by the oxidation of propyl alcohol or by the butyl alcohol fermentation process from cornstarch. It is a colorless volatile liquid with a characteristic pleasant odor. Acetone is used in commercial preparations of chloroform, iodoform, and other organic compounds. It is an

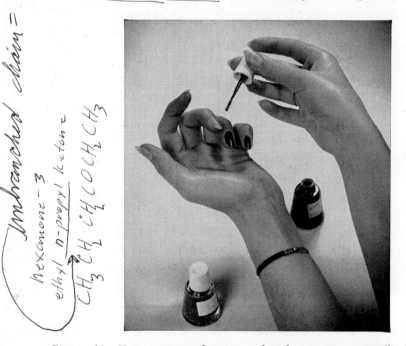

Figure 64. Ketones are used in many liquid cosmetics, especially fingernail polish and remover.

[handwritten margin notes:]

other mining systems for Acetone at bottom od p. 153

Unbranched chain = normal (n)

hexanone - 3

ethyl n-propyl ketone

$CH_3 CH_2 CH_2 COCH_2 CH_3$

$R COR' \xrightarrow{[O]}$ *some mixture of* $RCOOH$ *- can't predict exactly what comb. we will get.*

excellent solvent for cellulose derivatives and is used extensively in the manufacture of photographic film, acetate rayon, smokeless powders, lacquers, and explosives.

Another ketone similar to acetone is known as methyl ethyl ketone; it consists of a methyl group and an ethyl group attached to a carbonyl group. This ketone is used by the petroleum industry in the dewaxing of lubricating oils. It is also an excellent solvent for fingernail polish and is used as a polish remover (Fig. 64).

R COOH = acid (organic)

Organic Acids

Organic acids are closely related to alcohols and aldehydes since the oxidation of either of these compounds could result in the formation of an acid. An organic acid might be considered as a derivative of an aldehyde in which the aldehyde group has been oxidized to a

carboxyl group
acid radical

carboxyl group which is written C—OH or more simply COOH. The first three members of a homologous series of organic acids are illustrated as follows:

BUTYRIC ACID

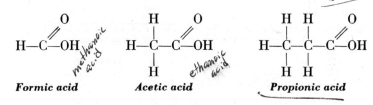

| Formic acid | Acetic acid | Propionic acid |

methanoic acid   *ethanoic acid*

$$R-\overset{O}{\underset{}{\overset{\|}{C}}}-OH$$ *ic ending*

The carboxyl group is the functional group of organic acids and is responsible for their acid properties. Most organic acids are weak acids since they ionize only slightly when dissolved in water. The only hydrogen atom that ionizes is the hydrogen of the carboxyl group as shown in the following:

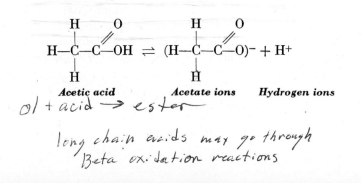

| Acetic acid | Acetate ions | Hydrogen ions |

ol + acid → ester

long chain acids may go through Beta oxidation reactions

$CH_3 COOH$ = acetic acid

The hydrogen ions released in solution impart all the characteristic properties of an acid to the organic acids.

Common organic acids such as formic and acetic acids which contain one *carboxyl* group are called *monobasic* acids. *Dibasic* acids contain two, and *tribasic* acids, three carboxyl groups. Oxalic acid, COOH—COOH, is an example of a dibasic acid, while citric acid, CH_2—COOH—COH—COOH—CH_2—COOH, is tribasic. Many organic acids contain hydroxyl groups in addition to the OH of the carboxyl group and are classified as *hydroxy acids*. Lactic acid, CH_3—CHOH—COOH, tartaric acid, COOH—CHOH—CHOH—COOH, and citric acid are common examples of hydroxy acids.

Reactions of Organic Acids

A characteristic property of organic acids is their ability to react with inorganic hydroxides (bases) to form *organic salts* and with organic hydroxides (alcohols) to form *esters*.

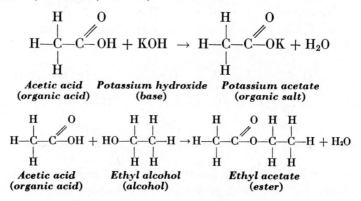

FORMIC ACID—HCOOH.   Small amounts of this acid occur free in nature and its presence is made known in an unpleasant fashion. Anyone who has been bitten by an ant, stung by a bee or brushed against stinging nettles has felt the irritating effect of formic acid injected under the skin. Fórmic acid is prepared industrially by heating powdered sodium hydroxide with carbon monoxide gas under pressure. The sodium formate produced by this reaction is treated with sulfuric acid to release the formic acid.

Important Organic Acids

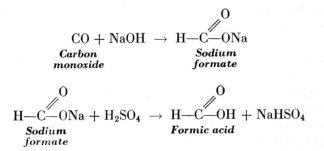

Formic acid is a colorless liquid with a sharp, irritating odor. It is a strong organic acid and will produce blisters when it comes in contact with the skin. Since it is stronger than most organic acids, yet not as strong as mineral acids, it finds many uses as an acid agent. It is used in the manufacture of esters, salts and oxalic acid.

ACETIC ACID—CH_3COOH. This acid has been known for centuries as an essential component of vinegar. It is formed from the oxidation of ethyl alcohol produced from the fermentation of fruit juices in the preparation of the vinegar. Cider vinegar from fruit juices contains about 4 per cent acetic acid in addition to flavoring and coloring agents from the fruit. White vinegar is prepared by diluting acetic acid to the proper concentration with water.

Acetic acid is produced commercially by the oxidation of acetaldehyde. The acetaldehyde for this process is produced by the oxidation of ethyl alcohol or the hydration of acetylene.

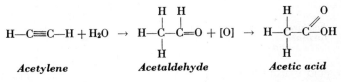

Some acetic acid is also produced from the controlled oxidation of natural gas as discussed previously. Commercially produced acetic acid is about 99.5 per cent pure and is called glacial acetic acid since on cold days it freezes to an icelike solid.

Acetic acid is produced in large quantities and is used extensively in industries where a low-cost organic acid is required. For example, considerable quantities are used in the manufacture of white lead, cellulose acetate for the production of rayon, cellophane, photographic film, plastics, and organic solvents.

LACTIC ACID—$CH_3CHOHCOOH$. This acid is formed when lactose (milk sugar) is fermented by Lactobacillus bacteria. The taste of sour milk and buttermilk is due to the presence of lactic acid. In the process of muscular contraction, lactic acid is formed by the muscle tissues and is found in the blood. In many of the so-called "cycles" involved in the oxidation of carbohydrates, lipids, and proteins to produce energy in the body, lactic acid is an essential component. It is made commercially by the fermentation of sugar or starch by a strain of lactic acid bacteria. It is a strong organic acid similar in strength to formic acid. Lactic acid esters are useful as solvents in the preparation of lacquers and plastics. Salts of lactic acid, the lactates, are used in medicine—for example, in calcium therapy—and also in several food products.

OXALIC ACID—$COOHCOOH$. Oxalic acid occurs as a salt in the leaves of vegetables such as rhubarb and is one of the strongest naturally occurring acids. Its preparation is closely related to that of formic acid since the sodium salt of oxalic acid is produced by heating 2 molecules of sodium formate. The sodium oxalate is then converted to oxalic acid by the addition of a suitable acid.

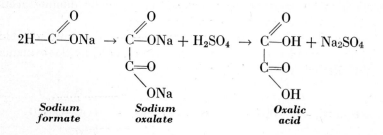

Sodium	*Sodium*	*Oxalic*
formate	*oxalate*	*acid*

Oxalic acid is used to remove iron stain from fabrics and from porcelain ware, and to bleach straw and leather goods. It will also remove stains made by inks that contain iron.

CITRIC ACID—$CH_2COOHCOHCOOHCH_2COOH$. Citric acid is a normal constituent of citrus fruits. Since it occurs in a concentration of 6 to 7 per cent in lemon juice, it is commercially feasible to prepare it from lemons. Large quantities are produced by a fermentation process from starch or molasses. It is commonly employed to impart a sour taste to food products and beverages. In fact, most of the citric acid produced each year is used by the food and soft drink industries.

Organic Salts

Any of the organic acids that have just been discussed will react with an inorganic base to form an organic salt. Salts of acetic acid are probably the most common and most extensively used.

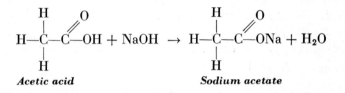

Acetic acid   **Sodium acetate**

A common reaction of all organic salts is the release of their corresponding organic acids when they are treated with a mineral acid. Organic salts are often intermediate compounds in the production of organic acids. They are also usually more stable and more convenient to handle than the acids.

Important Organic Salts

Sodium acetate is often used for its buffering effect in reducing the acidity of inorganic acids. Lead acetate, sometimes called sugar of lead because of its sweet taste, is used externally to treat poison ivy and certain skin diseases. Commercially it is used in large quantities in the manufacture of white lead paint. Paris green is a complex salt that contains copper acetate and is used as an insecticide. Aluminum acetate is used in certain processes in the dyeing of textile fibers. Calcium propionate is added to bread to prevent molding. The calcium salt of lactic acid is sometimes used to supplement the calcium of the diet. Many infants receive additional iron in their diets from the salt, ferric ammonium citrate. Magnesium citrate has long been used as a saline cathartic. A solution of sodium citrate is used to prevent the clotting of blood during transfusions, and potassium oxalate will prevent the clotting of blood specimens drawn for analysis in the clinical laboratory.

Esters

The compound formed in the reaction between an acid and an alcohol is called an *ester*. *Hydrolysis of ester → acid + ol* *Breakdown or*

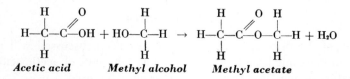

Acetic acid   **Methyl alcohol**   **Methyl acetate**

Esters differ from organic salts in that they do not ionize in water solution. Therefore they react very slowly with other compounds unless a catalyst is present. One of their most important reactions is hydrolysis, i.e., reaction with water to form an acid and an alcohol:

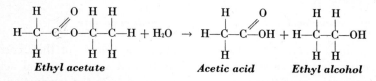

Ethyl acetate   **Acetic acid**   **Ethyl alcohol**

The number of organic esters that can be prepared is almost limitless. Each organic acid has a homologous series of esters. For example, methyl acetate, ethyl acetate, propyl acetate, and so on make up one such series. In addition, we may have esters of aromatic and cyclic acids. Commercially, only a few of the esters are produced in large quantity. The two most important are ethyl acetate and butyl acetate which are used as solvents, especially for nitrocellulose in the preparation of lacquers. Some of the higher molecular weight esters are plastics while others are used in the production of plastics.

Many esters occur in free form in nature and are responsible for the odor of most fruits and flowers. The characteristic taste and odors of different esters find application in the manufacture of artificial flavoring extracts and perfumes. Synthetic esters that are commonly used as food flavors are amyl acetate for banana, octyl acetate for orange, ethyl butyrate for pineapple, amyl butyrate for apricot, isobutyl formate for raspberry, and ethyl formate for rum. Esters used for the manufacture of perfumes are usually esters of aromatic or cyclic acids.

Other esters are commonly used as therapeutic agents in medicine. Ethyl acetate is employed as a stimulant and antispasmodic in colic, and bronchial irritations. It is also applied externally in the treatment of skin diseases caused by parasites. Ethyl nitrite, when mixed with alcohol, is called elixir of niter and is used as a diuretic and antispasmodic. Amyl nitrite is used to lower blood pressure temporarily and causes relaxation of muscular spasms in asthma and in the heart *handwritten:* $-N=N-$ = highly colored

$1S^1, 2S^2, \overline{(2P^1, 2P^1, 2P^1)}$ formally usually 3 bonds

N = at. no. = 7

condition known as angina pectoris. Glycerol trinitrate or nitroglycerin is a vasodilator that has a physiological action similar to amyl nitrate.

Amides

Amides may be considered as derivatives of organic acids which contain an amino (NH_2) group. It is perhaps more accurate to consider them as derivatives of ammonia in which hydrogen is replaced by an acyl group. The removal of an OH from the COOH group of an organic acid results in an *acyl* group. Amides may be prepared from an acid chloride and ammonia.

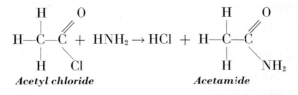

$$H-\underset{\underset{H}{|}}{\overset{\overset{H}{|}}{C}}-\overset{O}{\overset{\|}{C}}-Cl + HNH_2 \rightarrow HCl + H-\underset{\underset{H}{|}}{\overset{\overset{H}{|}}{C}}-\overset{O}{\overset{\|}{C}}-NH_2$$

Acetyl chloride   *Acetamide*

Formamide, a derivative of formic acid, is a liquid, while all other amides are solids. Even though amides are derived from ammonia, they are neutral compounds and do not exhibit basic properties in solution. Apparently, the basic properties of the amino group are balanced by the acid properties of the carboxyl group in the amides. Formamide and molten acetamide are used as solvents for other organic compounds and in the synthesis of organic compounds.

handwritten left margin: RNH_2 - primary amine / $RNHR'$ - secondary / R''' R'' R' - tertiary

handwritten: amine = 3 bonds on N derivative of ammonia

Amines

handwritten: MONO AMINES · $R-NH_2$ 1 substitution

Amines are organic derivatives of ammonia in which one or more of the hydrogen atoms have been replaced by an alkyl group. The characteristic or functional group present in amines is called the *amino group* and is written NH_2. The name amine is derived from ammonia, and the relation of the simple amines to ammonia is shown as follows:

$$H-N-H$$
$$\overset{|}{H}$$
Ammonia

$$H-\overset{\overset{H}{|}}{C}-N-H$$
$$\underset{H\ \ H}{}$$
Methyl amine

$$H-\overset{\overset{H}{|}}{C}-\overset{\overset{H}{|}}{C}-N-H$$
$$\underset{H\ \ H\ \ H}{}$$
Ethyl amine

handwritten bottom: derivatives of ammonium radical = either quaternary ammonium compounds or ethyl amine hydrochloride — N has 4 bonds

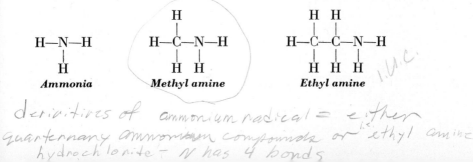

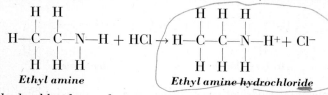

Methyl and ethyl amines are known as primary amines since only one of the hydrogens in ammonia is replaced by an alkyl group. Replacement of two or three of the hydrogens of ammonia by alkyl groups produces *secondary* and *tertiary* amines. Amines may be prepared by treating ammonia with the proper alcohol or alkyl halide in the presence of a suitable catalyst.

Amines exist as gases or liquids with unpleasant odors that combine the odor of ammonia with that of decayed fish. The simple amines are soluble in water and in most organic solvents. One of the outstanding characteristics of amines is their basic properties. For example, methyl amine and ethyl amine are stronger bases than ammonia and react with inorganic acids such as hydrochloric to form hydrochlorides.

Ethyl amine   **Ethyl amine hydrochloride**

The hydrochloride may be written more simply as $CH_3CH_2NH_3^+Cl^-$ or as $CH_3CH_2NH_2 \cdot HCl$. Secondary and tertiary amines are also stronger bases than ammonium hydroxide. The strongest of the amine bases are the *quaternary bases;* for example, tetramethyl ammonium hydroxide $(CH_3)_4NOH$ is comparable in basicity to potassium hydroxide.

Methyl amine and dimethyl amine are used in the tanning industry as dehairing agents. Butyl amine and amyl amine are used as antioxidants, corrosion inhibitors, and in the preparation of soaps that are soluble in oil. These amines find many uses as organic bases in the manufacture of pharmaceutical and cosmetic products.

Another type of important organic compounds that contain amino groups are *amino acids.* Amino acids may be considered as organic acids containing an amino group. Two simple amino acids are illustrated as follows:

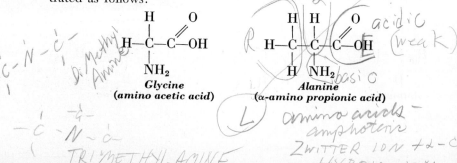

Glycine   **Alanine**
(amino acetic acid)   **(α-amino propionic acid)**

a semetric carbon atom — 4 dif. groups
7 on C atom — called L

insulin has -s-s- bond
SH (sulfhydryl) ⇄ reduce -s-s- (disulfide)

Amino acids are the fundamental units in the protein molecule and will be discussed later in greater detail under the chemistry of proteins.

glutathione — in all cells — function unknown — 3 sulfide

Review Questions

4 amino acids contain sulfur — either -s-s- -s-

1. Why is a knowledge of the characteristic group of a class of organic compounds important?
2. Write the formula for an aliphatic hydrocarbon that contains 8 carbon atoms. How would you name the compound? What relation does this compound have to commercial gasoline?
3. Define and illustrate isomerism in organic compounds.
4. What effect would the exhaustion of all petroleum supplies have on the progress of a nation at war, and at peace?
5. Write the formula for a saturated aliphatic compound and an unsaturated compound. How is unsaturation indicated in the formula of a compound?
6. What is a homologous series; a homolog?
7. Write the structural formulas for two halogen derivatives of hydrocarbons. Compare chloroform and carbon tetrachloride as to their usefulness in medicine and in industry.
8. Compare inorganic and organic radicals. Write the formulas for the common alkyl radicals.
9. Name and write the formula for a primary alcohol; a secondary alcohol.
10. Write an equation for the oxidation of primary butyl alcohol. What products are usually formed on complete oxidation of an alcohol?
11. In what ways are alcohols similar to inorganic bases? In what ways do they differ?
12. Why is methyl alcohol poisonous when taken internally?
13. List several important uses for ethyl alcohol.
14. What is meant by denatured alcohol? Why is denatured alcohol frequently used in the hospital and in industry?
15. Name and write the formula for an alcohol containing two hydroxyl groups; three hydroxyl groups.
16. Compare the advantages and disadvantages of ethyl ether, Vinethene, and metopryl.
17. Write the formula for an aldehyde other than acetaldehyde. Circle the characteristic group in the compound.
18. Why are aldehydes good reducing agents? How is this reducing property applied to the determination of sugar in the urine?
19. Write the formula for a ketone other than acetone. Discuss the uses of this ketone.
20. Compare the properties and reactions of organic and inorganic acids.
21. Starting with propyl alcohol, show the steps involved in the oxidation of this compound to form propionic acid.
22. Differentiate between the following terms: monobasic, dibasic, tribasic, and hydroxy acids. Give an example of each.
23. Why is lactic acid an important hydroxy organic acid?

AMINO ACID + NaOH → Negative amino at high pH
" " " + acid → Positive " " low pH
(HCl)

ZWITTER ION

LYSINE

ISOLEUCINE

24. Write an equation for the formation of a typical organic salt.
25. What organic salts are often used to supplement the calcium or iron content of the diet? Which are used as cathartics?
26. Write the formula for the ester that would be formed by the reaction of ethyl alcohol and propionic acid. What would the ester be called?
27. List several medical uses of esters.
28. Give an example of an amine. Would this compound be acidic or basic in reaction? Why?
29. If an amide is prepared from ammonia, why shouldn't it exhibit basic properties?

Toxicity of alcohol   *relative scale of lethal doses*

	man & others compounded	cats	rabbit heart
methyl	1.0	1.0	1.0
ethyl	1.25	1.2	1.3
propyl	2.5	2.95	4.4
butyl	3.8	19.7	10.0
amyl	5.0	39.0	39.0

higher molecular wt → greater toxicity

methyl alcohol oxidizes slowly – sub lethal dosage more dangerous than ethyl alcohol

primary
$$RCH_2OH + (O) \rightarrow RCHO \xrightarrow{(O)} RCOOH \xrightarrow{(O)} CO_2 + H_2O$$

secondary
$$RCHOHR' \xrightarrow{(O)} RCOR'$$

tertiary
$$RCHOR' \xrightarrow{(O)} comb. \ of \ al \ & \ one \ o^{..} \ break \ up \ molecule$$
R''   *NON PREDICTABLE*

Quarternary ammonium compounds

$N R_4^+ Cl^-$

detergents & germicides have large molecules

ISOELECTRIC POINT IS POINT of pH of amino acids at which ionization is at minimum & compound doesn't move toward either side of pole (ston)

Chapter 12

Cyclic Compounds

In addition to the aliphatic, or straight chain carbon compounds, that have just been considered, another major type of organic compound is derived from the cyclic hydrocarbon, benzene. Originally these cyclic hydrocarbons were termed *aromatic* compounds, since they were first isolated from aromatic substances such as gum benzoin and the volatile oils of cloves, wintergreen, vanilla, cinnamon, and bitter almonds. As additional cyclic compounds were discovered, the classification based on aroma was found to be too narrow in scope. At present, the term aromatic compounds is applied only to benzene and its derivatives. For this reason, organic compounds are now divided into aliphatic and cyclic compounds. If a ring structure consists entirely of carbon atoms, the compounds are called *carbocyclic;* when other kinds of atoms besides carbon are in the ring, they are called *heterocyclic* compounds.

Hydrocarbons

Benzene

The basic aromatic hydrocarbon benzene was named from the aromatic substance gum benzoin. In 1833, Mitscherlich obtained this hydrocarbon by the treatment of benzoic acid which had been isolated from gum benzoin. The empirical formula for benzene was found to be C_6H_6. This formula indicates a high ratio of carbon to hydrogen, and, if written as an open chain structure, it would be a very unsaturated hydrocarbon. Its chemical properties, however, more closely resemble those of a saturated hydrocarbon. For many years, chemists were unable to decide on a structural formula that would account for all of the reactions and properties of benzene. The structural formula for benzene was first represented as six carbons combined in the form of a hexagon with alternate single and double bonds by Kekulé in 1865.

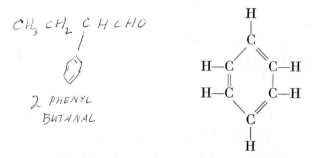

CH_3 CH_2 C H c HO

2 PHENYL BUTANAL

BARBITUATES — Sc. Am.

The alternate double bonds satisfy the valence requirements of the carbon atoms when one hydrogen atom is attached to each carbon atom. Since the properties of benzene are not similar to those of an unsaturated compound, it has been assumed that the double bonds between the carbon atoms in a ring are not as easily broken as those in an open chain compound.

For ease of representation, benzene is usually indicated as a hexagon with or without the double bonds. Aromatic hydrocarbon radicals may be formed in a fashion similar to aliphatic radicals by the removal of an atom of hydrogen from a molecule of benzene. The specific radical of benzene is known as the *phenyl* radical while in general aromatic hydrocarbon radicals are known as *aryl* groups.

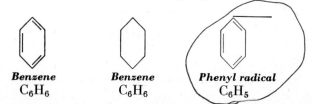

Benzene
C_6H_6

Benzene
C_6H_6

Phenyl radical
C_6H_5

In.using these symbols, it must be kept in mind that alternate double bonds are present, and that a hydrogen atom is attached to each carbon atom. If an element or radical has replaced a hydrogen atom on the ring, this must be indicated.

Until recent years, benzene was produced almost exclusively from coal gas and coal tar. The increased demand for benzene during and since World War II has resulted in the development of a synthetic method for its production. This method involves the cyclization of

[handwritten annotations: CYCLIC WITH RESONANCE → STABLE / NO REACTION WITH H₂ / SUB. REACTIONS]

alkanes such as hexane in petroleum to a cyclohexane, in the presence of suitable catalysts. The cyclohexanes can then be dehydrogenated to yield benzene. The production of benzene from hexane is illustrated in the following reaction:

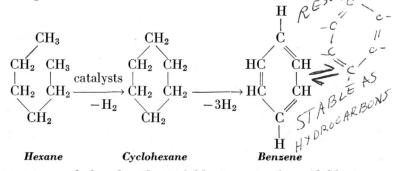

| *Hexane* | *Cyclohexane* | *Benzene* |

Benzene is a colorless liquid, insoluble in water but soluble in alcohol and ether. It is used as a solvent for fat, resins, paint, varnishes, and rubber. Commercially, it is used as the starting material in the manufacture of many important aromatic compounds such as phenol, styrene, and aniline. Prior to World War II, large quantities of benzene were mixed with gasoline and used as a fuel in internal combustion engines. Benzene is toxic when taken internally and must be used with proper precautions in any commercial process. Prolonged inhalation of its vapors by industrial workers results in a decreased production of red and white corpuscles in the blood, which may prove fatal.

Halogen Derivatives of Benzene

Aromatic hydrocarbons such as benzene react readily with halogens as do the alkane hydrocarbons. For example, chlorine and bromine react with benzene to form substitution products in which one or more of the hydrogen atoms are replaced by halogen atoms.

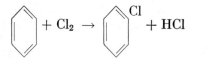

[handwritten: phenol, or, phenol]

When two or more halogen atoms are substituted on the benzene ring, their relative position is important. For example, there are three dichlorobenzenes which may be represented as follows:

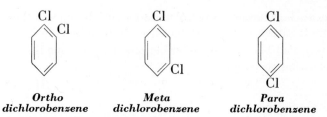

Ortho   *Meta*   *Para*
dichlorobenzene   *dichlorobenzene*   *dichlorobenzene*

The isomer in which the two chlorine atoms are on adjacent carbon atoms is called *ortho*, abbreviated *o-*. When there is one carbon atom between the two substituted groups, the isomer is known as *meta* *(m-)*, while the isomer in which there are two carbon atoms between the two chlorine atoms is termed *para (p-)*.

Any two groups that are substituted for hydrogen on the benzene ring will be in the ortho, meta, or para position. When three or more groups are substituted for the hydrogen in benzene, their positions are indicated by numbers:

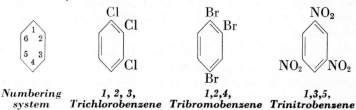

Numbering   *1, 2, 3,*   *1,2,4,*   *1,3,5,*
system   *Trichlorobenzene*   *Tribromobenzene*   *Trinitrobenzene*

Structure of Benzene

Although the Kekulé formula for benzene is commonly used, it is not completely satisfactory. It would, for example, permit the existence of two ortho dibromobenzenes in which the bromine atoms are attached to two carbon atoms joined by a single bond or by a double bond:

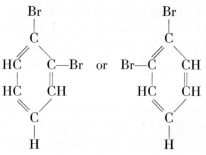

To account for the existence of only one ortho dibromobenzene, Kekulé proposed that the double bonds in benzene could exist in either of two positions as shown:

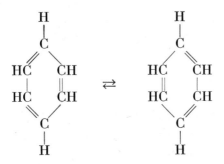

The most satisfactory structure for benzene, at present, is based on resonance between the above formulas. According to the *theory of resonance* there is a ready shift of double bonds from one position to the other. This explains the behavior of the two forms proposed by Kekulé and also accounts for the lack of unsaturation properties exhibited by benzene. Until a simple means of illustrating the resonance form of benzene is developed, it will be written in the common Kekulé form.

Homologs of Benzene

Any radical or group of elements, attached to the benzene ring was called a side chain by Kekulé. The characteristic 6 carbon group was called the ring or nucleus of the aromatic hydrocarbons. There are higher members or homologs in the benzene series that are similar to the homologs of the methane series. These homologs of benzene may be defined as hydrocarbons, which contain an alkyl group in the place of one or more of the hydrogen atoms. The first higher homolog is *toluene* or methyl benzene, $C_6H_5CH_3$. It is produced commercially from the light oil distilled from coal tar and may also be made synthetically from alkanes in petroleum. Toluene is a colorless liquid which is insoluble in water and has a characteristic odor. It is used as a solvent, as a preservative for urine specimens and for the preparation of many more complicated aromatic compounds. During World War II, large quantities of toluene were required for the manufacture of the explosive trinitrotoluene, commonly called TNT.

The second higher homolog of benzene is known as *xylene*. Since xylene contains two methyl groups, it may exist as the ortho, meta, or para isomer. Toluene and the isomers of xylene may be written structurally as follows:

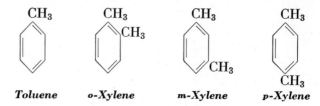

Toluene   **o-Xylene**   **m-Xylene**   **p-Xylene**

The xylenes, obtained from the light oil distilled from coal tar, have properties similar to toluene.

Condensed Aromatic Hydrocarbons

Two or more benzene rings may combine to form aromatic compounds with condensed or fused benzene rings. The simplest compound of this type is *naphthalene*. It consists of two rings fused

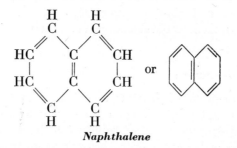

Naphthalene

together so that 2 carbon atoms are common to each ring. Naphthalene is obtained from coal tar and exists as a white crystalline solid. Large quantities of this compound are used in the preparation of moth balls. Derivatives of naphthalene find many important uses in industry. The naphthols which contain a hydroxyl group on the ring are important dye intermediates, and large quantities are used for the synthesis of other types of dye intermediates. Methyl naphthalene has a rating of zero as a diesel fuel and is used as a standard in testing fuels for diesel engines. Naphthoquinones are an integral part of the vitamin K molecule while other naphthalene derivatives are used as wetting agents, and as auxins, which accelerate the growth of plants.

Another similar substance obtained from coal tar is *anthracene* which is composed of three fused benzene rings.

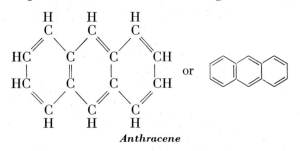

Anthracene

The most important derivative of anthracene is anthraquinone which is used in the manufacture of anthraquinone dyes.

An isomer of anthracene is phenanthrene which is obtained from coal tar.

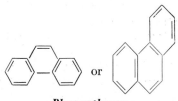

Phenanthrene

Phenanthrene is an integral part of the sterols, steroid hormones and vitamins which will be studied in detail in the section on Biochemistry.

Sources of Aromatic Hydrocarbons

The most important source of benzene and its homologs is coal. When coal is heated to a high temperature in the absence of air, volatile products are removed and a residue of impure carbon, called coke, remains behind. This process, which may be termed the destructive distillation of coal, has been used for years to produce large quantities of coke. Most of the coke is used for the reduction of ores in blast furnaces while a fraction of it is used also as a smokeless fuel in industry and in homes. The volatile products from this process include coal gas, ammonia gas, and coal tar. The destructive distillation of 1 ton of coal produces about 1500 pounds of coke, 11,000 cubic feet of gas, 3.5 gallons of a light oil, and 10 gallons of coal tar.

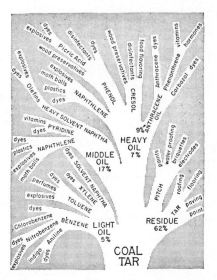

Figure 65.   Coal tar is a source of many important products. Some of these products are illustrated on the coal tar tree.

COAL GAS.   Coal gas consists chiefly of hydrogen and methane with smaller amounts of carbon monoxide, carbon dioxide, nitrogen, ethane, ethylene, and benzene. It also contains ammonia, hydrogen sulfide, and hydrogen cyanide. After removing the ammonia by washing with sulfuric acid, and the hydrogen sulfide and hydrogen cyanide by washing with water the gas may be used directly as illuminating gas. Before natural gas lines were installed, many cities used artificial or coal gas for illumination, cooking, and heating.

COAL TAR.   Coal tar is a heavy black liquid with an unpleasant odor. It is separated into its components by a process of fractional distillation. The various fractions from light oil to the pitchlike residue and the many important products derived from them are shown on the coal tar tree (Fig. 65). The importance of coal tar is reflected in the following common statements: "This drug is a coal tar derivative," or "these are coal tar dyes."

Aromatic Compounds

Aromatic hydrocarbons have oxygen derivatives that correspond to the aliphatic oxygen compounds. Therefore, we have aromatic alcohols, aldehydes, ketones, and acids that contain the same characteristic groups we encountered in the aliphatic series. Other aromatic compounds including amines, esters and salts will also be considered in this chapter. When a characteristic group or radical is in a side chain attached to the benzene ring, the compound reacts in a similar fashion to the corresponding aliphatic compound.

Alcohols

Aromatic alcohols have the OH group in the side chain. Benzyl alcohol and phenyl ethyl alcohol are the two lowest members in the series:

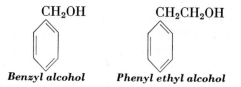

Benzyl alcohol   **Phenyl ethyl alcohol**

Both of these alcohols possess pleasant odors and are used in the manufacture of perfumes. Derivatives of these aromatic alcohols are benzyl acetate used in the preparation of perfume, and ortho-hydroxy-benzyl alcohol, a component of the fever-reducing substance salicin. *Benadryl*, the important antihistaminic drug, is also a derivative of aromatic alcohols. Benzyl and phenyl ethyl alcohols are even more reactive than their counterparts methyl and ethyl alcohols in the aliphatic series and are readily oxidized to produce the corresponding aldehydes and carboxylic acids.

Aralkyl Amines

Aralkyl amines are so named because they consist of alkyl amines attached to an aromatic ring. These compounds are very similar to the aromatic alcohols in structure, the two simplest being benzyl amine and phenyl ethyl amine.

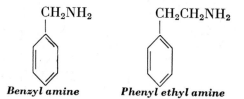

Benzyl amine   **Phenyl ethyl amine**

Several drugs, including Benzedrine, ephedrine, and epinephrine, are closely related to phenyl ethyl amine.

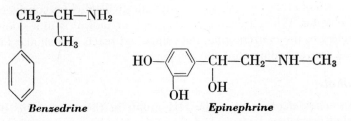

Benzedrine   **Epinephrine**

These drugs stimulate the central nervous system, producing among other effects an increased blood pressure, an accelerated heart beat, and dilation of the pupils of the eyes. *Benzedrine* produces a temporary stimulation of the physical and mental facilities of the body. However, when the effect of the drug wears off, the body pays for this "fast living" with increased muscular fatigue and mental depression. *Ephedrine* and closely related compounds are used in the treatment of bronchial asthma, and as components of nose drops to relieve nasal congestion in colds. Epinephrine is the active principle elaborated by the medullary portion of the adrenal gland. It not only has a powerful effect on the central nervous system, but is also related to the metabolism of carbohydrates.

Phenols

When the hydroxyl group is attached directly to the benzene ring, the aromatic derivatives are known as *phenols*. The simplest member of this series is known as phenol or carbolic acid, and has a single hydroxyl group attached to the benzene ring. Other phenols may contain two hydroxyl groups on the ring such as resorcinol, or be derivatives of toluene such as ortho-cresol, or contain methyl groups as thymol.

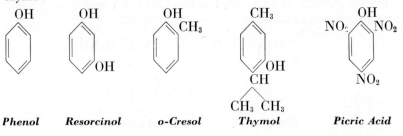

Phenol   **Resorcinol**   **o-Cresol**   **Thymol**   **Picric Acid**

The hydroxyl group in phenols is more acidic than that in aliphatic or aromatic alcohols. In general, phenols are weak acids that will readily react with sodium hydroxide to form salts. Substituted phenols, especially those containing nitro groups, are much stronger acids than phenol itself. Phenols are colorless liquids and solids that are soluble in alcohol and ether, and usually have a characteristic odor.

Phenol is produced in large quantities by the hydrolysis of chlorobenzene. It has strong antiseptic properties, but is a poison when taken internally. If it comes in contact with the skin, it causes blisters or deep burns and should therefore be washed off immediately with alcohol or ether. A dilute solution (3 per cent) of phenol is an effective disinfectant for containers used in hospitals (Figure 66). Most of the phenol produced in the United States is used in the manufacture of the phenolformaldehyde type of resins and plastics. Other uses for phenol are in the manufacture of dyes, drugs, and explosives.

Resorcinol is a representative of a phenol containing two hydroxyl

Figure 66. Phenol derivatives are widely used as disinfectants in the hospital. (Bard-Parker Company, Inc.)

groups. It may be obtained as a distillation product of natural resins or it may be made synthetically. It is used in the manufacture of dyes, adhesives, and antiseptics. Resorcinol containing the hydrocarbon hexane substituted for the hydrogen on carbon number four is a very effective antiseptic known as hexylresorcinol.

The *cresols* may be considered as methyl derivatives of phenol or hydroxy derivatives of toluene. They are obtained from coal tar and are commonly used commercially as a mixture of the ortho-, meta-, and para-cresols. Cresols are more effective antiseptics than phenol and are less toxic. The common disinfectant Lysol is composed of a mixture of cresols in a soap solution. Since the introduction of a methyl group side chain to phenol increased its antiseptic properties, the effect of longer hydrocarbon side chains was tested. It was found that hexane attached to phenol increased its antiseptic properties several hundred times and that hexylresorcinol was an even more satisfactory antiseptic. The cresols are essential constituents of creosote which is used extensively for wood preservation.

Thymol, obtained from the oils of thyme and mint, is a cresol derivative with a pleasant odor. It is an effective antiseptic used in mouthwashes, toothpastes, and in the treatment of hookworm. Another derivative of phenol, 2,4,6-trinitrophenol or picric acid, is formed by heating phenol with a mixture of nitric and sulfuric acids. *Picric acid* is a bright yellow solid that is sometimes used with other dyes to color wool and silk. Ammonium picrate is sometimes used as an explosive. For many years picric acid has been used in the treatment of burns since it forms insoluble compounds with the proteins of the skin and damaged tissue, covering the burn with a protective coating. Butesin picrate is a salve that combines picric acid with a local anesthetic to relieve the pain of burns. The weed killer or herbicide, 2,4-D, is a phenol derivative with chlorine atoms in the 2,4 position of an acetic acid-substituted phenol.

Aldehydes

The aromatic aldehydes contain the aldehyde group—CHO attached to one of the carbons in the benzene ring or attached to a carbon in a side chain. The simplest aromatic aldehyde, *benzaldehyde,* is a constituent of the seeds of bitter almonds and was once called oil of bitter almond. It can be prepared synthetically by several methods. One of the common methods for its manufacture is the oxidation of toluene in the presence of a suitable catalyst.

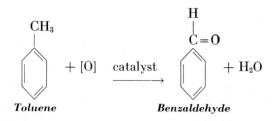

Toluene   *Benzaldehyde*

Benzaldehyde is a liquid with a pleasant almond-like odor. Its aldehyde group is readily oxidized forming the simple aromatic acid benzoic acid. Benzaldehyde is used to a limited extent in flavoring agents and perfumes. However, its main use is in the manufacture of drugs and dyes.

Other aldehydes of importance are *cinnamic aldehyde* and *vanillin*.

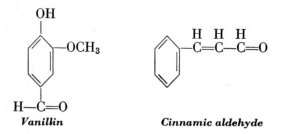

Vanillin   *Cinnamic aldehyde*

Cinnamic aldehyde is the major constituent of oil of cinnamon obtained from cinnamon bark. It can be readily synthesized by a condensation reaction between benzaldehyde and acetaldehyde. It is used mainly as a flavoring agent.

Vanillin is found in vanilla beans and is responsible for the taste and odor of vanilla extract. Vanillin and vanilla extract were originally prepared from vanilla bean. Since vanillin can be synthesized at a fraction of the cost of separating it from the bean, the majority of vanilla extracts are prepared from synthetic vanillin. In recent years, vanillin has been used to neutralize objectionable odors from paint, plastics, and rubber. Vanillin is also used in the manufacture of perfumes.

Ketones

The characteristic ketone group—CO—is present in aromatic ketones where it may be attached to two aromatic rings or be connected by an aromatic and an aliphatic group. The two most important aromatic ketones, *benzophenone* and *acetophenone,* illustrate this type of attachment.

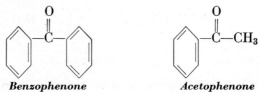

Benzophenone   *Acetophenone*

Benzophenone is used in the preparation of perfumes and in the manufacture of certain organic compounds. Acetophenone is a colorless oil with a characteristic odor possessing the properties of a hypnotic. It is also used as an intermediate in the preparation of other organic compounds and in the preparation of perfumes. If one of the hydrogens on the carbon atom at the end of the side chain is replaced by a chlorine atom, the compound chloroacetophenone is formed. This compound is a lachrymator and is commonly used as tear gas.

Acids

Many important organic compounds are included in the class of aromatic acids and their derivatives. These acids may have the carboxyl group (—COOH) attached to a carbon in the benzene ring or in the side chain. Benzoic acid, which is the simplest aromatic acid, was isolated from gum benzoin in the sixteenth century. It may be prepared by the oxidation of toluene in the presence of suitable catalysts as illustrated, or by the hydrolysis of benzyl trichloride.

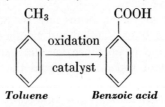

Toluene   *Benzoic acid*

Benzoic acid is used in the synthesis of several organic compounds while the sodium salt, sodium benzoate, is used as a preservative for food.

Of the three hydroxyl derivatives of benzoic acid, the most important is the ortho isomer known as *salicylic acid*. The sodium salt of salicylic acid is used extensively as an antipyretic or fever-lowering agent, and as an analgesic in the treatment of rheumatism and arthritis.

Salicylic acid   *Sodium salicylate*

Two other aromatic acids that form important derivatives are *para-aminobenzoic acid* and *benzene sulfonic acid*.

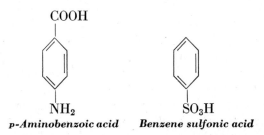

p-Aminobenzoic acid   *Benzene sulfonic acid*

Para-aminobenzoic acid is classified as a vitamin. It is apparently necessary for the proper physiological functioning of chickens, rats, mice, and bacteria, but as yet has not been proved essential in the diet of human beings. Certain derivatives of this acid are used as local anesthetics. Procaine, or Novocain, is probably the most important local anesthetic derived from *p*-aminobenzoic acid. Several derivatives of benzene sulfonic acid are used as dyes or indicators, sweetening agents, and antiseptics. Chloramine T is a sulfonic acid derivative of toluene which is used as an antiseptic. Phenolsulfonephthalein (phenol red) is a derivative of sulfobenzoic acid and phenol; it is used as a *p*H indicator and as a dye in kidney function tests. *Saccharin* is a derivative of *o*-sulfobenzoic acid which has a relative sweetness several hundred times that of sucrose. It is used as a sweetening agent when the sugar intake must be restricted. Recently another derivative of *o*-sulfobenzoic acid named *Sucaryl* has been developed. This sweetening agent has properties similar to saccharin and is available in both liquid and solid forms.

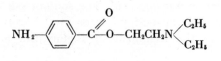

Procaine   *Saccharin*

Esters

An unlimited number of aromatic esters may be formed from aromatic acids. Some of these esters have pleasant tastes and odors similar to the aliphatic esters. For example, such simple esters as *methyl benzoate* and *methyl salicylate* are used in the manufacture of perfumes and flavoring agents. Methyl benzoate has the odor of new-mown hay while methyl salicylate smells and tastes like wintergreen. One of the most important esters of salicylic acid is that formed with acetic acid. *Acetylsalicylic acid*, or aspirin, is a common antipyretic and analgesic drug used by millions of people. Over 5000 tons of aspirin are produced in the United States every year. An increasing number of drugs for relief from simple headaches and the pain of rheumatism and arthritis contain aspirin combined with other pharmaceutical agents. For example, aspirin combined with antacid and buffering agents (Fig. 67) is absorbed more rapidly from the intestinal tract, and should therefore afford more rapid relief from aches and pains.

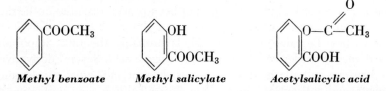

Methyl benzoate   *Methyl salicylate*   *Acetylsalicylic acid*

Several esters of p-aminobenzoic acid act as local anesthetics. Butesin is the butyl ester while Novocain is the diethylaminoethyl ester of this acid.

Amines

Aromatic compounds that contain the amino group—NH_2 are known as aromatic amines. As in the case of aliphatic amines, there are primary, secondary, and tertiary aromatic amines. The simplest

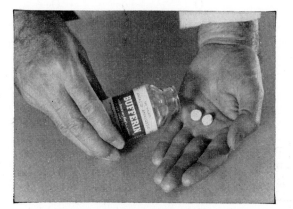

Figure 67. This common drug, which contains aspirin, is used extensively for headaches, fevers, and in rheumatic diseases.

primary aromatic amine, aminobenzene, is commonly called *aniline.* Aniline is prepared commercially by the reduction of nitrobenzene, or by the action of ammonia on chlorobenzene.

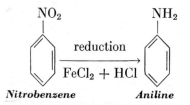

Nitrobenzene *Aniline*

Commercially, aniline is used to synthesize other important organic compounds used as dyes and dye intermediates, rubber accelerators, antioxidants, and drugs.

Several derivatives of the aromatic amines have medical properties and are used as drugs. One of the first such compounds used as a drug was *acetanilid* which is produced by the acetylation of aniline with acetic anhydride. For several years it was used as an antipyretic and analgesic drug. The toxicity of this compound in the body resulted in a search for similar compounds that were less toxic. Phenacetin which is closely related to acetanilid was found to be less toxic and to possess the beneficial effects of acetanilid.

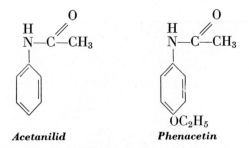

Acetanilid   *Phenacetin*

Sulfanilamide, the first of the sulfa drugs, is also a derivative of an aromatic amine. This compound can be synthesized from aniline although it is usually prepared commercially from acetanilid. In 1936, sulfanilamide was found to be effective in the treatment of patients with streptococcus infections, pneumonia, puerperal fever, gonorrhea, and gas gangrene. Since the administration of this drug caused toxic reactions in the body, many other similar derivatives were prepared and tested. Sulfapyridine, sulfathiazole, sulfaguanidine, and sulfadiazine were among the derivatives.

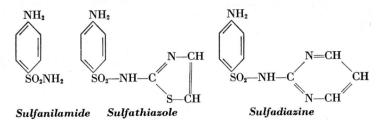

Sulfanilamide   Sulfathiazole   *Sulfadiazine*

Extensive studies of the therapeutic properties of each of the sulfa drugs were carried out in the ten years following the discovery of sulfanilamide. This resulted in better treatment and control of various infectious diseases. *Sulfadiazine,* for example, is less toxic than the other sulfa drugs, yet is one of the most effective in the treatment of pneumonia and staphylococcus infections.

Heterocyclic Compounds

Aromatic or cyclic organic compounds that have been considered thus far are *carbocyclic* compounds. Carbocyclic compounds contain only carbon atoms in the closed ring structure. If the ring of a cyclic compound contains elements other than carbon, it is known as a heterocyclic compound. The elements that are most commonly found in the ring with carbon are oxygen, nitrogen, and sulfur. Heterocyclic compounds are usually derived from a five- or six-membered ring which is called the *heterocyclic nucleus.*

Several important heterocyclic compounds are derived from the five-membered ring containing nitrogen known as *pyrrole.*

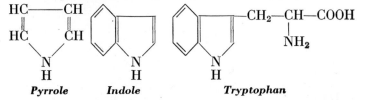

Pyrrole   **Indole**   **Tryptophan**

Pyrrole can be synthesized by the organic chemist and occurs as a liquid that gradually forms dark-colored resins on exposure to air. It is a constituent of hemoglobin, the respiratory pigment of the blood, and of chlorophyll, the plant pigment. It is also present in certain drugs and amino acids.

If pyrrole is condensed with a benzene ring, another type of heterocyclic nucleus called *indole* is produced. Indole and 3-methyl indole, which is called *skatole,* are formed during the putrefaction of proteins in the large intestine. They are responsible for the characteristic odor of feces. One of the most important derivatives of the indole nucleus is the amino acid *tryptophan.* Tryptophan is present in most proteins and is an essential constituent of the diet of growing animals.

Five-membered rings containing two elements other than carbon such as the imidazole nucleus with 2 nitrogen atoms and the thiazole nucleus with 1 nitrogen and 1 sulfur atom are found in the important amino acid *histidine* and the antibiotic *penicillin* (Fig. 68).

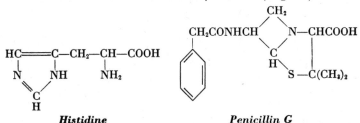

Histidine   **Penicillin G**

In 1957, the synthesis of a penicillin, called penicillin V, was reported. This development culminated a research project requiring nine years.

Figure 68. The valuable therapeutic agent penicillin is a heterocyclic compound produced by the green mold, *Penicillium*. (E. R. Squibb & Sons.)

Heterocyclic compounds also contain six-membered rings, for example, pyridine with 1 nitrogen atom.

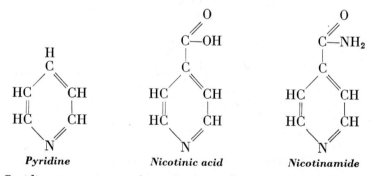

Pyridine is a common heterocyclic compound obtained from coal tar. It is a liquid with a characteristically disagreeable odor. Pyridine ionizes as a weak base and is a good solvent for organic and inorganic compounds. One of the main uses for pyridine is as a denaturant for ethyl alcohol. It is also used in the manufacture of sulfapyridine and in the synthesis of several organic compounds. *Nicotinic acid* and *nicotinamide* contain the pyridine nucleus and are members of the vitamin B complex. Nicotinic acid, renamed "niacin," is essential for the prevention of the dietary disease pellagra. At present it is used with other vitamins in the fortification of flour and cereals.

Pyrimidines and Purines

An important six-membered ring with two nitrogens is *pyrimidine.*

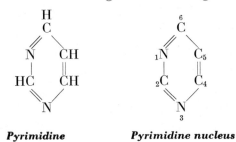

Pyrimidine   **Pyrimidine nucleus**

Pyrimidine derivatives are found in the nucleoproteins which are essential constituents of all living cells. Three important pyrimidines in nucleoproteins are *cytosine* (2-oxy, 6-amino pyrimidine), *uracil* (2, 6-dioxy pyrimidine), and *thymine* (2, 6-dioxy, 5-methyl pyrimidine). Other important derivatives of pyrimidine are *thiamine* or vitamin B_1, which contains a pyrimidine nucleus joined to a thiazole nucleus; and the *barbiturates.*

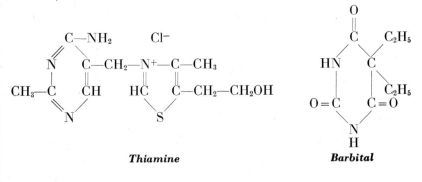

Thiamine   **Barbital**

Thiamine is one of the most important members of the vitamin B complex; its absence from the diet produces the deficiency disease known as beriberi or polyneuritis. *Barbital,* originally called Veronal, has been used as a hypnotic for about fifty years. Several derivatives of barbital have been prepared to increase the speed of action and decrease the unpleasant aftereffects of the drug. *Phenobarbital, Amytal,* and *Seconal* are examples of these barbital derivatives. In recent years the barbiturates have been used in such large quantities by the public that an attempt is being made to control their distribution.

Another class of compounds closely related to the pyrimidines are the *purines.* The purine nucleus is composed of a pyrimidine ring fused to an imidazole ring.

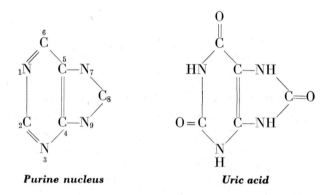

Purine nucleus   **Uric acid**

The purines present in nucleoproteins are adenine (6-amino purine) and guanine (2-amino, 6-oxy purine). The end product of metabolism or oxidation of purines in the body is *uric acid* which is 2,6,8-trioxy purine. Uric acid is present in the blood and is excreted in the urine. Under abnormal conditions uric acid may form insoluble deposits or stones in the kidney or bladder or may crystallize in the joints, causing the painful condition known as gout. The stimulants *theophylline* in tea and *caffeine* in tea and coffee are methylated purines. Theophylline is used in certain heart conditions and in bronchial asthma. It is also a constituent of Dramamine which is used for the prevention of seasickness or air sickness. Caffeine is a very active stimulant which is consumed in large quantities in coffee, cocoa, and other stimulating beverages.

Alkaloids

Alkaloids are basic nitrogen-containing substances that occur in plants. They are usually compounds containing a heterocyclic ring structure and are characterized by marked physiological activity. Most of the alkaloids are white crystalline solids with a bitter taste. Alkaloids are often classified according to the heterocyclic nucleus they contain. Some important alkaloids classified in this manner are shown in the table appearing on page 188. Typical alkaloids that contain the pyridine nucleus are *coniines* and *nicotines*. Coniine is the active principle of the poison hemlock plant while nicotine is the alkaloid contained in the tobacco plant.

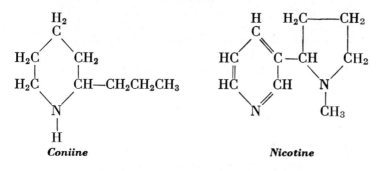

Coniine   *Nicotine*

Nicotine is an oil that has a burning taste and a sharp odor. Large quantities of this alkaloid are used in the preparation of insecticides and plant sprays (Fig. 69). It is also used to destroy lice on poultry.

Some Important Alkaloids

NAME OF ALKALOID	HETEROCYCLIC NUCLEUS	PLANT SOURCE	ACTIVITY OR APPLICATION
Coniine	Pyridine	Hemlock	Poison
Nicotine	Pyridine	Tobacco	Insecticide
Atropine	Tropane	Belladonna	Dilate pupil of eye
Cocaine	Tropane	Erythroxylum cocoa	Local anesthetic
Quinine	Quinoline	Cinchona bark	Antimalarial
Cinchonine	Quinoline	Cinchona bark	Antipyretic
Morphine	Piperidine	Opium	Analgesic, soporific
Codeine	Piperidine	Opium	Analgesic

Figure 69.   Insecticides and plant sprays often contain alkaloids such as nicotine. (Piper Aircraft Corporation.)

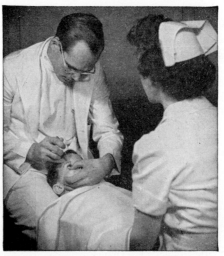

Figure 70.   Atropine solution is being used to dilate the pupil of the eye. (Paton in Cecil, The Specialties in General Practice.)

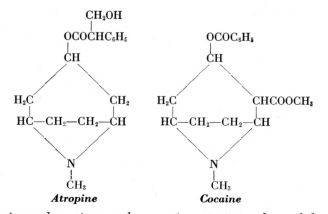

Atropine   **Cocaine**

Atropine and cocaine are the most important members of the group of alkaloids which are derivatives of the heterocyclic nucleus tropane. Atropine is present in the root of the deadly nightshade or bella-donna plant. This alkaloid is commonly used to dilate the pupil of the eye to facilitate examination of its interior (Fig. 70). Cocaine obtained from the leaves of the cocoa plant was formerly used as a local anesthetic in dentistry and eye surgery. It also has a stimulating action on the central nervous system and increases physical endurance. The drug exhibits toxic effects. Its continued use is habit-forming and eventually produces mental deterioration. A local anesthetic known as procaine or Novocain was prepared that had none of the toxic effects of cocaine.

Both quinine and cinchonine occur in the bark of the cinchona tree. Quinine has been used for many years in the treatment of malaria. It is able to poison the parasite that causes malaria without harming the host. Cinchonine is an antipyretic agent that is used to reduce fever. An alkaloid with an antimalarial action similar to quinine is Atabrine.

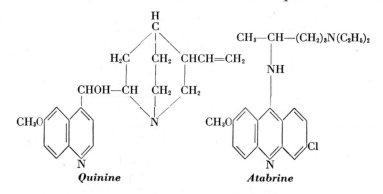

Quinine   **Atabrine**

During World War II when the supplies of quinine from Java were cut off, Atabrine was used extensively in the treatment of malaria.

Morphine and codeine alkaloids are obtained from the opium poppy. Morphine has a complex chemical structure containing a phenanthrene nucleus and a piperidine nucleus. Codeine is a methyl ester of morphine. Morphine depresses the central nervous system to produce an analgesic action. In larger doses it produces sleep. Codeine has a weaker analgesic action than morphine, although it is not as toxic. Both morphine and codeine are habit-forming narcotics and their continued use results in addiction.

Review Questions

1. Differentiate between the terms aromatic, carbocylic, and heterocyclic.
2. Write the complete structural formula for benzene. How do we usually represent a molecule of benzene in writing organic reactions?
3. Differentiate between ortho, meta, and para derivatives of organic compounds.
4. Write the formula for 1,3,6-trihydroxy benzene; 1-chloro-4,6-dinitro benzene; and 1,2,3-tribromo-5-hydroxybenzene.
5. Why are toluene and the xylenes classified as homologs of benzene?
6. Why is coal tar considered such a valuable by-product?
7. Why is benzylamine called an aralkyl amine? Discuss the use of two aralkyl amines in the practice of medicine.
8. Write the formulas for three different phenols. What properties of phenol, cresols, and picric acid are applied in nursing practice?
9. Write the formulas for an aromatic alcohol, aldehyde, ketone, acid, and salt. Name each compound.
10. Write the formula for two aromatic acids. Name one derivative of each acid and describe its medical applications.
11. In what class of aromatic compounds does aspirin belong? What is the chemical name for this compound? Write the formula for aspirin.
12. List three medically important aromatic amines and discuss their therapeutic value.
13. What is a heterocyclic nucleus? Give examples of a five and six membered ring.
14. Name and describe the use of two important heterocyclic compounds derived from a five membered ring.
15. Name three therapeutic agents that contain the pyrimidine nucleus.
16. What is the purine nucleus? Write the formula for uric acid, and name it as a derivative of a purine.
17. List several alkaloids that are used in medicine, and the heterocyclic nucleus they contain.

Chapter 13

Carbohydrates

In the previous chapters concerned with organic chemistry, the emphasis was on reactions, properties, synthesis and industrial applications of organic compounds. In contrast, little attention was paid to the presence or significance of these compounds in plants or animals. In this and subsequent chapters, we will consider the plant and animal kingdom with particular emphasis on the composition, nutritional requirements, and metabolic reactions of the human body. In studying the composition of plants, animals and foodstuffs, we will consider three major classes of organic compounds: carbohydrates, lipids, and proteins.

Carbohydrates will be discussed in the present chapter since they possess the simplest chemical structure. As a class of compounds, they include simple sugars, starches, and celluloses. Simple sugars such as glucose, fructose, and sucrose are constituents of many fruits and vegetables. Starches are the storage form of carbohydrates in plants, and cellulose is the main supporting structure of trees and plants.

Synthesis

Carbohydrates are formed in the cells of plants from carbon dioxide and water. In the presence of sunlight and chlorophyll, the green pigment of leaves, these two compounds react to form simple sugars:

$$6CO_2 + 6H_2O + \text{solar energy} \xrightarrow[\text{sunlight}]{\text{chlorophyll}} \underset{\text{simple sugar}}{C_6H_{12}O_6} + 6O_2$$

This important process by which plants form food material through the energy of sunlight is called *photosynthesis*. Although photosynthesis is represented as a simple chemical reaction, it involves complex mechanisms that are not as yet completely understood. Since radioactive elements have become available, the reactions of photosynthesis are being studied with the help of radioactive carbon and isotopic oxygen, O^{18}, as tracers.

Animals lack the ability to synthesize carbohydrates from inorganic materials and must obtain their supply of carbohydrates by eating plants. When animals take in carbohydrates in their diet, the oxygen from respiration oxidizes the sugar to carbon dioxide and water, liberating energy which is used by the body:

$$C_6H_{12}O_6 + 6O_2 \rightarrow 6CO_2 + 6H_2O + \text{energy}$$

The above reactions represent a cycle in which plants and animals are the participants. In the process of photosynthesis, plants liberate oxygen, which is essential to animal life. During respiration animals give off carbon dioxide, which is used by the plant to synthesize carbohydrates and other food materials. It has been stated that there is no reaction known to man which is of greater importance than that of photosynthesis. This is one of the few reactions that convert the energy of the sun into the chemical energy of foods. It is estimated that about 1 per cent of the energy of the sunshine falling on the plant is converted into energy, which is then stored in the form of carbohydrates.

Composition

Carbohydrates are composed of carbon, hydrogen, and oxygen, and the hydrogen and oxygen are usually in the proportion of two to one, the same as in water. The name carbohydrate (which signifies hydrate of carbon) is based on this relationship of hydrogen and oxygen. The term is misleading, however, because water does not exist as such in a carbohydrate. The classical definition of a carbohydrate stated that they were compounds of C, H, and O in which the H and O were in the same proportion as in water. However, certain compounds such as acetic acid, $C_2H_4O_2$, and lactic acid, $C_3H_6O_3$, fit this definition but are not classed as carbohydrates, while a carbohydrate such as rhamnose, $C_6H_{12}O_5$, does not fit the definition. Carbohydrates are now defined as derivatives of polyhydric alcohols containing an aldehyde or ketone group. A sugar that contains an aldehyde group is called an aldose, one that contains a ketone group is termed a *ketose*.

Classification

The simplest carbohydrates are known as *monosaccharides*, or *simple sugars*. Monosaccharides are straight chain polyhydric alcohols, and are classified according to the number of carbon atoms in the chain. A sugar with 2 carbon atoms is called a diose, with 3 a triose, with 4 a tetrose, with 5 a pentose, and with 6 a hexose. The ending *-ose* is characteristic of sugars. When two monosaccharides are linked together by splitting out a molecule of water, the resulting compound is called a *disaccharide*. The combination of three monosaccharides results in a *trisaccharide,* while a compound sugar composed of several monosaccharides is called a *polysaccharide.*

Physiologically important carbohydrates may be classified as follows:

I. Monosaccharides
$\qquad$ Pentose—$C_5H_{10}O_5$:
$\qquad\qquad$ Aldoses—Arabinose
$\qquad\qquad\qquad$ Xylose
$\qquad\qquad\qquad$ Ribose
$\qquad$ Hexoses—$C_6H_{12}O_6$:
$\qquad\qquad$ Aldoses—Glucose
$\qquad\qquad\qquad$ Galactose
$\qquad\qquad$ Ketoses—Fructose

II. Disaccharides—$C_{12}H_{22}O_{11}$
$\qquad$ Sucrose (glucose + fructose)
$\qquad$ Maltose (glucose + glucose)
$\qquad$ Lactose (glucose + galactose)

III. Polysaccharides
$\qquad$ Hexosans:
$\qquad\qquad$ Glucosans—Starch
$\qquad\qquad\qquad$ Glycogen
$\qquad\qquad\qquad$ Dextrin
$\qquad\qquad\qquad$ Cellulose

SIMPLE

Trioses

The trioses are not normally encountered in the laboratory, but are important compounds in muscle metabolism, and are the basic sugars to which all monosaccharides are referred. The definition of a simple sugar may readily be illustrated by the use of the trioses. The polyhydric alcohol from which they are derived is glycerol.

Oxidation on the end carbon atom would produce the aldose sugar known as glycerose; oxidation of the center carbon would result in the keto triose, dihydroxy acetone.

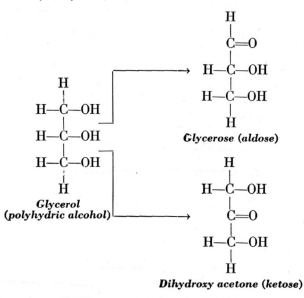

Glycerose (aldose)

Glycerol
(polyhydric alcohol)

Dihydroxy acetone (ketose)

Pentoses

The pentoses are sugars whose molecules contain 5 carbon atoms. They most commonly occur in nature, combined in polysaccharides, from which the monosaccharides may be obtained by hydrolysis with acids. Arabinose is obtained from gum arabic and the gum of the cherry tree. Xylose is found in wood, straw, and corn cobs. Ribose is a constituent of a nucleic acid found in plants.

Hexoses

The most important monosaccharides from a biochemical stand-point are the hexoses. Three of these are nutritionally important. Two belong to the aldose group and are glucose and galactose. The third belongs to the ketose group and is called fructose.

Although all hexoses have the same empirical formula, $C_6H_{12}O_6$, each has a different molecular arrangement as illustrated in the structural formulas for glucose, fructose, and galactose.

Monosaccharides
→ 1 carbonyl group
OH on each other C

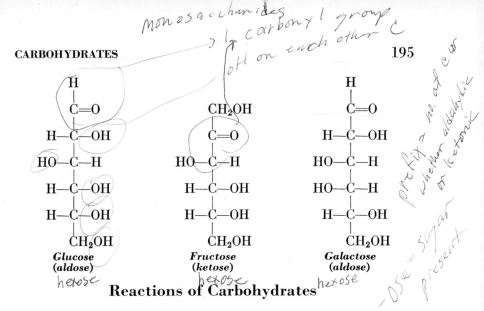

H		CH$_2$OH		H	
C=O		C=O		C=O	
H—C—OH		HO—C—H		H—C—OH	
HO—C—H		H—C—OH		HO—C—H	
H—C—OH		H—C—OH		HO—C—H	
H—C—OH		H—C—OH		H—C—OH	
CH$_2$OH		CH$_2$OH		CH$_2$OH	
Glucose		**Fructose**		**Galactose**	
(aldose)		*(ketose)*		*(aldose)*	

hexose   *hexose*   *hexose*

prefix → no. of C's
whether aldehyde or ketonic
ose = sugar present

Reactions of Carbohydrates

Reducing Power

Since aldehyde and ketone groups are reducing groups, sugars that contain these in a free form exhibit reducing powers. This reducing property can be utilized to test for the presence of these sugars in blood or urine. *Benedict's solution* is widely used in testing urine for glucose and may be considered as a solution of blue cupric hydroxide, Cu(OH)$_2$. When a sugar solution containing a free aldehyde or ketone group is heated with Benedict's solution, the Cu(OH)$_2$ is reduced to form an orange precipitate of Cu$_2$O. When only a small amount of sugar is present, the slight precipitate often appears green when its orange color is mixed with the blue color of Benedict's solution. The aldehyde or ketone groups of the sugar take up the oxygen that is released from the Cu(OH)$_2$ and are oxidized to form carboxyl groups.

ring called pyranose ring

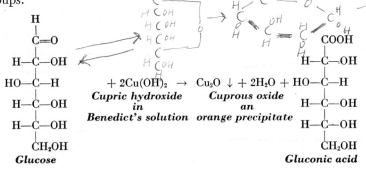

$$+ 2Cu(OH)_2 \rightarrow Cu_2O \downarrow + 2H_2O + \text{Gluconic acid}$$

Cupric hydroxide
in
Benedict's solution   **Cuprous oxide**
an
orange precipitate

Glucose

Gluconic acid

Other metallic hydroxides such as AgOH and Bi(OH)$_2$ are reduced by sugars to form metallic silver and bismuth respectively; these are also used to test for the presence of sugars.

Fermentation

The enzyme mixture called *zymase* present in common bread yeast will act on some of the hexose sugars to produce alcohol and carbon dioxide. The fermentation of glucose may be represented as follows:

$$C_6H_{12}O_6 \xrightarrow{\text{Zymase}} 2C_2H_5OH + 2CO_2$$

Glucose   *Ethyl alcohol*

The common hexoses (with the exception of galactose) ferment readily, but pentoses are not fermented by yeast. Disaccharides must first be converted into their monosaccharide constituents by other enzymes present in yeast before they are susceptible to fermentation by zymase.

There are many other types of fermentation of carbohydrates besides the common alcoholic fermentation. When milk sours, the lactose of milk is converted into lactic acid by a fermentation process. Citric acid, acetic acid, butyric acid, and oxalic acid may all be produced by special fermentation processes.

Oxidation of Carbohydrates

The alcohol, aldehyde, and ketone groups of sugars may be oxidized to produce a variety of oxidation products. When the primary alcohol group on the end of the carbon chain of glucose is oxidized to a carboxyl group, *glucuronic acid* is formed. This compound is the most important oxidation product of glucose; it unites with toxic substances in the body, forming nontoxic compounds which are eliminated in the urine. If the aldehyde group of glucose is oxidized, the product is called *gluconic acid*, while the oxidation of both the primary alcohol and the aldehyde group produces a compound called *saccharic acid*. Other sugars oxidize in a manner similar to that of glucose.

Reduction of Carbohydrates

Simple sugars may be reduced to form the polyhydric alcohols from which they are derived. On reduction, glucose yields *sorbitol*, fructose gives both sorbitol and *mannitol*, and galactose forms *dulcitol*.

Of these polyhydric alcohols, sorbitol is the most important because it is used in the manufacture of synthetic vitamin C.

Monosaccharides

Glucose

Glucose is also called *dextrose*, or *grape sugar*, and occurs with fructose in many sweet fruits. It ranks third in sweetness, being surpassed only by fructose and sucrose. It is the most important sugar from a physiological standpoint, as it is the normal sugar of the blood and tissue fluids. In diabetes mellitus, the amount of glucose in the blood increases and it often appears in the urine. In the United States, considerable quantities of glucose are made commercially by the acid hydrolysis of cornstarch. Corn syrup is prepared by the same process; it contains maltose and dextrins in addition to glucose. Many formulas for modifying cow's milk in infant feeding include corn syrup as a

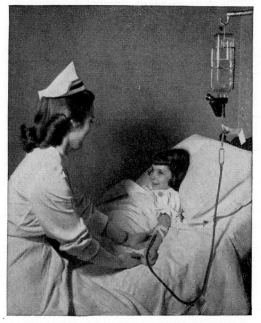

Figure 71. Glucose is often given intravenously as a source of dietary carbohydrates.

source of carbohydrates. Since glucose is the normal blood sugar, it is often given to patients intravenously (Fig. 71) when they are unable to take food by mouth.

Fructose

Fructose is often called *fruit sugar, or levulose,* and is the only important ketose sugar. It occurs with glucose in fruits and honey. It is the sweetest sugar known, having twice the sweetness of glucose and five times that of galactose. Fructose, usually prepared by the acid hydrolysis of the polysaccharide, inulin, is a constituent of the disaccharide sucrose, or cane sugar.

Galactose

This sugar is not formed free in nature but occurs as a constituent of the disaccharide lactose. *Agar-agar* is a polysaccharide of galactose that is used as a culture medium in bacteriology. Brain and nervous tissue in the animal body contain galactose as an essential constituent.

Disaccharides

A disaccharide is composed of two monosaccharides whose combination involves the splitting out of a molecule of water. The linkage is always made from the aldehyde group of one of the sugars to a hydroxyl or ketone group of the second. In order to reduce Benedict's solution, disaccharides must have an aldehyde or ketone group that is not involved in the linkage between the two sugars. A disaccharide such as sucrose in which the two monosaccharides are joined by a link between the aldehyde group of glucose and the ketone group of fructose will not reduce Benedict's solution. One such as maltose, however, in which the linkage connects the aldehyde group of one monosaccharide with a hydroxyl group of the other, will readily reduce Benedict's solution. In general, disaccharides such as maltose and lactose that reduce Benedict's solution possess properties similar to those of the monosaccharides.

Sucrose

Sucrose is commonly called *cane sugar* and is the ordinary sugar that is used for sweetening purposes in the home. It is found in many plants like sugar cane, sugar beets, sorghum cane, and in the sap of the sugar maple. Commercially it is prepared from sugar cane and sugar beets.

Sucrose is composed of a molecule of glucose joined to a molecule of fructose in such a way that the linkage involves the reducing groups of both sugars. It is the only common mono- or disaccharide that will not reduce Benedict's solution. When sucrose is hydrolyzed, either by the enzyme sucrase or by an acid, a molecule of glucose and a molecule of fructose are formed.

$$C_{12}H_{22}O_{11} + H_2O \rightarrow C_6H_{12}O_6 + C_6H_{12}O_6$$

Sucrose   *Glucose*   *Fructose*

The fermentation of sucrose by yeast is possible since the yeast contains both enzymes, sucrase and zymase. The sucrase first hydrolyzes the sugar and then the zymase ferments the monosaccharides to form alcohol and carbon dioxide.

Lactose

The disaccharide present in milk is lactose, or *milk sugar*. It is synthesized in the mammary glands of animals from the glucose in the blood. Commercially it is obtained from milk whey and is used in infant foods and special diets. Lactose, when hydrolyzed by the enzyme lactase or by an acid, forms a molecule of glucose and a molecule of galactose. Lactose will reduce Benedict's solution, but is not fermented by yeast. Certain bacteria contain enzymes that will ferment lactose to form lactic acid. This process occurs when milk sours. It has been suggested that one of the purposes of lactose in milk is to furnish galactose for the formation of brain and nervous tissue in infants.

Maltose

Maltose is present in germinating grains. Since it is obtained as a product of the hydrolysis of starch by enzymes present in malt, it is often called *malt sugar*. It is also formed in the animal body by the action of enzymes on starch in the process of digestion. Commercially it is made by the partial hydrolysis of starch by acid in the manufacture of corn syrup. Maltose reduces Benedict's solution and is fermented by yeast. On hydrolysis it forms two molecules of glucose.

Polysaccharides

The polysaccharides are complex carbohydrates that are made up of many monosaccharide molecules and therefore possess a high molecular weight. They differ from the simple sugars in many ways. They fail to reduce Benedict's solution, do not have a sweet taste, and are usually insoluble in water. When dissolved by chemical means, they form colloidal solutions because of their large molecules.

There are polysaccharides formed from pentoses or from hexoses, and the so-called mixed polysaccharides. Of these the most important are composed of the hexose glucose and are called *hexosans* or, more specifically, *glucosans*. As in a disaccharide, whenever two molecules of a hexose combine, a molecule of water is split out. For this reason, a hexose polysaccharide may be represented by the formula $(C_6H_{10}O_5)x$. The x represents the number of hexose molecules in the individual polysaccharide. Because of the complexity of the molecules, the number of glucose units in any one polysaccharide is still an estimate.

Starch

From a nutritional standpoint, starch is the most important polysaccharide. It is made up of glucose units and is the storage form of carbohydrates in plants. It consists of two types of polysaccharides: *amylase*, composed of a straight chain of glucose molecules; and *amylopectin*, which is a branched chain or polymer of glucose. Amylase has a molecular weight of about 50,000 compared with about 300,000 for amylopectin. The branching of the glucose chain in amylopectin occurs about every 24 to 30 glucose molecules.

In plant cells, starch exists as small granules, the shape of which is characteristic of the plant. The granules are covered by a layer of *amylopectin* which must be ruptured before the starch will mix with water to form a colloidal solution. Cooking destroys this outer layer, making the starch more readily digestible. Starch will not reduce Benedict's solution and is not fermented by yeast.

When starch is hydrolyzed by enzymes or by an acid, it is split into a series of intermediate compounds possessing smaller numbers of glucose units. The product of complete hydrolysis is the free glucose molecule. A characteristic reaction of starch is the formation of a blue compound with iodine. This test is often used to follow the hydrolysis of starch, since the color changes from blue through red to colorless with decreasing molecular weight:

Starch → amylodextrin → erythrodextrin →
blue   *blue*   *red*

achroodextrin → maltose → glucose
colorless   *colorless with iodine*

Dextrin

Dextrins are found in germinating grains but are usually obtained by the partial hydrolysis of starch. They are soluble in water and have a slightly sweet taste. Large quantities of dextrins are used in the manufacture of adhesives because they form sticky solutions when wet. An example of their use is the mucilage on the back of postage stamps.

Glycogen

Glycogen is the storage form of carbohydrate in the animal body and is often called animal starch. It is found in liver and muscle tissue. It is soluble in water, does not reduce Benedict's solution, and gives a wine-red color with iodine. The glycogen molecule is similar to amylopectin, although it has a much higher molecular weight. The branching of the glucose chain in glycogen occurs about every 12 glucose molecules. When glycogen is hydrolyzed in the animal body, it forms glucose to help maintain the normal sugar content of the blood.

Cellulose

Cellulose is a polysaccharide found in the framework or supporting structure of plants. It is made up of glucose units but is not hydrolyzed by any of the enzymes in the human digestive tract and therefore cannot be used as a source of dietary carbohydrates. Cellulose will not reduce Benedict's solution and is insoluble in water.

These properties of cellulose and in particular its insolubility are related to the molecular size (molecular weight between 300,000 and 500,000), the structure of the molecule, and the forces binding the molecules together.

The chemical treatment of cellulose has resulted in several important commercial products. For example, cotton, which is almost pure cellulose, takes on a silklike luster and increases in strength when treated under tension with a concentrated solution of sodium hy-

Figure 72. An array of fruits and vegetables in a modern supermarket. Cellophane, a common plastic prepared from cellulose, has increased the convenience in packaging and displaying these products. (Du Pont Co.)

droxide. This process, called mercerization, produces mercerized cotton which is used in large quantities in the manufacture of cotton cloth. When treated with nitric acid, cotton is converted into cellulose nitrates which are esters of commercial importance. Guncotton is a nitrocellulose containing about 13 per cent nitrogen and is used in the production of smokeless powder and high explosives. Another nitrocellulose is pyroxylin which can be made into celluloid, motion picture film, artificial leather, and lacquers for automobile finishes. Cellulose acetates also have several applications such as in the manufacture of safety motion picture films, plastics, and acetate yarn. Rayon is produced by treating cellulose with sodium hydroxide and carbon disulfide. The solution that results from this treatment is forced through fine holes into dilute sulfuric acid to make the rayon fibers. Cellophane is made by a process similar to that used for rayon (Fig. 72).

In addition to the esters of cellulose, certain ethers such as methylcellulose, ethylcellulose, and carboxymethylcellulose have become important. Methylcelluloses are used as sizing and finish for textiles, for pastes and for cosmetics. Ethylcellulose is soluble in organic solvents and resistant to the action of alkalies, properties which make it a valuable agent in the manufacture of plastic coatings and films. Carboxymethylcellulose is used as a sizing agent for textiles, and as a builder in the manufacture of synthetic detergents.

Review Questions

1. Chlorophyll is necessary in photosynthesis for the production of sugar from carbon dioxide and water. What role would you assume chlorophyll to play in this reaction? Why?
2. How does photosynthesis in plants and oxidation in animals fit into a cycle that is beneficial to both plants and animals?
3. Give the classical and modern definition of carbohydrates. Which is the more accurate? Explain.
4. Define the following terms: aldose, ketose, disaccharide, polysaccharide, pentose, and hexose. Give an example of each.
5. Glucose, fructose, and galactose have the same empirical formula. Why does each exhibit different properties and reactions?
6. What two fundamental reactions occur in the Benedict's test? Which is the more important with respect to the interpretation of the test?
7. Name two types of fermentation. What products are formed in the fermentation of sugars by zymase in yeast?
8. Give three names for glucose. Why is this sugar so important from a physiological standpoint?
9. Explain why the disaccharide sucrose fails to reduce Benedict's reagent whereas maltose will reduce it.
10. What agents may be used to hydrolyze the three important disaccharides? What products would result from the hydrolysis of sucrose, lactose, and maltose?
11. Is sucrose fermented by yeast? Explain the process.
12. Why is lactose nutritionally important to infants?
13. In what ways do polysaccharides differ from the simple sugars?
14. How would you describe chemically a polysaccharide composed of pentose units?
15. What are the steps in the process of gradual hydrolysis of starch to form glucose? What simple test may be used to detect the presence of intermediate products during the hydrolysis of starch?
16. Name six important products that are made from cellulose.
17. Compare starch, dextrins, glycogen and cellulose as to size of molecule, chemical composition, color with iodine, and importance.

Chapter 14

The Lipids

In addition to the carbohydrates, another important class of organic compounds that serve as foods and body constituents are the lipids. Their molecules are more complex than the carbohydrates and are composed of carbon, hydrogen, and oxygen, and, occasionally, phosphorus and nitrogen. Lipids as a class are insoluble in water but soluble in such fat solvents as ether, chloroform and acetone. They are essential constituents of all types of body tissue, especially brain and nervous tissue. In the body they serve as a reserve food supply, and, when utilized for energy, yield twice the amount available from an equal weight of carbohydrate or protein.

The important lipids may be classified as follows:

Fats—esters of fatty acids and glycerol.

Waxes—esters of fatty acids with alcohols other than glycerol.

Phospholipids—substituted fats containing phosphoric acid and a nitrogenous base.

Glycolipids—compounds that contain a fatty acid, a carbohydrate, a complex alcohol, and nitrogen.

Sterols—high molecular weight cyclic alcohols.

Fatty Acids

Since all fats are esters of fatty acids and glycerol, it may be well to consider the composition and properties of these substances before discussing lipids in general. Fatty acids, although not lipids themselves, are found in all of the above types of lipids except the sterols. The fatty acids that occur in nature almost always have an even number of carbon atoms in their molecules. They are usually straight chain organic acids which may be saturated or unsaturated. Some of the important fatty acids that occur in natural fats are listed in the table below.

In the series of saturated fatty acids, those up to and including capric acid are liquid at room temperature. The most important saturated fatty acids are *palmitic* and *stearic acids*. They are components of the majority of the common animal and vegetable fats.

Unsaturated fatty acids are characteristic constituents of oils. *Oleic acid*, which contains one double bond, is the most common unsaturated fatty acid. Its formula is written:

$$(CH_3CH_2)_7CH = CH(CH_2)_7COOH$$

NAME	FORMULA	CARBON ATOMS	OCCURRENCE
1. *Saturated*			
Acetic	CH_3COOH	2	
Butyric	C_3H_7COOH	4	Butter fat
Caproic	$C_5H_{11}COOH$	6	Butter fat
Caprylic	$C_7H_{15}COOH$	8	Coconut oil
Capric	$C_9H_{19}COOH$	10	Palm kernel oil
Lauric	$C_{11}H_{23}COOH$	12	Coconut oil
Myristic	$C_{13}H_{27}COOH$	14	Nutmeg oil
Palmitic	$C_{15}H_{31}COOH$	16	Animal and vegetable fats
Stearic	$C_{17}H_{35}COOH$	18	Animal and vegetable fats
2. *Unsaturated*			
Oleic (1 =)*	$C_{17}H_{33}COOH$	18	Olive oil
Linoleic (2 =)	$C_{17}H_{31}COOH$	18	Linseed oil
Linolenic (3 =)	$C_{17}H_{29}COOH$	18	Linseed oil
3. *Hydroxy*			
Ricinoleic (1 =)	$C_{17}H_{32}(OH)COOH$	18	Castor oil
4. *Cyclic*			
Chaulmoogric	$C_{17}H_{31}COOH$	18	Chaulmoogra oil

* Number of double bonds.

Ricinoleic acid is an unsaturated fatty acid characterized by the presence of a hydroxyl group and is found in castor oil. Its formula is as follows:

$$CH_3(CH_2)_5CHOHCH_2CH = CH(CH_2)_7COOH$$

Salts of ricinoleic acid are sometimes used to detoxify the intestinal contents in cases of colitis.

Chaulmoogric acid is a cyclic fatty acid found in chaulmoogra oil:

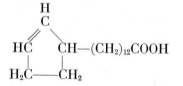

This oil and the ethyl ester of the fatty acid were formerly used as a cure for leprosy, but at present, other therapeutic agents are being used with greater success.

From a nutritional standpoint, the three most commonly occurring fatty acids in edible animal and vegetable fats are palmitic, stearic, and oleic acids.

Glycerol

The polyhydric alcohol, *glycerol,* is a common constituent of all fats and oils:

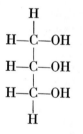

The hydroxyl groups of glycerol will readily form esters with organic acids. The formation of a simple ester may be illustrated by the reaction of the hydroxyl group of methyl alcohol and the carboxyl group of acetic acid:

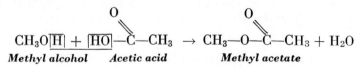

In this equation and in the following one, the fatty acid is written with its carboxyl group turned around facing the hydroxyl group of the alcohol. This is done to bring the two reactive groups close together to better illustrate the splitting out of a molecule of water when the ester linkage is formed.

Since glycerol contains three hydroxyl groups, it will form a triple ester with fatty acids.

Fats

From the standpoint of organic chemistry, fats are esters of fatty acids and glycerol. The formation of a fat molecule from glycerol and fatty acids may be illustrated as follows:

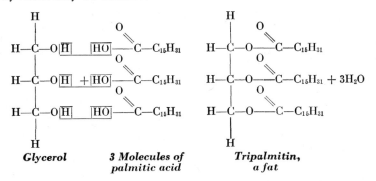

| Glycerol | 3 Molecules of palmitic acid | Tripalmitin, a fat |

Tripalmitin is known as a simple glyceride because all of the fatty acids in the fat molecule are the same. Other examples of simple glycerides would be tristearin and triolein. In most naturally occurring fats, different fatty acids are found in the same molecule. These are called *mixed glycerides* and may contain both saturated and unsaturated fatty acids.

Both fats and oils are esters of fatty acids and glycerol. The main difference between fats and oils is the relatively high content of unsaturated fatty acids in the oils. The common saturated fatty acids exist as solids, therefore fats are solid at room temperature, compared to the liquid oils. A fat that contains short chain fatty acids may also exist as a liquid at room temperature.

Most of the common animal fats are glycerides that contain saturated and unsaturated fatty acids. Since the saturated fatty acids predominate these fats are solid at room temperature. Beef fat, mutton fat, lard and butter are important examples of animal fats. Butter fat is readily distinguished from other animal fats because of its relatively high content of short chain fatty acids.

Glycerides that are found in vegetables usually exist as oils rather than fats. Vegetable oils such as olive oil, corn oil, cottonseed oil, and linseed oil are characterized by their high content of oleic, linoleic, and linolenic acids. Coconut oil, like butter fat, contains a relatively large percentage of short chain fatty acids.

In addition to their function as foodstuffs and as constituents of protoplasm and body tissues, fats and oils are used in many commercial processes. The manufacture of soap, paint and varnish, oilcloth, linoleum, printing inks, ointments, and creams represents a few of their industrial applications.

Waxes

Waxes are simple lipids which are esters of fatty acids and high molecular weight alcohols. Fatty acids such as myristic, palmitic, and carnaubic are combined with alcohols that contain from 12 to 30 carbon atoms. Common naturally occurring waxes are beeswax, lanolin, spermaceti, and carnauba wax. *Beeswax* is found in the structural part of the honeycomb. *Lanolin,* from wool, is the most important wax from a medical standpoint since it is widely used as a base for many ointments, salves, and creams. *Spermaceti,* obtained from the sperm whale, is used in cosmetics, some pharmaceutical products and in the manufacture of candles. *Carnauba wax* is obtained from the carnauba palm and is widely used in floor waxes and in automobile and furniture polishes.

Paraffin wax, petrolatum, and lubricating oils are not to be confused with the simple lipids discussed above because they are merely mixtures of hydrocarbons.

Phospholipids

The phospholipids are found in all animal and vegetable cells. They are composed of an alcohol, fatty acids, phosphoric acid, and a nitrogenous base. The three main types of phospholipids are the lecithins, cephalins, and sphingomyelins.

Lecithins

The lecithins are constituents of brain, nervous tissue, and egg yolk. The formula for a typical lecithin may be written as follows:

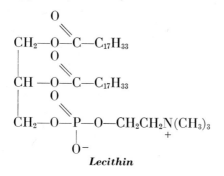

Lecithin

A lecithin may be considered as a glyceride or fat in which one of the fatty acid molecules is replaced by phosphoric acid and the nitrogenous base choline. The phosphoric acid is joined to glycerol in an ester linkage, and choline is joined by the same type of linkage to phosphoric acid.

From a physiological standpoint, lecithins are important in the transportation of fats from one tissue to another and serve as a source of phosphoric acid for the synthesis of new cells. In industry, lecithin is obtained from soybeans, and finds wide application as an emulsifying agent. Large quantities of this substance are used in the manufacture of chocolate candies, margarine, aviation gasoline, and medicines.

If the oleic acid on the central carbon atom of lecithin is removed by hydrolysis, the resulting compound is called *lysolecithin*. Disintegration of the red blood cells, or hemolysis, is caused by intravenous injection of lysolecithin. The venom of snakes such as the cobra contains an enzyme capable of converting lecithins into lysolecithins, which accounts for the fatal effects of the bite of these snakes. A few insects and spiders produce toxic effects by the same mechanism.

Cephalins

The cephalins are especially abundant in brain tissue. Their chemical composition resembles that of lecithin except that choline is replaced by ethanolamine (amino ethyl alcohol) or serine. A typical cephalin that contains ethanolamine may be represented as follows:

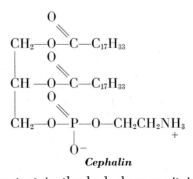

Cephalin

Cephalin is important in the body because it is one of the factors involved in the blood-clotting process.

Sphingomyelins

The composition of the sphingomyelins differs markedly from that of the lecithins or cephalins. They are not glycerides but contain an amino alcohol, called sphingosinol, in place of glycerol. Only one fatty acid is present in the molecule, along with phosphoric acid and choline. The sphingomyelins are essential constituents of brain and nervous tissue and may serve as a source of phosphoric acid in the body. The formula of a typical sphingomyelin may be written as follows:

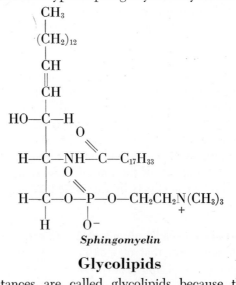

Sphingomyelin

Glycolipids

These substances are called glycolipids because they contain a carbohydrate as part of their molecule. They are also often called cerebrosides since they occur in large amounts in brain tissue. Their structure is similar to the sphingomyelins except that the carbohydrate, galactose, replaces phosphoric acid and choline in the molecule. *Phrenosin* and *kerasin* are the most commonly occurring cerebrosides. It has been suggested that since galactose is an essential constituent of cerebrosides, milk sugar is important in the diet of children during the development of their brain and nervous system.

Sterols

The sterols are high molecular weight cyclic alcohols that occur in all living cells. The most common sterol is *cholesterol*, which is found in the brain and nervous tissue and in gallstones. Cholesterol and the other sterols are derivatives of the cyclopentanoperhydrophenanthrene nucleus, also called the sterol nucleus.

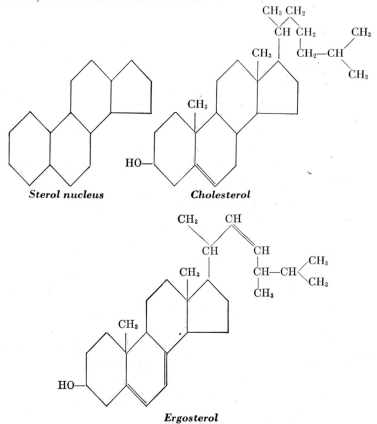

Sterol nucleus   Cholesterol

Ergosterol

Ergosterol is an important plant sterol that has two more double bonds and one more methyl group than cholesterol. When ergosterol is exposed to ultraviolet light, a mixture of sterols is formed. One of these, called *calciferol,* has vitamin D activity and is administered as a source of this vitamin. Calciferol is also called *drisdol* and, when in an oil solution, is known as *viosterol.* Other substances of physiological importance that contain the sterol nucleus are the bile salts, the sex hormones, and the hormones of the adrenal cortex.

Reactions of Fats

Glycerol Portion

When glycerol or a liquid containing glycerol is heated with a dehydrating agent, *acrolein* is formed.

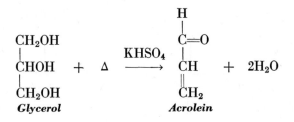

Acrolein has a very pungent odor and is sometimes formed by the decomposition of glycerol in the fat of frying meats. The formation of acrolein is often used as a test for fats, since all fats yield glycerol when they are heated.

Hydrolysis

Fats may be hydrolyzed to form free fatty acids and glycerol by the action of acid, alkali, superheated steam, or the enzyme lipase. In hydrolysis of a fat, the three water molecules (that were split out when the three fatty acid molecules combined with one glycerol molecule in an ester linkage to make the fat molecule) are replaced with the resultant splitting of the fat into glycerol and fatty acids. Commercially, fats are a cheap source of glycerol for use in the manufacture of high explosives and pharmaceuticals. For this purpose, the

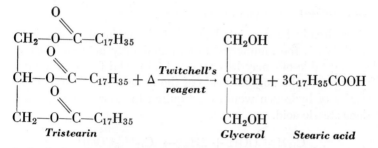

$$CH_2-O-\overset{O}{\overset{\|}{C}}-C_{17}H_{35}$$
$$CH-O-\overset{O}{\overset{\|}{C}}-C_{17}H_{35} + \Delta \xrightarrow[\text{reagent}]{\text{\textit{Twitchell's}}} CHOH + 3C_{17}H_{35}COOH$$
$$CH_2-O-\overset{O}{\overset{\|}{C}}-C_{17}H_{35}$$

| *Tristearin* | *Glycerol* | *Stearic acid* |

fat is hydrolyzed with superheated steam and *Twitchell's reagent*, which contains naphthalene, oleic acid, and sulfuric acid. The advantage of this method is that glycerol is readily separated from the fatty acids. Hydrolysis by an alkali is called *saponification,* and produces glycerol and salts of the fatty acids which are called soaps. In the laboratory, fats are usually saponified by an alcoholic solution of an alkali. The fats are more soluble in hot alcohol and the reaction is therefore more rapid.

Rancidity

Many fats develop an unpleasant odor and taste when they are allowed to stand in contact with air at room temperature. The two common types of rancidity are *hydrolytic* and *oxidative.* Hydrolytic changes in fats are the result of the action of enzymes or microorganisms producing free fatty acids. If these acids are of the short chain variety, like butyric acid, the fats develop a rancid odor and taste. This type of rancidity is common in butter.

The most common type of rancidity is the oxidative type. Oxidation of the fat molecule results in the formation of some short chained aldehydes and ketones which have objectionable tastes and odors. The oxygen of the air is necessary for the development of this type of rancidity. The prevention of rancidity of lard and vegetable shortenings that are used in the manufacture of crackers, pretzels, pastries, and similar food products has long been an important problem. Modern packaging has helped considerably in this connection, although a more important contribution has been the development of *antioxidants.* These compounds are usually phenolic in structure and inhibit the oxidation of fats. The majority of the vegetable shortenings on the market as well as certain brands of lard are protected from rancidity by the addition of antioxidants.

Hydrogenation

It has already been pointed out that the main difference between oils and fats is the number of unsaturated fatty acids in their molecules. Vegetable oils may be converted into solid fats by the addition of hydrogen to the double bonds of the unsaturated fatty acids. Two molecules of hydrogen would be required to saturate linoleic acid to produce stearic acid.

$$C_{17}H_{31}COOH + 2H_2 \rightarrow C_{17}H_{35}COOH$$

   Linoleic acid   *Stearic acid*

This process has important applications in industry and is used to prepare lard substitutes and shortening from vegetable oils, such as cottonseed oil. The extent of hydrogenation is controlled to produce a fat of the desired consistency since complete saturation would result in a brittle tallow-like product. The resultant fat, commercial examples of which are "Crisco" and "Spry," contains approximately 20 to 25 per cent of saturated fatty acids, 65 to 75 per cent of oleic acid, and 5 to 10 per cent of linoleic acid.

Analysis of Fats

Fats are usually characterized by the determination of *fat constants*. Some of the important physical constants are the specific gravity, viscosity, melting point, and solidification point. Two of the most common chemical constants are the saponification number and the iodine number.

Saponification Number

The saponification number may be defined as the number of milligrams of potassium hydroxide that will combine with the fatty acids present in 1 gm. of fat. *The saponification number is used as a measure of the size of the fat molecule.* In general, a high saponification number signifies a low molecular weight fat, while a low saponification number means a high molecular weight fat. For instance, butter fat, which contains a large number of small molecular weight fatty acids in its molecule, has a high saponification number (about 227) compared with lard (about 197).

Iodine Number

Iodine or a mixture of iodine and bromine, which is a more reactive form, will combine with the double bonds of the unsaturated fatty acids in a fat molecule. This combination may be illustrated by the reaction of iodine with oleic acid:

$$
\begin{array}{cc}
\text{H} \quad \text{H} & \text{H} \quad \text{H} \\
| \quad | & | \quad | \\
CH_3(CH_2)_7C{=}C(CH_2)_7COOH + I_2 \rightarrow & CH_3(CH_2)_7C{-}C(CH_2)_7COOH \\
& | \quad | \\
& I \quad I
\end{array}
$$

The iodine number is defined as the number of grams of iodine absorbed by 100 gm. of fat. *The iodine number, therefore, is a measure of the degree of unsaturation of a fat or oil.* For example, beef tallow has an iodine number of 35 to 40 compared with linseed oil which has an iodine number of 175 to 200.

Soaps

The process of saponification or alkaline hydrolysis of a fat produces soap as one of the end products. *Soaps* may be defined as metallic salts of fatty acids. The saponification of a fat may be represented as follows:

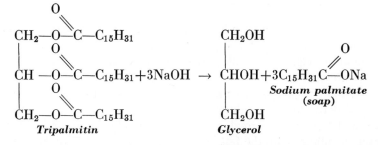

Sodium salts of fatty acids are known as *hard soaps,* while potassium salts form *soft soaps.* The ordinary cake soaps used in the home are sodium soaps. Certain cake soaps float because air has been blown into the soap before it is formed into cakes. Yellow laundry soap contains resin which increases the solubility of soap and its lathering properties and has some detergent action. *Tincture of green soap,* commonly used in hospitals, is a solution of potassium soap in alcohol.

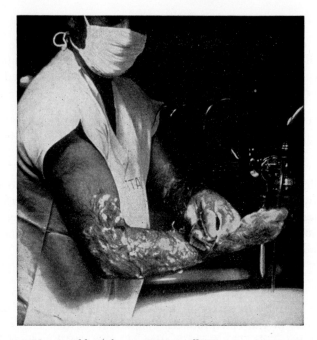

Figure 73. Scrubbing for an operation illustrates one important use of soap in a hospital. (Dept of Surgery, University of Iowa Hospitals.)

When sodium soaps are added to hard water, the calcium and magnesium salts present replace sodium to form insoluble calcium and magnesium soaps. The familiar soap curd formed in hard water is due to these *insoluble soaps.*

Insoluble calcium soaps are found in the feces of children with celiac disease. In this condition, fatty acids are not absorbed from the intestinal tract in a normal manner. The calcium present in the intestine combines with the fatty acid to form insoluble soaps which are subsequently eliminated from the body.

The cleansing power of soaps depends on their ability to lower surface tension and act as emulsifying agents. By emulsifying the grease or oily material that holds the dirt on the skin or clothing, the particles of grease and dirt may be rinsed off with water.

All soaps have mild antiseptic properties; prolonged scrubbing of the hands and arms with soap and water will remove bacteria from the skin. This procedure is employed by surgeons and nurses when they scrub for an operation (Fig. 73). These antiseptic properties are sometimes increased by the addition of mercury compounds or carbolic acid. Zinc stearate is an insoluble soap used in talcum powders for infants because of its antiseptic properties.

Detergents

Various compounds are now being marketed as soap substitutes. These compounds are a mixture of the sodium salts of the sulfuric acid esters of lauryl and cetyl alcohols. They may be used in hard water because they do not form insoluble compounds with calcium and magnesium. They are the major components of such products as Dreft, Drene, Swirl, Vel, and Tide, and are often used in the washing of silk and woolen material, since they contain no excess alkali. Sodium lauryl sulfate is used as a cleansing agent in toothpastes and powders. Similar substances are employed commercially in Irium and Lusterfoam. In recent years, extensive research on new detergents and emulsifying agents has resulted in the development of several hundred products possessing almost any desired property.

Review Questions

1. How could you readily distinguish between carbohydrates and lipids in the laboratory?
2. What is meant by the following terms: saturated fatty acid, unsaturated fatty acid, hydroxy fatty acid, and cyclic fatty acid? Give an example of each.
3. Give two examples of the use of fatty acids in medicine.
4. Write the equation for the formation of a fat from palmitic acid and glycerol. What linkage is involved in this process?
5. What is a mixed glyceride? A simple glyceride?
6. What is the difference between: (1) a fat and an oil; (2) a fat and a wax? For what purpose are waxes used in medicine?
7. Compare lecithin and lysolecithin from a chemical standpoint; from a physiological standpoint.
8. What is cephalin? What is its function in the body?
9. How would you define a glycolipid? Why are phrenosin and kerasin often called cerebrosides?
10. Write the formula for the sterol nucleus. Name two compounds that contain this nucleus.

11. What relation exists between the sterols and vitamin D? What is calciferol?
12. Which of the following compounds would give a positive acrolein test: fat, phospholipid, sterol? Explain your reasoning.
13. Discuss two methods for the hydrolysis of a fat. What products are formed in each method?
14. What happens when butter becomes rancid? When crackers become stale?
15. What changes in chemical and physical properties take place during the hydrogenation of a vegetable oil?
16. Write an equation to illustrate the saponification of a fat.
17. What are hard soaps, soft soaps, and insoluble soaps? What is tincture of green soap?
18. Give an example of a soap that has antiseptic properties.
19. What is a detergent? What advantages do detergents have over ordinary soap?

Chapter 15

Proteins

As a class, proteins are the most important organic compounds found in the body. Chemically speaking, they are more complex molecules than carbohydrates or lipids. They are fundamental constituents of the cells and tissues in the body, and are present in all fluids except the urine, which is an excretory product, and the bile, which has excretory functions. They were named from a Greek word, "proteios," meaning "of prime importance," by Mulder in 1839. He coined the term for a group of nitrogen-containing compounds that he believed were fundamental constituents of protoplasm. Proteins are also essential constituents of the diet required for the synthesis of body tissue, enzymes, certain hormones, and protein components of the blood.

Proteins are made by plant cells from such simple inorganic substances as carbon dioxide, water, nitrates, sulfates, and phosphates. The complicated synthesis is at present not well understood. Animals are unable to synthesize proteins from inorganic material, so they are dependent on plants or other animals for their source of dietary protein. Proteins are used in the body for growth of new tissue, for maintenance of existing tissue, and as a source of energy. When used for energy, they are broken down by oxidation to form simple substances such as water, carbon dioxide, sulfates, phosphates, and simple nitrogen compounds, which are excreted from the body. These same products are formed in decaying plant and animal matter. The simple nitrogen compounds such as amino acids and urea (Fig. 74), are converted into ammonia, nitrites, and nitrates. The growing plants then use these inorganic compounds to form new proteins and the cycle is completed.

Elementary Composition

The five elements that are present in all naturally occurring proteins are carbon, hydrogen, oxygen, nitrogen, and sulfur.

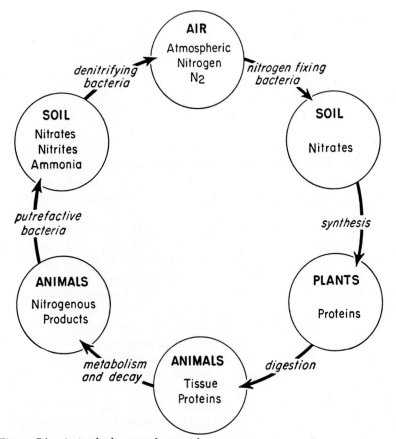

Figure 74. A simple diagram showing the events occurring in the nitrogen cycle.

Small amounts of phosphorus, iron, and iodine are present in some proteins. For example, casein of milk is a phosphoprotein, hemoglobin contains iron, and the protein of the thyroid gland contains iodine. Most proteins show little variation in their elementary composition; the average content of the five main elements is as follows:

ELEMENT	AVERAGE PER CENT
Carbon	53
Hydrogen	7
Oxygen	23
Nitrogen	16
Sulfur	1

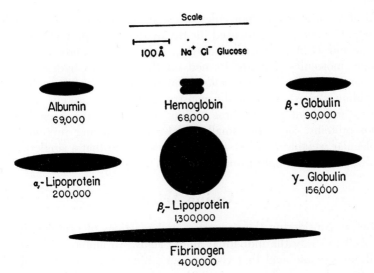

Figure 75. The relative dimensions of various protein molecules. (Oncley, J. L.: Conference on the Preservation of the Cellular and Protein Components of Blood, published by the American Red Cross, Washington, D. C.)

The relatively high content of nitrogen differentiates proteins from fats and carbohydrates.

Molecular Weight

Protein molecules are very large, as indicated by the approximate formula for oxyhemoglobin:

$$C_{2932}H_{4724}N_{828}S_8Fe_4O_{840}$$

The molecular weight of oxyhemoglobin would thus be about 68,000. The common protein egg albumin has a molecular weight of about 34,500. In general, protein molecules have weights that vary from 34,500 to 50,000,000. Their extremely large size can readily be appreciated when they are compared to the molecular weight of a fat such as tripalmitin which is 807, of glucose which is 180, or of an inorganic salt such as sodium chloride, which is 58.5 (Fig. 75).

Hydrolysis

In addition to their large size, protein molecules are also very complicated. Like any complex molecule, they may be broken down by hydrolysis into smaller molecules whose structure is more easily determined. Common reagents used for the hydrolysis of proteins are acids (HCl and H_2SO_4), bases (NaOH), and enzymes (proteases). The simple molecules that are formed on the complete hydrolysis of a protein are called *amino acids*. Amino acids are often called the "building stones" used in the construction of the protein molecule. There are about twenty-three amino acids that have been isolated from proteins. Since the smallest naturally occurring protein has a molecular weight of 34,500, it has been estimated that a single protein molecule contains approximately 250 amino acids.

Amino Acids

Before considering the properties and reactions of proteins, it may be well to study the individual amino acids. An amino acid is essentially an organic acid that contains an amino group. If we replace a hydrogen by an amino group on the carbon atom that is next to the carboxyl group in acetic acid, CH_3COOH, we will form the simple amino acid *glycine:*

$$CH_2COOH$$
$$|$$
$$NH_2$$

The chemical name for this amino acid would be amino acetic acid. The carbon atom next to the carboxyl group is called the alpha (a) carbon; the next, beta (β); the next, gamma (γ); the next, delta (δ), and the fifth from the carboxyl group is called the epsilon (ϵ) carbon atom. Since all naturally occurring amino acids have an amino group attached to the alpha carbon atom, they are known as *alpha amino acids*.

The amino acids are divided into groups according to their chemical structure. Examples of each group are given in the following classification:

I. Aliphatic amino acids
    A. With 1 amino and 1 carboxyl group:
        Glycine (amino-acetic acid)

$$CH_2{-}COOH$$
$$|$$
$$NH_2$$

Alanine (α-aminopropionic acid)

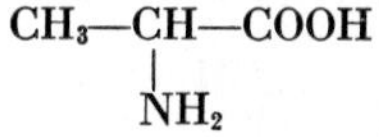

$$CH_3—CH—COOH$$
$$\quad\quad\quad |$$
$$\quad\quad\quad NH_2$$

B. With 1 amino, 1 carboxyl, and 1 hydroxyl group:
   Threonine (α-amino-β-hydroxybutyric acid)

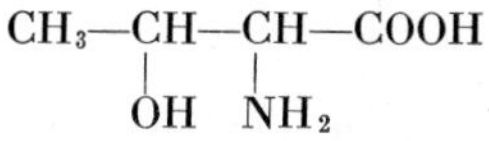

$$CH_3—CH—CH—COOH$$
$$\quad\quad\quad |\quad\quad |$$
$$\quad\quad\quad OH\quad NH_2$$

C. With 1 amino and 2 carboxyl groups:
   Glutamic acid (α-aminoglutaric acid)

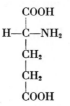

D. With 2 amino and 1 carboxyl group:
   Lysine (α-ε-diaminocaproic acid)

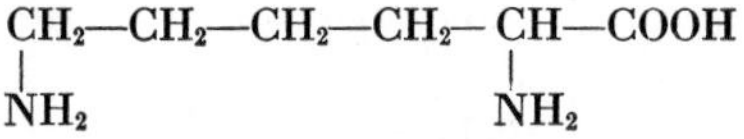

$$CH_2—CH_2—CH_2—CH_2—CH—COOH$$
$$\;|\qquad\qquad\qquad\qquad\quad |$$
$$NH_2\qquad\qquad\qquad\qquad NH_2$$

E. Sulfur-containing amino acids:
   Cystine di (α-amino-β-thiopropionic acid)

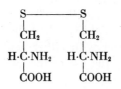

II. Aromatic amino acids
    Tyrosine (α-amino-β-parahydroxyphenylpropionic acid)

$$CH_2—CH—COOH$$
$$\quad\quad\quad |$$
$$\quad\quad\quad NH_2$$

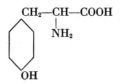

III. Heterocyclic amino acids
   Tryptophan (α-amino-β-indolpropionic acid)

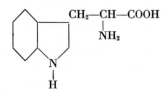

In the above classification, the common name of an amino acid is given first, followed by the more complex chemical name. These formulas should help to emphasize the statement that the chemical structure of the protein molecule is complicated.

Amphoteric Properties of Amino Acids

Amino acids behave both as weak acids and as weak bases since they contain at least one carboxyl and one amino group. Substances that ionize as both acids and bases in aqueous solution are called *amphoteric*. An example would be glycine, in which both the acidic and basic groups are ionized in solution to form dipolar ions or *zwitterions*.

$$CH_2-COO^-$$
$$|$$
$$NH_3^+$$

The glycine molecule is electrically neutral since it contains an equal number of positive and negative ions. The zwitterion form of glycine would thus be isoelectric, and the pH at which the zwitterion does not migrate in an electric field is called the isoelectric point. Amphoteric compounds will react with either acids or bases to form salts. This is best illustrated by the use of the zwitterion form of the amino acid:

$$CH_3-CH-COO^- + HCl \rightarrow CH_3-CH-COOH$$
$$\quad\quad\; | \quad\quad\quad\quad\quad\quad\quad\quad\quad\quad\;\; |$$
$$\quad\; NH_3^+ \quad\quad\quad\quad\quad\quad\quad\quad\quad NH_3^+Cl^-$$

$$CH_3-CH-COO^- + NaOH \rightarrow CH_3-CH-COO^-Na^+ + H_2O$$
$$\quad\quad\; | \quad\quad\quad\quad\quad\quad\quad\quad\quad\quad\quad\quad\quad |$$
$$\quad\; NH_3^+ \quad\quad\quad\quad\quad\quad\quad\quad\quad\quad\;\; NH_2$$

From these equations it can be seen that the addition of a H^+ to an isoelectric molecule results in an increased positive charge (NH_3^+), since the acid represses the ionization of the carboxyl group. Conversely, the addition of a base to an isoelectric molecule results in an increased negative charge (COO^-), since the base represses the ionization of the amino group. Since proteins are composed of amino acids, they are amphoteric substances with specific isoelectric points, and are able to neutralize both acids and bases. This property of proteins is responsible for their buffering action in blood and other fluids.

Protein Structure

As has already been stated, hydrolysis of protein results in the formation of alpha amino acids. To understand the structure of the protein molecule we must know how the amino acids are joined together to form the large molecules. Several complicated theories have been proposed to explain protein structure. The most reasonable theory, suggested by Emil Fisher, is that amino acids are joined by the peptide linkage.

The *peptide linkage* is formed when the carboxyl group of one amino acid combines with the amino group of another, with the loss of a molecule of water. This type of linkage may be illustrated by the union of a molecule of alanine and a molecule of glycine:

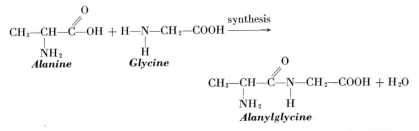

The compound, alanylglycine, which resulted from this linkage, is called a *dipeptide*. The union of three amino acids would result in a *tripeptide*, while the combination of several amino acids by the peptide linkage would be called a *polypeptide*. Proteins may be considered as complex polypeptides. The above dipeptide may readily be hydrolyzed by the addition of water, to form alanine and glycine:

Since egg albumin has a molecular weight of 34,500, it has been estimated that its molecule contains approximately 250 amino acids, Complete hydrolysis of such a protein that consisted of 250 amino acids joined together in a long polypeptide chain would require the addition of 249 molecules of water and result in the formation of 250 individual amino acid molecules. The number of possible combinations of the twenty-three different amino acids to form a protein is beyond comprehension. It is therefore impossible to write a structural formula for a molecule so large and complex as a protein molecule.

Classification of Proteins

Proteins are usually divided into three main groups on the basis of their variation in chemical composition. *Simple proteins* are those that yield only amino acids or their derivatives on hydrolysis. The simple proteins are further classified according to their differences in solubility. *Conjugated proteins* are simple proteins combined with some nonprotein compound. The conjugated proteins are named and classified according to the nature of the nonprotein molecule. Several protein classifications include a group called *derived proteins*, which are not naturally occurring proteins and may be considered as protein derivatives that are produced by the action of enzymes, chemical reagents, and various physical forces on simple or conjugated proteins. So many protein derivatives have been reported in the extensive investigations on proteins that an attempt to classify them would only result in confusion. For this reason, the derived proteins have been omitted from the following protein classification.

Simple Proteins

Albumins

The albumins are soluble in water and are coagulated by heat. Typical albumins are egg albumin in egg white, lactalbumin in milk, and serum albumin in blood.

Globulins

The globulins are insoluble in water, but are soluble in dilute salt solution (such as 5 per cent sodium chloride), and are coagulated by heat. Serum globulin in blood plasma, and lactoglobulin in milk are examples of globulins.

Glutelins

The glutelins are insoluble in water and dilute salt solutions, but are soluble in dilute acid and alkali, and are coagulated by heat. Examples are glutenin in wheat and oryzenin in rice.

Prolamines

The prolamines are soluble in 70 to 80 per cent alcohol, but are insoluble in water or absolute alcohol. Typical prolamines are gliadin in wheat and zein in corn.

Albuminoids

The albuminoids are insoluble in the protein solvents mentioned above and are dissolved only by hydrolysis. The keratin in hair, horn, feathers, and fingernails, and elastin in tendons are examples of albuminoids.

Histones

The histones are soluble in water and dilute acid, but are insoluble in dilute ammonium hydroxide, and are not coagulated by heat. They are slightly basic proteins due to a predominance of the basic amino acids. Examples are the globin in hemoglobin, and thymus histone.

Protamines

The protamines are soluble in water, dilute acid, and dilute ammonium hydroxide, and are not coagulated by heat. They are strongly basic in reaction and are the simplest of all naturally occurring proteins. Salmine and sturine in the sperm of fish are examples of protamines.

Conjugated Proteins

Nucleoproteins

Nucleoproteins consist of a basic protein combined with nucleic acid. They are present in the nuclei of living cells and are abundantly distributed in glandular tissue.

Glycoproteins

A glycoprotein is the combination of a protein and a carbohydrate. Typical examples are mucin in saliva and mucoids in tendon and cartilage.

Phosphoproteins

Phosphoproteins are proteins that are linked with phosphoric acid. Casein in milk and vitellin in egg yolk are phosphoproteins.

Chromoproteins

The chromoproteins are composed of a protein combined with a colored compound. Examples are hemoglobin in blood and melanin in hair and feathers.

Lipoproteins

Lipoproteins are combinations of proteins with fatty acids or fats. Examples are the lipoprotein complexes in serum and brain tissue.

Determination of Protein

It is often desirable to know the protein content of various foods and biological material. The analysis of the protein content of such material is based on its nitrogen content. Since the average nitrogen content of proteins is 16 per cent, the protein content of a substance may be obtained by multiplying its nitrogen value by the factor 6.25.

The *Kjeldahl method* is commonly used to determine the amount of nitrogen in organic materials. In brief, the procedure consists of heating the material with concentrated sulfuric acid in the presence of a catalyst (such as a copper or selenium compound). This *digestion process* converts the nitrogen from the organic form to the inorganic salt, ammonium sulfate. Excess sodium hydroxide is added to the $(NH_4)_2SO_4$ and the ammonia that is liberated is distilled into an excess of acid of known concentration. The amount of acid that was neutralized by the ammonia is determined by titration and the amount of ammonia formed is calculated. From this latter value, the nitrogen content of the material can be calculated and, when multiplied by 6.25, gives the protein content of the organic material.

Color Reactions of Proteins

The color reactions of proteins depend on the presence of certain linkages or specific amino acids in the protein molecules. They are often used to follow the extent of hydrolysis of a protein and for the detection of certain amino acids.

Biuret Test

When a protein solution is mixed with a sodium hydroxide solution and a few drops of a very dilute solution of copper sulfate are added, a violet color is produced. Amino acids and dipeptides do not give the biuret test. A positive test apparently depends on the presence of two or more *peptide linkages*, therefore the biuret test is a good test for proteins or polypeptides. It is often used to follow the hydrolysis of a protein. When the hydrolysate gives a negative biuret test, it can contain only dipeptides and amino acids.

Unoxidized Sulfur Test

We have already seen that naturally occurring proteins contain an average of 1 per cent of sulfur. Part of this sulfur is in the form of the amino acid, *cystine*. When a protein containing cystine is boiled for a few minutes in a solution of sodium hydroxide containing a small amount of lead acetate, the solution turns black. The black color is due to the formation of lead sulfide from the unoxidized sulfur of cystine and the lead of lead acetate.

Millon's Test

Millon's reagent consists of mercuric nitrate and nitrite in a mixture of nitric and nitrous acids. When this reagent is added to a protein solution, the protein precipitates as a mercury salt which turns red when the solution is heated. A positive test is given by any protein that contains *tyrosine*. Millon's test is therefore specific for the amino acid tyrosine in the protein molecule.

Hopkins-Cole Test

A layer of concentrated sulfuric acid is carefully placed under a mixture of a protein and a glyoxylic acid (CHO—COOH) solution. A violet ring will appear at the zone of contact of the two liquids if tryptophan is present in the protein. The Hopkins-Cole test is thus a test for *tryptophan* in the protein molecule.

Xanthoproteic Test

If concentrated nitric acid is added to a protein solution, the protein first precipitates and then dissolves, forming a yellow color. If the solution is made alkaline with sodium hydroxide, the yellow color changes to an orange. A positive test depends upon the presence of amino acids that contain the benzene ring, such as *tyrosine* and *tryptophan.*

Precipitation of Proteins

A characteristic property of proteins is the ease with which they are precipitated by certain reagents. Many of the normal functions in the body are essentially precipitation reactions, for example, the clotting of blood, or the precipitation of casein by rennin during digestion. Since animal tissues are chiefly protein in nature, however, reagents which precipitate protein will have a marked toxic effect if introduced into the body. Bacteria, which are mainly protein, are effectively destroyed when treated with suitable precipitants. Many of the common poisons and disinfectants act in this way.

Precipitation reactions are used in clinical and analytical laboratories to identify and separate protein components.

The following paragraphs contain a brief summary of the most common methods of protein precipitation.

By Heat Coagulation

When most protein solutions are heated, the protein becomes insoluble and precipitates, forming coagulated protein. Many protein foods coagulate when they are cooked. Tissue proteins and bacterial proteins are readily coagulated by heat. Routine examinations of urine specimens for protein are made by heating the urine in a test tube to coagulate any protein that might be present.

By Concentrated Inorganic Acids

Proteins are precipitated from their solutions by concentrated acids, such as hydrochloric, sulfuric, and nitric acid. Casein, for example, is precipitated from milk as a curd when acted on by the hydrochloric acid of the gastric juice. A clinical test for protein in urine is known as Heller's ring test. It depends upon the precipitation of any protein present when concentrated nitric acid is added.

By Salts of Heavy Metals

Salts of heavy metals, like mercuric chloride and silver nitrate, precipitate proteins. These salts are used for their disinfecting action and are toxic when taken internally. A protein solution such as egg white or milk, when given as an antidote in cases of poisoning with heavy metals, combines with the metallic salts. The precipitate that is formed must be removed by the use of an emetic before the protein is digested and the heavy metal is set free to act on the tissue protein. A silver salt such as argyrol is used in nose and throat infections, while silver nitrate is used to cauterize wounds and to prevent gonorrheal infection in the eyes of newborn babies.

By Salting Out

Most proteins are insoluble in a saturated solution of a salt such as ammonium sulfate. When it is desirable to isolate a protein from a solution without appreciably altering its chemical nature or properties, the protein may be precipitated by saturating the solution with $(NH_4)_2SO_4$. After filtration the excess $(NH_4)_2SO_4$ is usually removed by dialysis. This salting out process finds wide application in the isolation of biologically active proteins.

By Alcohol

Alcohol coagulates proteins other than the prolamines. A 70 per cent solution of alcohol is commonly used to sterilize the skin since it effectively penetrates the bacteria. A 95 per cent solution of alcohol is not effective because it merely coagulates the surface of the bacteria and does not destroy them.

By Alkaloidal Reagents

Tannic, picric, and tungstic acids are common alkaloidal reagents that will precipitate proteins from solution. Tannic and picric acids are used in the treatment of burns. When a solution of either of these acids is sprayed on extensively burned areas, it precipitates the protein to form a protective coating; this excludes air from the burn and prevents the loss of water. In an emergency, strong tea may be used as a source of tannic acid for the treatment of severe burns. Many other therapeutic agents have been used in the treatment of burns, the most recent being penicillin. Nevertheless, considerable quantities of tannic and picric acid preparations are still employed for this purpose. Tungstic and phosphotungstic acids are often used to precipitate the proteins from blood before analyzing the blood for various constituents of clinical importance.

Review Questions

1. What elements are present in proteins? Which element helps distinguish proteins from fats and carbohydrates?
2. A molecule of egg albumen is approximately how many times as large as a molecule of sucrose?
3. What products result from the complete hydrolysis of a protein? Why would it be difficult to write the structural formula for a protein even though you knew the chemical formulas of the products of hydrolysis?
4. How would you define a protein?
5. What is an amino acid? Write the formulas and names of three amino acids.
6. Why are amino acids classed as amphoteric substances? Would proteins also be amphoteric? Explain.
7. What is the peptide linkage? What simple substance is always split off when the peptide linkage is formed?
8. Illustrate the formation of a tripeptide from three molecules of alanine.
9. Under what three main types are proteins classified? How would you differentiate between the three types?
10. A certain food product was analyzed by the Kjeldahl method and found to have a nitrogen content of 4.0 per cent. What percentage of protein does this food contain?
11. Why is the biuret test used to determine when a protein is completely hydrolyzed?
12. A positive Millon's test would indicate the presence of what amino acid in a protein? A positive Hopkins-Cole test?
13. List five important processes involving the precipitation of proteins.
14. How would you treat a patient who had accidentally swallowed a mercuric chloride solution?

Chapter 16

Enzymes and Digestion

In previous chapters we have considered the chemistry of organic compounds with emphasis on the type of compounds occurring as food and body constituents. The food taken in by the body cannot be utilized until it undergoes the process of digestion and absorption. Since so many of the reactions of organic compounds proceed slowly compared with those of inorganic compounds, the action of catalysts is important. The great majority of reactions that occur in the body are between organic molecules, and require catalysts for the proper rate of reaction. These catalysts which govern the rate of chemical reactions in the body tissues are called *enzymes*. An enzyme is an organic catalyst that is formed by living cells but does not require the presence of the cell for its action.

Properties of Enzymes

It is generally accepted at the present time that enzymes are protein in nature. This view is strengthened by the observation that all of the enzymes that have been isolated in a crystalline form are proteins. In general, enzymes in solution are destroyed or inactivated by any treatment that precipitates or coagulates the protein material. Excessive heat, alcohol, salts of heavy metals, and concentrated inorganic acids will rapidly inhibit the activity of an enzyme.

The substance on which the enzyme acts is called the *substrate*. The modern system for naming enzymes is to add the ending *-ase* to the root of the name of the substrate. For example, the enzyme that hydrolyzes lipids is called a *lipase* and one that hydrolyzes maltose is called *maltase*. Certain enzymes had common names that had been used for years before this system was introduced. These enzymes retain their original name; for example, pepsin and trypsin are protein-splitting enzymes present in the stomach and intestine respectively. These two enzymes could also be called gastric and intestinal proteases.

The ability of an enzyme to act as a catalyst is thought to be related to an "active center" in the protein molecule. This active center combines with the substrate, and initiates the reaction that is catalyzed by the enzyme. An important property of an enzyme is that of *specificity* of action. For every reaction that takes place in the body there is a specific enzyme. A lipase will hydrolyze only lipids and has no effect on carbohydrates or proteins. Similarly, maltase attacks only its substrate maltose and will not split sucrose or lactose into their constituent sugars.

Factors that Influence the Rate of Enzyme Action

The rate of enzyme activity is influenced by several factors. The two most important are the temperature and the hydrogen ion concentration of the solution. Other factors that affect the speed of reaction are the concentration of the enzyme and substrate, the nature of the end products, the presence of electrolytes, and light.

The speed of most chemical reactions is increased two or three times for each 10° C. rise in temperature. This is also true for reactions in which an enzyme is the catalyst. Beyond a certain point, however, an increase in temperature will coagulate the enzyme and inactivate it. Every enzyme has an *optimum temperature* at which it exhibits maximum activity. The optimum temperature of the enzymes that are present in the body ranges between 37° and 50° C. (98.6° and 122° F.).

The hydrogen ion concentration, or pH, of the solution also influences the rate of enzyme action. For every enzyme there is an *optimum* pH at which activity is maximum. For example, pepsin is most active at a pH of 1.6, while trypsin has an optimum pH of 8.2. If the pH of the solution is too far from the optimum pH of an enzyme, it will exhibit no activity. Pepsin will not act in an alkaline solution, nor will trypsin act in an acid solution. In solutions where the pH is less than 1 or greater than 13, enzymes have no activity.

Activation and Inhibition of Enzymes

Certain enzymes are produced by cells in an inactive form. These are called *zymogens* or *proenzymes*. Proenzymes must be activated before they can catalyze their specific reactions. Some zymogens are activated by inorganic compounds, some by other enzymes, and some activate themselves in the presence of the proper *p*H. For example, the cells of the stomach produce a proenzyme called *pepsinogen* which in the presence of hydrochloric acid forms a small amount of pepsin. This active enzyme then converts the remainder of the pepsinogen into pepsin. Another proenzyme is *trypsinogen* that is made in the pancreas and activated in the intestine by the enzyme enterokinase. In addition to activators, most enzymes require the presence of certain organic molecules for their activity. These substances are called *coenzymes*. There is no sharp distinction between *activators* and coenzymes although in general activators are inorganic while coenzymes are organic in nature.

The activity of enzymes is inhibited by any substance that precipitates proteins, such as salts of heavy metals, cyanides, alcohol, and heat. Inhibitors of enzyme action in the body are called *antienzymes*. These substances are believed to be present in the lining of our stomach and intestine to prevent the protein-splitting enzymes from digesting our own tissue. Tapeworms are not digested in the intestine of the host because they are protected by antienzymes in their bodies.

Classification of Enzymes

Since the reactions of the body are catalyzed by enzymes, there must be different kinds of enzymes to influence the many types of reactions carried out by the body. Enzymes may therefore be classified according to the type of reaction they influence. The most important classes are *hydrolytic enzymes,* which produce hydrolysis of complex molecules; *fermenting enzymes,* which bring about fermentation; *oxidizing* and *reducing enzymes,* which control oxidation and reduction reactions respectively; *deaminizing enzymes,* which form ammonia; and *coagulating enzymes,* which produce coagulation of proteins. Each class may be subdivided into enzymes that act on the various foodstuffs as, for example, the hydrolytic enzymes that hydrolyze carbohydrates, fats, and proteins.

Common Enzymes and the Reactions They Influence

ENZYME	OCCURRENCE	SUBSTRATE	END PRODUCTS
I. Hydrolytic enzymes			
A. Carbohydrases:			
1. Amylases			
Ptyalin	Saliva	Starch	Dextrins and maltose
Amylopsin	Pancreatic juice	Starch	Maltose
2. Sucrase	Intestinal juice	Sucrose	Glucose + fructose
3. Lactase	Intestinal juice	Lactose	Glucose + galactose
4. Maltase	Intestinal juice	Maltose	Glucose + glucose
B. Lipases:			
1. Steapsin	Pancreatic juice	Fats	Fatty acids and glycerol
C. Proteases:			
1. Pepsin	Gastric juice	Proteins	Proteoses and peptones
2. Trypsin	Pancreatic juice	Proteins	Proteoses and peptones and polypeptides
D. Peptidases:			
1. Aminopoly-peptidase	Intestinal juice	Polypep-tides	Smaller peptides and amino acids
2. Carboxypoly-peptidase	Pancreatic juice	Polypep-tides	Smaller peptides and amino acids
3. Dipeptidase	Intestinal juice	Dipeptides	Amino acids
II. Fermenting enzymes			
1. Zymase	Yeast	Monosac-charides	Ethyl alcohol and carbon dioxide
2. Lactic acidase	Lactic acid bacteria	Lactose	Lactic acid
III. Oxidizing enzymes			
1. Catalase	Plant and animal tissue	Hydrogen peroxide	Oxygen
2. Peroxidase	Plant and animal tissue	Organic peroxides	Oxygen
IV. Deaminizing enzymes			
1. Urease	Animal tissue	Urea	Ammonia and carbon dioxide
V. Coagulating enzymes			
1. Rennin	Gastric juice	Casein	Paracasein
2. Thrombin	Blood	Fibrinogen	Fibrin

Digestion

The majority of the food that is taken into the body is made up of large complex molecules. Before they can be absorbed and utilized by the body they must be broken down into small, relatively simple molecules. The process in which complex food material is changed into simple molecules is called *digestion*. Digestion involves the hydrolysis of carbohydrates into monosaccharides, fats into glycerol and fatty acids, and proteins into amino acids by the action of the hydrolytic enzymes.

Many of the changes that take place during the preparation of food may be considered preliminary digestive processes. The cooking of starch aids digestion by rupturing the insoluble amylopectin layer that surrounds the starch granule and by converting the starch into dextrin. The connective tissue of meat is changed into gelatin and the meat is made more tender by cooking. In addition to meat, other protein foods such as egg whites are made more digestible by cooking. In recent years, the use of soybean meal in animal, poultry, and human nutrition has increased considerably. It is well known that cooking increases the nutritive value of soybeans. Undesirable microorganisms are often destroyed in the cooking process, thus protecting the body from food poisoning. Storage of meats, fruits, and vegetables often produces a more desirable food due to the action of enzymes during the storage period. A diagram of the digestive tract is shown in Figure 76.

Salivary Digestion

Food taken into the mouth is broken into smaller pieces by chewing and is mixed with *saliva*, which is the first of the digestive fluids. The saliva is secreted by three pairs of glands, the parotid, the submaxillary, and the sublingual. It is an almost neutral solution with a pH of about 6.8 and a water content of 99.5 per cent. Saliva contains *mucin*, a glycoprotein which makes the saliva slippery, and *ptyalin*, an enzyme that hydrolyzes starch to maltose. It also contains several inorganic salts such as chlorides and phosphates that are present in the blood.

A normal person secretes approximately 1500 cc. of saliva daily. The flow of saliva is controlled by the nervous system; the sight, odor, or even the thought of food will cause the salivary glands to secrete. The presence of food in the mouth and the mere process of chewing stimulate the flow of saliva.

Ptyalin. Ptyalin is the enzyme responsible for the digestive action

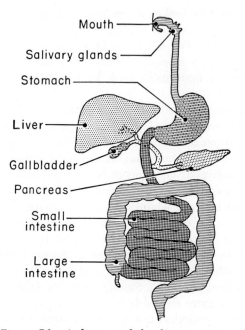

Figure 76. A diagram of the digestive system.

of the saliva. It hydrolyzes starch to soluble starch, erythrodextrin, achroodextrin, and finally maltose. Ptyalin is active over a pH range of 4 to 9 with an optimum pH of 6.6. It is inactivated in the stomach, where the pH may drop to about 1.5. Since this enzyme has little time to act on starches in the mouth, its main activity takes place in the stomach before it is inactivated by the acid gastric contents. Food that is well mixed with saliva may undergo salivary digestion for twenty to thirty minutes in the stomach before the ptyalin is inactivated.

The most important functions of saliva are to moisten and lubricate the food for swallowing and to initiate the digestion of starch to dextrins and maltose.

Gastric Digestion

When the food is swallowed, it passes through the esophagus into the stomach. The upper end of the stomach, into which the esophagus opens, is called the *fundus*, while the part leading into the intestine is called the *pylorus*. As the food enters the stomach, it distends the muscular wall and collects in the fundic portion. The stomach therefore acts as a storage organ for undigested food. During the process of digestion, the food is mixed with the gastric juice and moves toward the pyloric opening, where it is discharged into the intestine. The food remains in the stomach for one to five hours, depending on the type of meal that is eaten.

There are many small tubular glands located in the walls of the stomach that are responsible for the secretion of *gastric juice*. These glands are stimulated in various ways. The sight, smell, or thought of appetizing foods will cause an increased flow of gastric juice. The presence of food in the stomach is thought to cause the production of a hormone called *gastrin* which diffuses into the blood stream and stimulates secretion by the gastric glands. Gastrin is believed to be identical with *histamine*, which will stimulate the flow of gastric juice when it is injected into the blood stream. The average person secretes 2000 to 3000 cc. of gastric juice a day.

Gastric Juice. As secreted, gastric juice is a pale yellow, strongly acid solution containing the enzymes pepsin, rennin, and lipase. The acidity of the gastric juice is due to free hydrochloric acid, which may be present in a concentration as high as 0.5 per cent. The acidity of the normal stomach contents corresponds to a 0.2 per cent solution of HCl and has a pH of about 1.6 to 1.8. In certain pathological conditions, the acidity of the stomach contents varies considerably. An increase in acidity over the normal is called *hyperacidity*, which is frequently a symptom of gastric ulcers (Fig. 77).

A decrease in acidity is known as *hypoacidity*, a condition commonly associated with cancer and anemia. The acidity of the gastric juice is often determined clinically as a diagnostic procedure.

Pepsin is the principal enzyme in the gastric juice. The inactive form, pepsinogen, is produced by the cells in the lining of the stomach, and is converted into active pepsin in the presence of hydrochloric acid. Pepsin acts on the protein in the food, hydrolyzing it into the smaller, more soluble molecules of *proteoses* and *peptones*. The optimum pH of pepsin is 1.5 to 2; thus it is ideally suited for the digestion of protein in normal stomach contents, whose pH is 1.6 to 1.8.

Rennin is another protease found in gastric juice. It acts on casein, the main protein of milk, changing it into the soluble paracasein. The

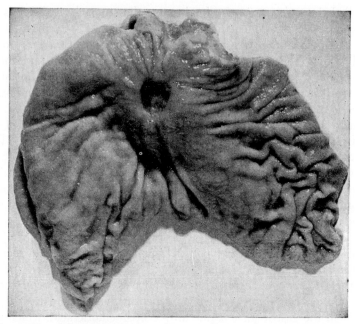

Figure 77.   A large gastric ulcer. (From Bockus, H. L.: Gastro-enterology.)

calcium present in the milk combines with paracasein to form the insoluble *calcium paracaseinate curd.* This curdling of milk in the stomach is important because the solid material remains in the stomach longer and is acted on by pepsin. Rennin is especially important in the stomach of young mammals whose sole diet is milk.

Evacuation of the Stomach.   As digestion in the stomach proceeds, the food gradually assumes a liquid consistency. The wavelike contractions of the stomach musculature mix the contents with the gastric juice; this liquid mixture is called *chyme.* As the chyme is forced toward the pyloric opening, the pyloric valve relaxes and allows a portion of the stomach contents to pass into the intestine. After the acid chyme is neutralized by the pancreatic juice and bile, another portion of chyme is allowed to pass into the intestine. The time required for gastric digestion and evacuation of the stomach depends on the character of the food that is eaten. A meal which is mainly carbohydrate in nature remains in the stomach about two hours, while a heavy meal of fatty foods and meat remains in the stomach for five hours.

Intestinal Digestion

The acid chyme passes into the small intestine as it leaves the stomach. The first ten inches of the small intestine is known as the *duodenum* and is the most important section from the standpoint of digestion. The next section is called the *jejunum*, while the main portion of the small intestine is known as the *ileum*.

The three digestive juices, namely, the pancreatic juice, intestinal juice, and bile, enter the intestine through the duodenum. These juices are alkaline in reaction and together neutralize the acidity of the chyme.

Pancreatic Juice. The pancreas is a long, glandular organ lying close to the duodenum. Two secretions are formed by the pancreas, an internal secretion called *insulin*, which diffuses into the blood stream and regulates carbohydrate metabolism, and an external secretion called *pancreatic juice* which is carried to the duodenum through ducts. The flow of pancreatic juice occurs only when chyme enters the duodenum. The acid in the chyme converts *prosecretin* in the duodenal wall into *secretin*, a hormone which diffuses into the blood stream. Secretin is thus carried to the pancreas and stimulates the flow of pancreatic juice. Normally about 500 to 800 cc. of pancreatic juice (*p*H 7.5 to 8) is produced in a day.

Pancreatic Enzymes. There are enzymes present in the pancreatic juice that are capable of digesting proteins, fats, and carbohydrates. The pancreatic proteases are *trypsin, chymotrypsin,* and *carboxypolypeptidase.* The first two named are secreted as the proenzymes, *trypsinogen* and *chymotrypsinogen.* Trypsinogen is activated by the *enterokinase* present in the intestinal juice, while chymotrypsin is activated by trypsin. Both of these enzymes act on native proteins, forming proteoses, peptones, and polypeptides. Trypsin has an optimum *p*H of 8.2. Chymotrypsin, in particular, possesses the property of clotting milk and may act as a safety factor in infants to take care of any milk that passes through the stomach without being coagulated by rennin. Carboxypolypeptidase further hydrolyzes the polypeptides to form simpler peptides and amino acids.

The pancreatic lipase called *steapsin* hydrolyzes fats into glycerol and fatty acids. The activity of this enzyme is greatly enhanced by the presence of bile, since the bile salts lower the surface tension and cause emulsification of fats.

The pancreatic juice also contains an amylase similar to ptyalin in saliva, called *amylopsin*. This enzyme splits starch to maltose, with an optimum activity in a neutral to slightly alkaline medium.

The Intestinal Juice. The intestinal juice or *succus entericus* is produced mainly in the duodenum, with smaller amounts being formed in the jejunum and ileum. Although the juice contains enzymes, the main activity is confined to the intestinal mucosa.

Intestinal Enzymes. The most important enzymes present in the intestinal juice are the *peptidases* and the three disaccharide-splitting enzymes, *sucrase, lactase,* and *maltase.*

There are two intestinal peptidases: *aminopolypeptidase* hydrolyzes polypeptides to simpler peptides and amino acids, *dipeptidase* hydrolyzes dipeptides to amino acids. These two enzymes therefore complete the hydrolysis of native proteins that has been started by other enzymes. The intestinal peptidases have an optimum pH between 7 and 8.

The three disaccharidases present in intestinal juice account for the hydrolysis of the common disaccharides: sucrose, lactose, and maltose. Cane sugar is the main source of dietary sucrose, milk contains lactose, and maltose comes from the partial hydrolysis of starch by ptyalin and amylopsin. Sucrase, lactase, and maltase split these disaccharides into their constituent monosaccharides, thus completing the digestion of carbohydrates.

Bile

In addition to pancreatic and intestinal juice, bile is poured into the duodenum. Although bile contains no enzymes, it plays an important role in digestion. Bile is formed continuously by the liver; when it is not needed in the intestine it is stored in the gallbladder. Water is absorbed from the bile in the gallbladder, concentrating the bile and thus increasing the storage capacity of the gallbladder. When fat enters the small intestine the hormone *cholecystokinin* is liberated into the blood stream, causing the gallbladder to contract and empty the bile into the duodenum. It is estimated that a normal adult produces 600 to 800 cc. of bile per day.

Bile is an alkaline fluid with a yellow-brown to green color and a bitter taste. Its alkaline reaction aids in the neutralization of the acid chyme. From the standpoint of digestion, the *bile salts* are the most important constituents of bile. Several constituents including the *bile pigments* and cholesterol are excreted in the bile.

Bile Salts. The two most important bile salts are *sodium glycocholate* and *sodium taurocholate*. As mentioned previously, they are compounds that contain the sterol nucleus. Their main function in digestion is the emulsification of fats, which they accomplish by lowering the surface tension. The activity of the pancreatic lipase, steapsin, is greatly increased in the presence of bile salts. By increasing the speed with which fats are digested, they also indirectly assist in the digestion of proteins and carbohydrates; for if a considerable portion of the meal consists of fatty foods, the fat tends to coat the other food particles and must be removed before the other enzymes can act.

Bile Pigments. When red blood cells decompose, hemoglobin is oxidized to form *bilirubin*, which is excreted into the bile by the liver. Bilirubin is the main bile pigment and is reddish in color. On oxidation it is converted into the green pigment *biliverdin*, while on reduction it forms the brown *stercobilin*. Stercobilin is the normal pigment of the feces. Bilirubin is also reduced to form *urobilin*, which may be reduced to form *urobilinogen*. The chief pigment of the urine, called *urochrome*, is a mixture of urobilin and urobilinogen.

In cases of obstruction of the bile duct or impairment of the liver, there is an accumulation of bile pigments in the blood and the skin becomes yellow. This condition is called *jaundice*. The black and blue spot caused by an injury is a visual demonstration of the conversion of hemoglobin into bile pigments.

Cholesterol. This common sterol is excreted from the body by way of the bile. When the bile is concentrated in the gallbladder the cholesterol sometimes precipitates around a foreign body to produce *gallstones*. A gallbladder filled with gallstones is shown in Figure 78. Although there are other types of gallstones, the most common type formed in the human gallbladder is composed mainly of cholesterol.

Functions of Bile. The functions of bile may be summarized as follows: (1) It aids in the neutralization of the acid chyme, (2) it emulsifies and promotes solution of the fats, (3) it activates steapsin and accelerates its action, (4) it dissolves the insoluble fatty acids and assists in the absorption of fats, (5) it reduces intestinal putrefaction by stimulating peristalsis.

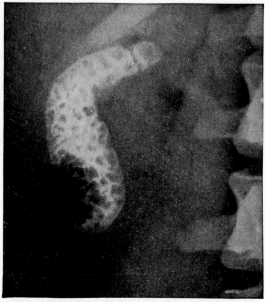

Figure 78. A gallbladder packed with gallstones.
(From Buckstein, J.: Clinical Roentgenology of the Alimentary Tract.)

Summary

The digestion of the three major foodstuffs as they pass down the alimentary canal is outlined in the table on page 245.

Absorption

The passage of the end products of digestion through the walls of the small intestine into the blood and tissues is called *absorption*. No food material is absorbed from the mouth and very little is absorbed from the stomach.

The small intestine is especially adapted for absorption. Although the superficial surface area measures about ½ square meter, the effective absorbing surface is nearly 10 square meters because of the folds in the mucous lining and the numerous finger-like projections called *villi*. The food usually remains in the small intestine from four to six hours for the process of intestinal digestion and absorption to take place. During this period, the end products of digestion are absorbed through the villi into the blood or lymph stream. The human small

Summary of Digestion

FOOD-STUFF	DIGESTED IN	ENZYME	SUBSTRATE	END PRODUCTS
Carbohy-drates	Mouth	Ptyalin	Starch	Dextrins and maltose
	Stomach Gastric juice Intestine	No carbohydrate-splitting enzymes		
	Pancreatic juice	Amylopsin	Starch	Maltose
	Intestinal juice	Sucrase	Sucrose	Glucose and fructose
		Lactase	Lactose	Glucose and galactose
		Maltase	Maltose	Glucose
Proteins	Mouth Saliva Stomach	No protein-splitting enzymes		
	Gastric juice	Pepsin	Proteins	Proteoses and peptones
		Rennin *not in humans*	Casein	Paracasein
	Intestine Pancreatic juice	Trypsin	Proteins, proteoses, peptones	Polypeptides
		Chymotrypsin	Proteins, proteoses, peptones	Polypeptides
		Carboxypoly-peptidase	Polypep-tides	Peptides and amino acids
	Intestinal juice	Aminopolypeptidase	Polypep-tides	Peptides and amino acids
		Dipeptidases	Dipeptides	Amino acids
Lipids	Mouth Saliva Stomach	No lipid-splitting enzymes		
	Gastric juice	Gastric lipase	Emulsified fats	Fatty acids and glycerol
	Intestine Pancreatic juice	Steapsin	Fats	Fatty acids and glycerol

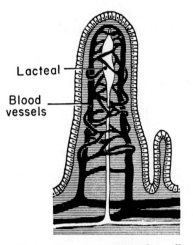

Figure 79. A diagram of a villus.

intestine contains from 4,000,000 to 5,000,000 villi. Each villus (Fig. 79) consists of a lining of cells that surround a central *lacteal* or lymph capillary. A network of blood capillaries surrounds the lacteal, thus providing a rapid circulation of blood close to the surface. The blood and lymph capillaries from several villi coalesce to form larger blood and lymph vessels.

Absorption of Carbohydrates

When the digestive process is completed, the carbohydrates exist as the monosaccharides glucose, fructose, and galactose. These monosaccharides are absorbed directly into the blood stream through the capillary blood vessels of the villi. They are carried by the blood to the liver, where they are converted into *glycogen* for storage and for subsequent conversion to glucose. Considerable evidence exists to indicate that the intestinal mucosa possesses the property of selective absorption not possessed by a dead membrane. For example, there is a difference in the rate of absorption of the three monosaccharides. Galactose is absorbed more rapidly than glucose which is absorbed more rapidly than fructose.

Absorption of Fats

The products of complete fat digestion are glycerol and fatty acids. These compounds, together with a mixture of mono-, di-, and triglycerides emulsified with bile salts, are present in the small intestine at the site of absorption. After years of research, there is as yet a lack of agreement on the exact mechanism of fat absorption. Most of the evidence at present suggests that bile salts are essential in the transport of lipid digestion products across the intestinal barrier. The overall mechanism may be summarized as follows: After a period of hydrolysis in the small intestine, the products of hydrolysis, with the assistance of bile salts, enter the lacteals almost quantitatively. These products then appear in the lymph stream as resynthesized triglycerides. The fat in the lymph is carried through the larger lymphatics to the thoracic duct, from which they enter the blood stream and are carried to the tissues and fat depots. The essential nature of bile salts in fat absorption is demonstrated by the marked decrease in absorption that occurs when bile is excluded from the small intestine.

Absorption of Proteins

The complete digestion of proteins yields amino acids, which are absorbed directly into the blood stream. Each amino acid, like the monosaccharides, has a different rate of absorption through the intestinal mucosa. The amino acids are carried to the tissues where they are used for building new tissue or are oxidized to produce energy. The body does not contain storage depots for protein as it does for fats and carbohydrates.

Formation of Feces

The intestinal contents are still fluid as they leave the ileum and pass through the ileocecal valve into the large intestine. They consist mainly of undigested food residues, remains of digestive and intestinal secretions, and cellular debris. This material normally remains in the large intestine for one to two days, where it is converted into feces by the reabsorption of water. In addition to the food residues, the feces contain bile salts, bile pigments, mucin, sterols, and inorganic salts. Approximately one fourth or more of the feces consist of bacteria.

The character of the feces does not depend entirely on the nature of the diet. An exclusive carbohydrate diet will produce feces with a composition similar to that produced on an exclusive protein diet. Starvation does not markedly alter the composition of the feces, so the feces must be derived mainly from secretions of the alimentary tract. Foods that contain a high percentage of cellulose produce a bulky feces. From 25 to 50 gm. of dry fecal matter are excreted per day on a normal mixed diet.

Bacterial Action in the Intestine

Increasing numbers of bacteria are found in the lower section of the small intestine, and they make up a considerable portion of the total contents of the large intestine. In certain animals such as cows, sheep, and horses, the intestinal bacteria play an active role in the digestion of cellulose. By splitting cellulose into simpler carbohydrates, they make available food material otherwise indigestible by ordinary enzymes.

The two main types of bacterial action in the human intestine are *fermentation* of carbohydrates and *putrefaction* of protein material. If any of the simple carbohydrates have escaped digestion or absorption, they undergo fermentation to form gases (hydrogen, carbon dioxide, and methane) and acids (acetic, lactic, and butyric). The gases may cause distention of the intestinal tract and the acids may cause diarrhea in infants by irritating the intestinal mucosa. Fermentative diarrhea in infants is often treated by decreasing the carbohydrate in their formula or by feeding milk of high protein and low carbohydrate content.

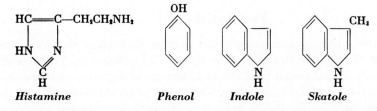

Histamine   *Phenol*   *Indole*   *Skatole*

Putrefaction of protein material in the large intestine results in the formation of products that may be toxic if absorbed into the blood stream. The bacteria split the proteins into amino acids, which they further decompose by the removal of carbon dioxide or ammonia.

Some typical products of intestinal putrefaction are histamine, phenol, indole, and skatole. *Histamine* has marked physiological properties, while *indole*, and *skatole* are responsible for the characteristic odor of the feces. Small amounts of these toxic compounds may be absorbed from the intestine and carried by the blood to the liver where they are detoxified. Indole, for example, is converted into nontoxic indican which is excreted in the urine. An abnormally large excretion of indican in the urine would indicate that excessive putrefaction was occurring in the large intestine.

Symptoms such as headaches, drowsiness, mental depression, and general malaise that accompany constipation have been attributed to the absorption of toxic compounds from the intestine. At the present time, it is considered that these symptoms are not caused by intestinal putrefaction. It should be kept in mind that a certain amount of intestinal putrefaction occurs normally and that mechanisms are present in the body to take care of these toxic products. If it is desirable to reduce the extent of putrefaction in the intestine, a high carbohydrate and low protein diet is beneficial.

Review Questions

1. Give an example of an enzyme and its substrate. What products would result from the action of this enzyme on its substrate?
2. Why should enzyme solutions not be boiled or treated with alcohol or concentrated acids?
3. What two factors have a strong influence on the rate of action of an enzyme?
4. Define optimum pH; optimum temperature. Give the optimum pH and optimum temperature of two enzymes.
5. What explanation would you give for the formation of enzymes in an inactive state by the cells?
6. List five general types of enzymes. Which type is the most important in digestion? Why?
7. How would you define digestion? What reaction always occurs in the digestion of food?
8. What are the main functions of saliva?
9. What enzyme is present in the saliva? Upon what substrate does it act?
10. Comment on the statement: "Salivary digestion takes place in the stomach for 20 to 30 minutes after the ingestion of food."
11. What characteristic of gastric juice distinguishes it from all other fluids in the body?

12. What abnormal conditions are frequently associated with hyperacidity of the gastric juice? With hypoacidity?

13. List the principal enzymes of the gastric juice with their substrates and end products of digestion.

14. Why is rennin most important in infant nutrition?

15. What is chyme? How is it formed?

16. How is the flow of pancreatic juice controlled?

17. Name the protein-splitting enzymes of the pancreatic juice.

18. List the important characteristics and composition of bile.

19. Why are the bile salts of importance in digestion?

20. Describe three locations in the body where you might observe bile pigments.

21. How are gallstones usually formed? What constituent predominates in gallstones?

22. List the important functions of bile.

23. What is absorption? In what part of the alimentary canal does it occur?

24. Why are the villi important in the process of absorption?

25. Describe briefly the absorption of carbohydrates, fats, and proteins.

26. What type of material is present in the feces?

27. What causes fermentative diarrhea in infants? How is it treated?

Chapter 17

Carbohydrate Metabolism

A study of the chemical nature, digestion, and absorption of the three major foodstuffs is preliminary to the most important consideration of the utilization of food by the body tissues. Strictly speaking, food material in the gastrointestinal tract is outside of the body. To be used in growth of bones and tissue, or to be utilized for energy, the material must be carried to the tissues by the blood stream. The changes that occur in body tissues after food is digested and absorbed are given the general name, *metabolism*. If the changes or reactions involve the synthesis of new tissue as in growth they are called *anabolism*, while the breakdown of tissues or food material into energy and waste products is called *catabolism*.

The Blood Sugar Level

The main end products of carbohydrate digestion in the body are the three important monosaccharides, glucose, fructose, and galactose. These sugars are absorbed into the blood stream and are carried by the portal circulation to the liver. Fructose and galactose are converted into glucose by the liver cells. The metabolism of carbohydrates therefore is essentially the metabolism of glucose.

The concentration of glucose in the general circulation is normally 70 to 90 mg. per 100 cc. of blood. This is known as the *normal fasting level* of blood sugar. After a meal containing carbohydrates, the glucose content of the blood increases, causing a temporary condition of *hyperglycemia*. In cases of severe exercise or prolonged starvation, the blood sugar value may fall below the normal fasting level, resulting in the state of *hypoglycemia*. One of the major functions of the tissues is to maintain blood of a constant composition, therefore several mechanisms are available to counteract changes in the blood sugar

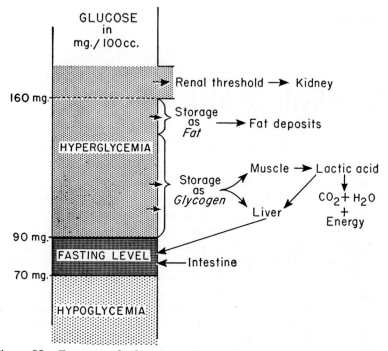

Figure 80.   Factors involved in the regulation of the glucose level of the blood.

level. After an ordinary meal, the glucose in the blood reaches hyperglycemic levels; this may be returned to normal by the following processes:

1. Storage
    (a) as glycogen
    (b) as fat
2. Oxidation to produce energy
3. Excretion by the kidneys

The operation of these factors in counteracting hyperglycemia is illustrated by the diagram in Figure 80. The space between the vertical lines may be compared to a thermometer with values expressed as milligrams of glucose per 100 cc. of blood. During active absorption of carbohydrates from the intestine, the blood sugar level rises, causing a temporary hyperglycemia. In an effort to bring the glucose concentration back to normal, the liver may remove glucose from the blood stream, converting it into glycogen for storage. The muscles will also take glucose from the circulation to convert it to glycogen or to oxidize it to produce energy. If the blood sugar level continues to rise, the glucose may be converted into fat and stored in the fat depots. These four processes usually control the hyperglycemia; however, if large amounts of carbohydrates are eaten and the blood sugar level exceeds 160 mg. of glucose per 100 cc., the excess is excreted by the kidneys. The blood sugar level at which the kidney starts excreting glucose is known as the *renal threshold* and has a value from 150 to 170 mg. per 100 cc.

Since carbohydrate metabolism is essentially the regulation of the blood sugar level, we will discuss the above factors in detail.

Glycogen Formation

During absorption of the carbohydrates, the excess glucose is stored as glycogen in the liver. Normally this organ contains about 100 gm. of glycogen but may store as much as 400 gm. The glycogen in the liver is readily converted into glucose and serves as a reservoir from which glucose may be drawn if the blood sugar level falls below normal. The formation of glycogen from glucose is called *glycogenesis*, while the conversion of glycogen to glucose is known as *glycogenolysis*. The muscles also store glucose as glycogen, but muscle glycogen is not as readily converted into glucose as is liver glycogen.

The process of glycogenesis is not just a simple conversion of glucose to glycogen. The glucose is phosphorylated by phosphoric acid with the aid of specific enzymes to form the compound known as glucose-1-phosphate. This compound which contains a phosphoric acid molecule attached to the aldehyde carbon of glucose is readily converted into glycogen by means of another specific enzyme. The process of glycogenolysis liberates glucose into the blood stream for the synthesis of muscle glycogen which is used in muscle contraction. During the process of muscular contraction, lactic acid is formed and diffuses into the blood stream. This lactic acid may be oxidized to produce energy or may be carried back to the liver and converted into liver glycogen. The series of events starting with glucose in the blood stream and ending with liver glycogen produced from lactic acid may be illustrated as follows:

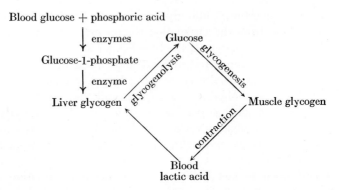

Blood glucose + phosphoric acid

↓ enzymes

Glucose-1-phosphate

↓ enzyme

Liver glycogen ⟶ *glycogenolysis* ⟶ Glucose ⟶ *glycogenesis* ⟶ Muscle glycogen

contraction

Blood
lactic acid

Substances other than the carbohydrates in food may be converted into glycogen. About 58 per cent of the amino acids from protein digestion, the glycerol portion of fats, and lactic acid from the contraction of muscles will form glycogen. These substances, therefore, contribute to the glucose supply of the body when they are needed.

Oxidation of Carbohydrates

Glucose is ultimately oxidized in the body to form carbon dioxide and water with the liberation of energy (Fig. 81). However, this process is complicated by the formation of several intermediate prod-

Figure 81. The major function of dietary carbohydrates is to supply energy for physical movement and exercise.

ucts whose interrelationships are not clearly defined. Although oxidation of glucose occurs in the various tissues of the body, our information is largely confined to the process in the muscles.

Much study has been devoted to the chemical changes which occur when carbohydrates are metabolized in the muscle. It has been known for many years that one of the products of muscular activity is lactic acid. About four fifths of the lactic acid that is formed in muscular contraction is changed back to glycogen in the muscle, or is carried as blood lactic acid to the liver, where it is converted into liver glycogen. The other fifth of the lactic acid is oxidized to carbon dioxide and water.

Muscle glycogen is apparently the source of energy for muscular activity. The first reaction is probably the hydrolysis of glycogen to form a hexose sugar. The hexose sugar then combines with phosphoric acid to form a hexose monophosphate which eventually is converted to a hexose diphosphate which is split into two triose monophosphates. The triose monophosphates are rearranged with the ultimate formation of pyruvic acid, which is then converted into lactic acid. The intermediate compounds which are thought to be involved in the oxidation of glycogen in the muscle are shown in the following outline:

Muscle glycogen
$\updownarrow$
Glucose—1—phosphate
$\updownarrow$
Glucose—6—phosphate
$\updownarrow$
Fructose—6—phosphate
$\updownarrow$
Fructose diphosphate
$\updownarrow$ _____ $\updownarrow$
Phosphoglyceric aldehyde $\rightleftharpoons$ Dihydroxyacetone phosphate
$\updownarrow$
Diphosphoglyceric acid
$\updownarrow$
Phosphoglyceric acid
$\updownarrow$
Phosphopyruvic acid
$\updownarrow$
Pyruvic acid $\rightleftharpoons$ ⟨Tricarboxylic acid cycle⟩ $\rightarrow CO_2 + H_2O$ + energy
$\updownarrow$
Lactic acid

The pyruvic acid and the one fifth of the lactic acid that is not converted to liver glycogen are eventually oxidized with the formation of carbon dioxide and energy. The lactic acid may be oxidized to reform pyruvic acid which is converted to compounds involved in the *tricarboxylic acid cycle* which eventually converts the pyruvic acid to CO_2, H_2O, and energy. Another mechanism for the oxidation of pyruvic acid involves the formation of acetic acid which enters the tricarboxylic acid cycle by combining with a complex molecule called coenzyme A. The endproducts of this series of reactions are also CO_2, H_2O, and energy.

The Action of Insulin and Epinephrine

Insulin

Insulin is a hormone that is formed by the pancreas. It is an essential factor in carbohydrate metabolism and is responsible for the regulation of the normal blood sugar level. The main functions of insulin are as follows:

1. It is necessary for the conversion of glucose into liver and muscle glycogen for storage.
2. It is necessary for the proper oxidation of carbohydrates in the body.
3. It prevents the breakdown of glycogen to glucose in the liver.

DIABETES MELLITUS. If the pancreas fails to produce sufficient insulin, a condition of *diabetes mellitus* results. The failure of the storage mechanisms in the absence of insulin causes a marked increase in the blood sugar level. Glucose is usually excreted in the urine because the renal threshold is exceeded. The impairment of carbohydrate oxidation causes the formation of an excess of ketone bodies. Many of these ketone bodies are acid in nature, and the severe acidosis that results from the lack of insulin causes *diabetic coma*, which is often fatal to a diabetic patient. When insulin is injected, carbohydrate metabolism is properly regulated and the above symptoms do not appear.

A more detailed description of diabetes will be presented in the chapter on hormones (Chap. 24).

Epinephrine (Adrenalin)

This substance is produced by the adrenal glands. It is antagonistic to the action of insulin in that it causes glycogenolysis in the liver with liberation of glucose. Continued secretion of epinephrine occurs under the influence of strong emotions such as fear and anger. In these cases, the epinephrine liberates glucose from liver glycogen and increases the blood sugar level. This mechanism is often used as an emergency function to provide carbohydrate for muscular work. The hyperglycemia that results often exceeds the renal threshold, and glucose is excreted in the urine.

Glucose Tolerance

Glucose Tolerance Test

The capacity of the body to assimilate large doses of glucose, without excreting sugar in the urine, has long been of clinical interest. This glucose tolerance is a valuable aid in the diagnosis of diabetes. The blood of a fasting person is analyzed for glucose. Then 50 to 100 gm. of glucose are administered by mouth and the glucose concentration is determined at intervals. The blood sugar level of a normal person will rise to a maximum during the first half-hour or hour interval and will return to approximately the normal fasting level at the end of two hours.

The rapid absorption of the ingested glucose apparently causes the pancreas to secrete insulin, which removes glucose from the blood until the normal level is reached. A diabetic person, lacking this controlling effect, cannot tolerate the large dose of glucose. The blood sugar level of the diabetic person would be higher at the start of the test and would probably reach a peak at the end of the second hour. The original level would not be reached for several hours, and large quantities of glucose would appear in the urine. The chart in Figure 82 illustrates the difference between glucose tolerance curves obtained from a normal and a diabetic patient.

Excretion of Glucose

Any condition which produces a hyperglycemia in excess of 180 mg. per 100 cc. of blood will result in the appearance of glucose in the urine. The kidney may be compared to a dam that holds back the glucose of the blood stream until it rises beyond the top of the dam and spills over into the urine. The renal threshold may be considered as the top of the dam. The blood sugar level of a patient with uncontrolled diabetes is usually above the renal threshold, causing glucose to be spilled into the urine almost continuously. It is not unusual for such a patient to excrete 200 to 300 gm. of glucose in the urine per day. In a completely diabetic patient, the main mechanism for removing glucose from the blood is that of excretion by the kidney.

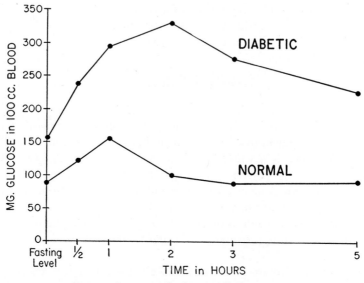

Figure 82. Typical glucose tolerance curves.

The presence of appreciable amounts of glucose in the urine is known as *glycosuria*. When a routine examination of a urine specimen reveals a positive Benedict's test, diabetes is usually suspected. However, there are several other conditions that may cause glycosuria and these may be outlined as follows:

ALIMENTARY GLYCOSURIA. This is a transitory type of glycosuria that results from the ingestion of a large quantity of sugar. The sugar is absorbed so rapidly that the body is unable to convert it into glycogen fast enough to maintain a blood sugar level below the renal threshold. After the excess sugar is excreted, the level returns to normal.

RENAL DIABETES. Glucose is excreted in the urine in renal diabetes because the renal threshold of the person is abnormally low; thus glucose is excreted even when the blood sugar level is normal.

EMOTIONAL GLYCOSURIA. The secretion of epinephrine that occurs in emotional excitement causes an increase in the blood sugar level. If the renal threshold is exceeded, glycosuria results. An especially difficult examination or the emotional stress of an athletic contest may produce glycosuria of this type.

PHLORHIZIN DIABETES.   Glycosuria may also be caused by the injection of the drug, phlorhizin, into experimental animals. This condition is called phlorhizin diabetes and is often used to study some of the factors in diabetes.

FALSE GLYCOSURIA.   A positive Benedict's test may be observed on urine specimens in the last stage of pregnancy and during lactation. This is due to the presence of lactose in the urine, and is called false glycosuria.

Conversion of Carbohydrate to Fat

It is a common observation that persons who consume an excessive amount of carbohydrates in their diet become fat. The body is able to convert carbohydrates into fat, but the mechanism for this change is not clear. The glycerol portion of a fat could easily be formed from glyceric aldehyde, which is an intermediate product in carbohydrate metabolism, by reduction of the aldehyde group to an alcohol. The long-chain fatty acids may possibly be built by the condensation of several molecules of a simple unit such as acetaldehyde, which contains two carbon atoms.

Review Questions

1. Explain the meaning of the terms: metabolism, anabolism, and catabolism.
2. Why is the metabolism of carbohydrates essentially the metabolism of glucose?
3. What is the normal fasting level of blood glucose? What values of blood glucose would be considered hypoglycemic, hyperglycemic?
4. What are the factors that maintain the glucose concentration of the blood at a fairly constant level?
5. How could you represent glycogenesis and glycogenolysis in one simple equation? Of what importance are these processes in carbohydrate metabolism?
6. What happens to the lactic acid that is formed by carbohydrate metabolism in the muscles?
7. What is the function of the tricarboxylic acid cycle in the oxidation of carbohydrates?
8. If the pancreas were unable to form insulin, what alterations would occur in carbohydrate metabolism?
9. When would a normal individual have the most need for (1) insulin, (2) epinephrine, with respect to carbohydrate metabolism?
10. What is meant by the statement that a diabetic cannot tolerate large doses of glucose by mouth?
11. Define the terms: glycosuria, renal threshold, and diabetes mellitus.
12. Glucose is sometimes excreted in the urine of apparently normal persons. Name three conditions that might result in this glycosuria. Explain each briefly.

Chapter 18

Fat Metabolism

Although the diet contains several types of lipids, the fats or triglycerides are most important in metabolism. They are a rich source of energy, and may be stored in fat depots to serve as future food supplies. Other lipids such as sterols and phospholipid are involved in separate metabolic processes and are essential constituents of the tissues.

Utilization of Fats

As discussed previously, the absorption of the end products of fat digestion is a complex process involving bile salts. The fat molecules are resynthesized in the intestinal mucosa, pass into the lymph, and are carried to the blood for circulation to the body tissues. After a meal containing fat, the increased amount of fat in the blood stream is utilized by the body as follows:

1. Synthesis of complex lipids
2. Storage
3. Oxidation to furnish energy

Synthesis of Complex Lipids

Certain lipids are essential constituents of protoplasm and are probably synthesized from fats of the food. Phospholipids such as sphingomyelin and lecithin are necessary in the formation of brain and nervous tissue. Lecithin is used in transporting fats to the various tissues and may be involved in the oxidation of fats. Another essential phospholipid is cephalin, which is a vital factor in the clotting of blood. Special fats and oils in the body, such as the natural oil of the scalp and the wax of the ear, are examples of lipids synthesized from the fat of the food.

Storage

Fats may be removed from the blood stream by storage in the various fat depots. When fat is stored under the skin, it is usually called *adipose tissue*. However, considerable quantities of fat may be stored around such organs as the kidneys, heart, lungs, and spleen. This type of depot fat acts as a support for these organs and helps to protect them from injury.

For many years it was believed that the fat stored in fat depots was relatively inert and used only for fuel when the body required it. In effect it was like putting money in the bank for future financial emergencies. Several studies on fat storage and utilization using fat whose fatty acids were tagged with deuterium have changed this point of view. At present, the storage fat is considered to exist in a dynamic state with its component fatty acids being continually interchanged with those from food fat.

The composition of the storage fat is generally characteristic for a given species of animal. If large amounts of fat are fed to an animal, the nature of the stored fat will be similar to that of the dietary fat. This may produce an undesirable fat from a commercial standpoint, for example, the fattening of hogs for market. Southern hogs that are fed cottonseed oil and peanut oil develop a soft storage fat that produces inferior bacon and hams. These hogs are often fed more saturated fats shortly before they are sold, in order to harden their storage fat.

OBESITY. Obesity is the condition in which excessive amounts of fat are stored in the fat depots. In a small percentage of cases, obesity is due to a disorder of certain endocrine glands, but as a general rule it results from eating more food than the body requires. Most of the food consumed by an adult is used to produce energy, and food in excess of that necessary to fulfill the energy requirements of the body is stored as fat. Thin people generally are more active than fat people, and are able to eat larger amounts of food without putting on weight.

Many people apparently eat all they want and yet maintain a fairly constant weight over long periods of time. This weight control may be due to the appetite, which is abnormally increased in people who are gaining weight and decreased in those who are losing weight. Many experiments have shown that the law of conservation of energy operates in this connection. A thin person can be made to gain weight by feeding him more food than he needs, whereas a fat person can lose weight by eating less than his energy requirements call for.

Oxidation of Fats

Since fats are converted into phospholipids for transportation in the blood stream, it is probable that the food or storage depot fat is presented to the tissues for oxidation in this form. The first step in the oxidation process is the hydrolysis of the phospholipid into glycerol and fatty acids. The glycerol is oxidized to glyceric aldehyde, which is an intermediate compound in carbohydrate metabolism, and thus enters the chain of reactions involved in the oxidation of carbohydrates. The fatty acids are oxidized to form carbon dioxide and water and a relatively large amount of energy. The oxidation of a gram of fat will produce more than twice the amount of energy obtained from the oxidation of a gram of carbohydrate or protein.

The intermediate steps in the oxidation of fatty acids in the tissues are not definitely known, although *Knoop's theory of beta-oxidation* is generally accepted as an explanation of the mechanisms. Knoop believed that the long-chain fatty acids were oxidized at the beta-carbon atom, forming a ketone group, after which the end two carbon atoms were split off, leaving a fatty acid with two less carbon atoms. It may be recalled that the a-carbon atom is next to the carboxyl group, thus the β-carbon atom would be next to the a-carbon atom. The oxidation of stearic acid to form palmitic acid may be illustrated as follows:

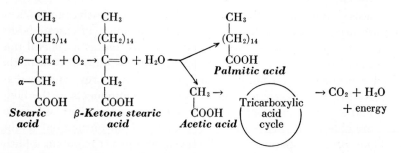

The palmitic acid may then be oxidized in a similar manner to form myristic acid (with 14 C atoms) and another molecule of acetic acid. The process of oxidation continues until butyric acid is formed. The butyric acid is oxidized to acetoacetic acid, acetic acid, then carbon dioxide and water as shown:

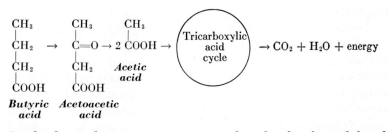

Butyric acid Acetoacetic acid Acetic acid

In the liver, the numerous acetic acid molecules formed by the process of β oxidation combine with coenzyme A to form acetyl coenzyme A. The acetyl coenzyme A molecules can combine to reform acetoacetic acid, which is then converted into acetone and β-hydroxybutyric acid. This process of fatty acid oxidation is called the *β-oxidation–acetic acid condensation theory* and is generally accepted as the mechanism for the formation of acetone bodies by the liver. The conversion of *acetoacetic acid* to *acetone* and *β-hydroxybutyric acid* is shown in the following scheme:

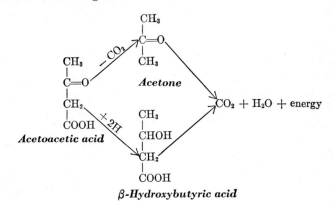

β-Hydroxybutyric acid

The above three compounds, acetoacetic and β-hydroxybutyric acids, and acetone, are known as the *acetone bodies*. For many years it was thought that the acetone bodies were products of abnormal metabolism, especially since they accumulated in the blood and were excreted in the urine in diabetes and in starvation. The modern viewpoint is that the acetone bodies are normally produced by the liver during metabolism of the fatty acids. The liver cannot oxidize them to CO_2, H_2O, and energy, but this process takes place in the muscle tissue. Under ordinary conditions when the body is metabolizing carbohydrates, fats, and proteins, the fatty acids and the acetone bodies that are formed are completely burned to CO_2, H_2O, and energy. During starvation when carbohydrates are lacking, or in diabetes when they are not properly utilized, the body must metabolize larger quantities of fats and proteins. Under these conditions the liver may produce more acetone bodies than the muscles can oxidize, thereby causing an accumulation in the blood and subsequent excretion in the urine. Acetone, being a volatile substance, may also be excreted by the lungs and is responsible for the fruity odor of the diabetic person's breath. The two acids neutralize the alkali of the blood and tissues and cause acidosis. Severe diabetes or prolonged starvation may result in the formation of such large quantities of these acids that the alkali reserve of the blood is lowered to a point where the patient goes into a coma from the acidosis. This *diabetic coma* is sometimes fatal.

It has long been agreed that carbohydrate can be converted into fat in the body. A brief discussion of the possible mechanism involved in this conversion was outlined in the last chapter. Conversion in the other direction, from fat to carbohydrate, has long been open to question. The glycerol portion of fat is closely related to the 3-carbon metabolites of carbohydrates, and there is no difficulty in portraying a reversible relation between glycerol and carbohydrates.

Fatty acids are oxidized in the liver to 4-carbon compounds such as acetoacetic acid and β-hydroxybutyric acid. These compounds are then carried by the blood stream to the extrahepatic tissues such as muscle tissue where they are oxidized to CO_2, H_2O, and energy. During this oxidation process in the extrahepatic tissues, acetic acid is formed. As described earlier, the 2-carbon compounds from acetoacetic acid form acetyl coenzyme A, and may thus enter the carbohydrate metabolism scheme through the tricarboxylic acid cycle to yield CO_2, H_2O, and energy.

Review Questions

1. How does the body bring the fat concentration of the blood back to normal after a meal containing fat?

2. Name four special lipids that must be synthesized from the fat in the diet.

3. Why is a certain amount of depot fat desirable in the body?

4. What method would you prescribe for a rapid reduction of excess body weight? What two principles are important in reducing?

5. Outline Knoop's theory of beta-oxidation.

6. Explain what is meant by the beta-oxidation—acetic acid condensation theory.

7. Why are acetone bodies often found in the urine of persons on drastic reducing diets?

8. What are the acetone bodies? Where are they formed?

9. Write an equation for the formation of acetone bodies from acetoacetic acid.

10. Why should an excess formation of acetone bodies result in a condition of acidosis?

11. Compare the fat metabolism of a normal individual with that of a diabetic patient.

12. Discuss the relationship of fat metabolism and carbohydrate metabolism.

Chapter 19

Protein Metabolism

Carbohydrate metabolism is concerned with the utilization of glucose while fat metabolism mainly involves the fate of triglycerides. The metabolism of proteins on the other hand is more complex, probably because of the wide variation in the chemical structure of the amino acids. In general, protein metabolism is concerned with the utilization of the individual amino acids. The nitrogen content of amino acids gives rise to pathways of metabolism not commonly encountered in carbohydrate or fat metabolism. Also, there are no storage depots for the amino acids that are absorbed into the blood stream after digestion as there are for carbohydrates and fats. The amino acids that enter the blood after a meal must therefore either be used to synthesize new body tissue or be oxidized to produce energy.

Utilization of Proteins

Amino acids from the protein of the diet or from the breakdown of tissue proteins are temporarily taken up by the tissues before being used by the body. From this pool of amino acids, the body draws its building stones for the construction of new tissue for growth, or for the synthesis of biologically active substances such as hormones and enzymes. Tissue proteins exist in a state of dynamic equilibrium similar to that of fat in the body's fat depots. Apparently there is a continuous exchange of amino acids between the tissue proteins and the temporarily stored amino acids (sometimes called the metabolic pool). For example, a tryptophan molecule may be released from a certain tissue protein and have its place taken by an amino acid from the metabolic pool. Since there are no facilities for permanent storage, the amino acids in the blood stream are always undergoing catabolism to yield energy and end products of protein metabolism.

The utilization of proteins may be represented as follows:

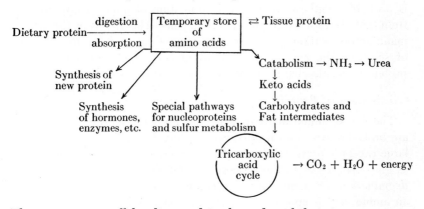

These processes will be discussed in the order of their importance to the body.

Synthesis of Protein

Growing children require large quantities of amino acids to build new tissue. The body apparently selects the proper assortment of amino acids from those temporarily stored in the tissues to construct the different proteins that are needed for the growth of various organs and muscle tissue.

The situation is somewhat different in adults. If they are neither gaining nor losing weight, the amino acids necessary for growth of new tissue are negligible. A small quantity of amino acids, however, is constantly required for the repair of body tissues. A wide assortment of amino acids from the diet and tissue protein exchange is used to form blood cells, hemoglobin, plasma proteins, and tissue fluids. The manufacture of these vital proteins probably requires a sizable quantity of amino acids, but they are nearly balanced by a similar quantity released when the blood cells, hemoglobin, or plasma proteins are broken down or used for food.

Synthesis of Hormones and Enzymes

The protein nature of enzymes is well accepted, and a supply of amino acids must be present for their synthesis. Several hormones are known to be protein in nature. Since hormones are synthesized in certain endocrine glands, a supply of amino acids must be made available to these glands. Insulin, the hormone made by the pancreas, is probably synthesized from a combination of amino acids different from that used for tissue protein or enzymes. The glands or tissues that manufacture certain hormones and enzymes must have the property of selecting the correct proportions of each amino acid to build a protein molecule characteristic of that gland or tissue.

Catabolism of Protein

The excess amino acids that are not used for synthesis of proteins are broken down to form urea, carbon dioxide, water, and energy. If a large excess is present, they may be converted into glucose and stored as glycogen or fat. In the process of catabolism, amino acids undergo *deamination.* Deamination is a reaction in which the amino group of an amino acid is split off, forming ammonia and a keto acid. An enzyme known as amino acid oxidase dehydrogenates the amino acids to the imino acids which then hydrolyze into the keto acid and ammonia. This process may be illustrated using the simple amino acid, alanine.

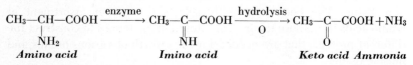

$$CH_3-\underset{\underset{NH_2}{|}}{CH}-COOH \xrightarrow{enzyme} CH_3-\underset{\underset{NH}{||}}{C}-COOH \xrightarrow[O]{hydrolysis} CH_3-\underset{\underset{O}{||}}{C}-COOH + NH_3$$

Amino acid   *Imino acid*   *Keto acid Ammonia*

The fate of the keto acid depends on the amino acid from which it is derived. In general the catabolism of each amino acid must be studied separately. Glycine is the simplest amino acid, yet it can be transformed metabolically to acetate, ethanolamine, aspartic acid, fatty acids, ribose, purines, and porphyrins. This amino acid may therefore play a role in carbohydrate, lipid, protein, nucleic acid, and hemoglobin metabolism. A complete discussion of the role of all amino acids in metabolism is beyond the scope of this book.

In addition to deamination another important type of reaction is involved in the interchange of amino acids between the metabolic pool and the body tissues and is known as *transamination.* The keto acids from deamination can react with excess amino acids to synthesize a new amino acid and a different keto acid. The dicarboxylic acids, aspartic and glutamic, are often involved in the transamination reactions. For example aspartic acid could react with pyruvic acid to produce alanine and oxalacetic acid.

FORMATION OF UREA. The ammonia, carbon dioxide, and water that result from the deamination and oxidation of the amino acids are combined to form urea. Urea formation takes place in the liver by a fairly complicated series of reactions. The NH_3 and CO_2 combine with the amino acid ornithine to form another amino acid—citrulline. Another molecule of NH_3 combines with citrulline to form the amino acid arginine which is then hydrolyzed by means of the enzyme arginase, present in the liver, to form urea and ornithine. The ornithine may enter the beginning of the cycle and combine with more NH_3 and CO_2 from protein catabolism. This so-called ornithine-citrulline-arginine cycle may be illustrated as follows:

$$
\begin{array}{cccccc}
& \text{NH}_2 & \text{NH}_2 & \text{NH}_2 & & \\
& | & | & | & & \\
& \text{C}=\text{O} & \text{C}=\text{NH} & \text{C}=\text{O} & & \\
& | & | & | & & \\
\text{NH}_2 & \text{NH} & \text{NH} & \text{NH}_2 & & \text{NH}_2 \\
| & | & | & | & & | \\
\text{CH}_2 & \text{CH}_2 & \text{CH}_2 & \textit{Urea} & & \text{CH}_2 \\
| \xrightarrow[\text{CO}_2]{\text{NH}_3} & | \xrightarrow{\text{NH}_3} & | \xrightarrow[\text{H}_2\text{O}]{\text{arginase}} & & + & | \\
\text{CH}_2 & \text{CH}_2 & \text{CH}_2 & & & \text{CH}_2 \\
| & | & | & & & | \\
\text{CH}_2 & \text{CH}_2 & \text{CH}_2 & & & \text{CH}_2 \\
| & | & | & & & | \\
\text{CHNH}_2 & \text{CHNH}_2 & \text{CHNH}_2 & & & \text{CHNH}_2 \\
| & | & | & & & | \\
\text{COOH} & \text{COOH} & \text{COOH} & & & \text{COOH} \\
\textit{Ornithine} & \textit{Citrulline} & \textit{Arginine} & & & \textit{Ornithine}
\end{array}
$$

As urea is formed in the liver, it is removed by the blood stream, carried to the kidneys and excreted in the urine. Urea is the main end product of protein catabolism and accounts for 80 to 90 per cent of the nitrogen that is excreted in the urine.

Nitrogen Balance

Since proteins are not stored in the body, an adult whose weight remains constant should excrete the same amount of nitrogen as is contained in his food. Any repair of tissues would merely represent an exchange of amino acids without appreciably affecting the intake or excretion of nitrogen. A person who excretes an amount of nitrogen in the urine, feces, and perspiration equal to that taken in as food is said to be in *nitrogen balance*.

A growing child will retain considerable quantities of nitrogen in the protein of newly formed body tissue. He will therefore excrete less nitrogen than is present in his diet; he is said to have a *positive nitrogen balance*. Any condition which results in the formation of new tissues in the body, such as recovery from a wasting illness or an extensive program of muscular development, will be characterized by a positive nitrogen balance.

When the nitrogen excretion is greater than the intake of nitrogen, the body is said to have a *negative nitrogen balance*. Starvation, prolonged fevers, malnutrition, and any wasting disease will produce a negative nitrogen balance. If a person continues on a negative nitrogen balance, the body tissues will eventually exhaust the protein available for energy production, and death will occur. Large amounts of sugar are often given to patients suffering from prolonged fevers to spare the protein tissue as much as possible.

Protein Minimum

Many investigators have attempted to determine the minimum amount of protein a person can eat and still maintain a nitrogen balance. From his extensive work in this field, Hinhede suggested that nitrogen balance could be maintained on an intake of 30 to 40 gm. of protein per day. If the protein of the diet contained the proper assortment of amino acids, as low as 15 gm. per day was sufficient. Modern nutritional workers recommend a daily intake of at least 60 gm. of protein to insure an adequate supply of the different amino acids required by the body. The average diet of today supplies 50 to 75 gm. of protein as compared to the higher protein intake (75 to 100 gm.) of a few years ago.

Essential Amino Acids

In order to synthesize such essential substances as tissue proteins, hormones, enzymes, bile salts, and hemoglobin, the body must have a complete assortment of amino acids. These amino acids may be supplied by the protein of the diet or may be synthesized by the body from other materials. A protein that is desirable from a nutritional standpoint should contain adequate amounts of the amino acids the body is unable to synthesize. Such protein is said to be *biologically complete*, or to have a high *biological value*.

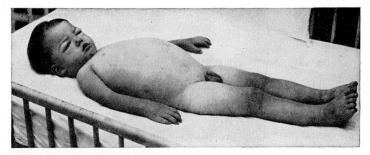

Figure 83. Edema in a child. This condition is attributed to a lowered level of serum albumin which may be caused by a protein deficiency in the diet. (Courtesy of Dr. P. C. Jeans.)

The amino acids that cannot be synthesized by the body and must therefore be supplied by the dietary protein are called *essential amino acids.* If an essential amino acid is lacking in the diet, the body is unable to synthesize tissue protein. If this condition occurs for any length of time, a negative nitrogen balance will exist and there will be a loss of weight, a lowered level of serum protein and a marked edema (Fig. 83). Extensive feeding experiments on laboratory rats have established the following amino acids as essential for growth:

Histidine	Isoleucine
Methionine	Leucine
Arginine	Lysine
Tryptophan	Valine
Threonine	Phenylalanine

In more recent studies on the amino acid requirements of man, it has been suggested that all of the above ten except histidine are essential to maintain nitrogen balance.

Many common dietary proteins are deficient in one or more of these essential amino acids. Gelatin, for example, lacks tryptophan and is therefore an *incomplete protein.* A person could eat a barrel of gelatin every day without building body tissues. Zein and gliadin, the prolamines of corn and wheat respectively, are deficient in lysine, while zein is also low in tryptophan. Although an incomplete protein will not support growth when it is the only protein in the diet, we seldom confine ourselves to the consumption of a single protein. In the ordinary mixed diet, several proteins are present, and each one acts as a supplement to the other. In fact, it would be rather difficult to plan an average diet that would be deficient in an essential amino acid.

Creatine and Creatinine

Creatine and creatinine are two nitrogen-containing compounds that are usually associated with protein metabolism in the body. *Creatine* is widely distributed in all tissues but is especially abundant in muscle tissue, where it is combined with phosphoric acid as *phosphocreatine.* In the contraction of muscles, phosphocreatine apparently plays an important role. The energy for the initial stages of muscular contraction probably comes from the hydrolysis of this compound to form creatine and phosphoric acid. These two substances are later combined during the recovery period of the muscle.

Creatinine is also present in the tissues but is found in much larger amounts in the urine. It is usually considered a waste product from the creatine of the tissues. The formulas for creatine and creatine phosphate and the relation of creatine to creatinine are shown below:

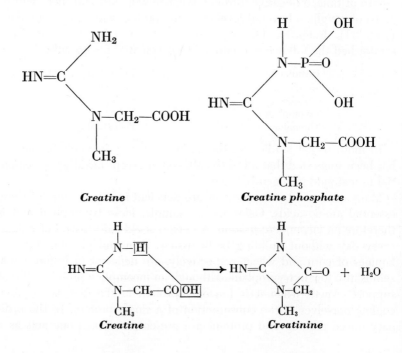

Sulfur Metabolism

The sulfur of the body is largely derived from the sulfur-containing amino acids, *cystine* and *methionine,* which are present in the proteins of food. Certain tissue proteins of the body, such as hair and fingernails, are rich in sulfur, containing from 10 to 15 per cent cystine. Taurocholic acid, a bile acid, contains sulfur, as does glutathione and vitamin B_1. The last two compounds are important in biological oxidation-reduction reactions.

When protein is catabolized in the body, the sulfur of cystine and methionine is converted into sulfates. This sulfur is known as *oxidized sulfur* and may be excreted in the form of *inorganic sulfates* or *ethereal sulfates* (organic). A small fraction of the sulfur is excreted without being oxidized and is called *neutral sulfur.* Cystine makes up the majority of the neutral sulfur. If abnormally large amounts of cystine are excreted in the urine, the condition is called *cystinuria.* An increase in the protein intake causes the excretion of more oxidized sulfur but has little effect on the neutral sulfur.

Nucleoprotein Metabolism

It has already been stated that nucleoproteins are constituents of nuclear tissue and are composed of a protein conjugated with nucleic acid. During the process of digestion, the protein is broken down to amino acids, and the nucleic acid is hydrolyzed by a series of enzymes to form purines, pyrimidines, phosphoric acid, and sugar. In metabolism, the amino acids and sugar follow the ordinary process of protein and carbohydrate utilization. The phosphoric acid is used to form other phosphorus compounds in the body or may be excreted in the urine as phosphates.

Purine Metabolism

Only the purines and pyrimidines follow a special course in metabolism. *Adenine* (the purine nucleus, with an amino group in position 6, more simply named 6-aminopurine [see p. 186]) and *guanine* (2-amino-6-oxypurine, or an amino group in position 2 and an oxygen connected by a double bond to position 6) are the two purines present in nucleic acid. These purines are deaminized and oxidized through

274 FUNDAMENTALS OF CHEMISTRY

a series of reactions to form *uric acid* (2,6,8-trioxypurine). These reactions may be illustrated as follows:

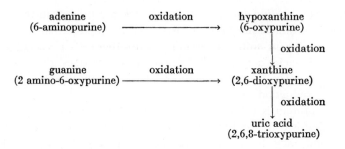

Mammals other than man and apes have an enzyme (uricase) which catalyzes the further oxidation of uric acid to *allantoin*. Uric acid, however, is the end product of purine metabolism in man and is excreted in the urine.

Little is known about the metabolism of pyrimidines except that they are probably changed to urea, which is excreted in the urine. There is ample evidence to suggest that both purines and pyrimidines may be synthesized in the body, even when they are not present in the diet. Since these substances are necessary in the formation of cells, this power of synthesis is extremely important. A growing baby lives on milk, which contains no purines, yet he is continually building new cells. A salmon travels miles up rivers to its spawning beds, with nothing to eat, yet it builds considerable nuclear material on the trip.

Correlation between Carbohydrate, Lipid, and Protein Metabolism

The correlation between carbohydrate and lipid metabolism has already been discussed. Since the catabolism of amino acids results in keto acids, such as pyruvic acid, it can readily be seen that these products could enter the metabolic scheme of the carbohydrates. The glycogenic or glucose-forming amino acids would also enter carbohydrate metabolism, while the ketogenic or ketone-body forming amino acids would enter the scheme of fat metabolism. The over-all correlation between the three major types of metabolism is represented in the following diagram:

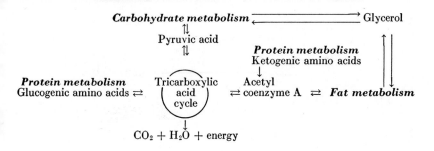

Review Questions

1. What main processes remove amino acids from the blood stream after a meal rich in protein?

2. Why is the synthesis of protein more important in the metabolism of a child than in that of an adult?

3. Write an equation to illustrate the catabolism of protein. How does the body utilize the end products of catabolism?

4. What essential difference exists between the end products of catabolism of proteins compared to those from carbohydrates or fats?

5. Outline with equations the formation of urea in the body.

6. Would it be possible for a person to be in nitrogen balance at one time, have a positive nitrogen balance at another, and a negative nitrogen balance at still another time? Explain.

7. Why is it inadvisable to feed growing children on a minimum amount of dietary protein?

8. Define the following terms: essential amino acid, complete protein, and incomplete protein.

9. Why are creatine and phosphocreatine important compounds in the body?

10. Name four important sulfur-containing compounds present in the body.

11. What happens to the sulfur of cystine and methionine when these substances undergo catabolism?

12. Why is purine metabolism an important aspect of nucleoprotein metabolism?

13. Outline the steps involved in the formation of uric acid in the body.

14. Plan a simple experiment to prove that purines and pyrimidines are synthesized in the body when they are not present in the diet.

15. Discuss the correlation between protein, carbohydrate, and lipid metabolism.

Chapter 20

The Blood

It has already been stated that the gastrointestinal tract is, in effect, outside of the body. The food molecules, after digestion and absorption, must be carried to the tissues and organs of the body before they can be utilized. Also, for effective correlation between the metabolism of carbohydrate, fat, and protein, the intermediate products involved must be transported to the proper sites in the body tissues for the chain of enzymatic reactions to be activated. Of most importance in this transportation is the blood, which receives valuable assistance from the *tissue fluid* and *lymph*. These circulatory systems carry nutrient material, enzymes, hormones, and other regulatory substances to all the tissues, and waste products to the organs of excretion. The blood moves within a closed system, and does not come in direct contact with the tissue cells; the tissue fluid surrounds all the tissues, while the lymph is carried by a system of vessels called the lymphatic system. The lymph and tissue fluid are collectively called the *interstitial fluid* and play an important role in the exchange of material between the blood and tissues.

Functions of the Blood

Some idea of the importance of blood to the body may be gained from a consideration of its major functions, which follow:

1. The blood transports nutrient material to the tissues and waste products of metabolism to the organs of excretion.

2. It functions in respiration by carrying oxygen to the tissues and carbon dioxide back to the lungs.

3. It distributes regulatory substances, such as hormones, vitamins, and certain enzymes, to the tissues in which they exert their action.

4. The blood contains white corpuscles, antitoxins, precipitins, and so on, which serve to protect the body against microorganisms.

5. It plays an important role in the maintenance of a fairly constant body temperature.

6. It aids in the maintenance of acid-base balance and water balance.

General Composition

Volume

Blood composes approximately 9 per cent, or one eleventh to one twelfth of the body weight. This means that a person weighing 120 pounds would have about 5 liters of blood. The loss of a small quantity of blood in bleeding or the donation of 500 cc. for transfusion or to the Red Cross does not cause adverse effects. The blood volume is rapidly regenerated after such loss, and the missing constituents are replaced in a reasonably short period. The volume of the blood decreases in hemorrhage, diarrhea, and vomiting, and increases in fever and pregnancy.

Formed Elements

The two major portions of blood are the formed elements and the plasma. When separated by centrifugation, the formed elements occupy from 40 to 45 per cent by volume of the blood. This fraction contains the red blood cells, white blood cells, and thrombocytes (platelets).

The red blood cells, or *erythrocytes*, contain the respiratory pigment hemoglobin and have several important functions. The number of red blood cells in men is approximately 5,000,000 per cubic millimeter, in women approximately 4,500,000. The determination of the number of red cells in the blood is often carried out in the laboratory since the value changes markedly in certain diseases. The red cell count is especially important in diagnosis and treatment of anemia, which is characterized by a lowered red cell count and a decrease in hemoglobin.

White blood cells, or *leukocytes*, are larger than red cells and have nuclei which red cells do not. Normally, there are from 5000 to 10,000 white cells per cubic millimeter of blood. There are several types of white blood cells, and they all function to combat infectious bacteria. In several diseases and especially in acute infections, the white cell count increases. Laboratory determinations of the number of white cells are therefore commonly used as diagnostic aids in such conditions as acute appendicitis.

Thrombocytes (platelets) are even smaller than red blood cells and do not contain a nucleus. There are from 250,000 to 400,000 thrombocytes per cubic millimeter in the blood of a normal person. Their major function is in the process of blood clotting, since they contain cephalin, a phospholipid involved in the early stages of clotting.

Serum and Plasma

When freshly drawn blood is allowed to stand, it clots and a pale yellow fluid soon separates from the clotted material. This fluid is called *serum* and is blood minus the formed elements and fibrinogen which is used in the clotting process. If, on the other hand, blood is centrifuged, the fluid portion that separates from the cells is called *plasma*. The plasma contains fibrinogen as well as other important proteins. From 55 to 60 per cent of the blood volume is plasma.

Plasma Proteins

The proteins of the plasma are present in a concentration of about 7 per cent. The most important of these are *albumin,* the *globulins,* and *fibrinogen.* Recently, the globulins have been separated into several fractions of different molecular size and properties by the modern technic of *electrophoresis,* as can be seen in the following table:

	PER CENT OF PLASMA PROTEINS
Albumin	60
Globulins	
alpha$_1$ (α_1)	5
alpha$_2$ (α_2)	9
beta (β)	11
gamma (γ)	10
Fibrinogen	5

The electrophoretic analysis of the plasma proteins (Fig. 84) is of great clinical interest since the proportion of the proteins varies considerably in certain diseases. For example, the changes in the protein components of plasma in multiple myeloma, cirrhosis or in nephrosis are so striking that the analysis may be used in diagnosis.

The plasma proteins have several functions in the body, of which the most essential is the maintenance of the effective osmotic pressure of the blood which controls the water balance of the body. The interchange of water between blood and tissue spaces depends on the plasma proteins, and a decrease, especially in albumin, will cause water to flow from the blood into the tissues, resulting in a condition of *edema*. The globulins contain the immunologically active antibodies against such diseases as diphtheria, influenza, mumps, and measles. These immune principles are especially concentrated in the *gamma globulin* fraction. *Fibrinogen* is an essential component in the blood clotting process. During the 1940's, methods of separating the proteins of the plasma were devised, and the clinical use of the fractions was studied. Two of the separated proteins, human serum albumin and gamma globulin, have already undergone considerable clinical trial. The concentrated serum albumin has been used in cases of shock, cirrhosis, nephrosis, extensive hemorrhage, and in edema, while gamma globulin has been used in the prevention and treatment of measles. Recently gamma globulin has also been used with some success in the treatment of *hypo-* or *agammaglobulinemia*. In this condition, patients exhibit a lack of gamma globulin in their plasma, and are subject to repeated infections that are not cured by antibiotics. Another fraction, fibrinogen, which is relatively easy to separate from the other plasma proteins, has been employed in the production of *fibrin films, fibrinogen plastics,* and *fibrin foam.* The films have been fabricated into sheets, threads, and tubes for use in surgery, whereas the foam finds extensive use as a hemostatic agent in surgery and neurosurgery. Severely burned areas of the skin have been protected by precipitating a fibrin film over the surface of the burn.

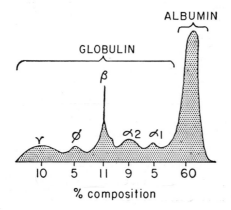

% composition

Figure 84. An electrophoretic pattern of plasma from a normal individual.

Blood Clotting

There have been many theories proposed to explain the complex mechanisms of the clotting of blood. Perhaps the most commonly accepted is the modern version of Howell's original theory, a rough approximation of which is shown below in outline form:

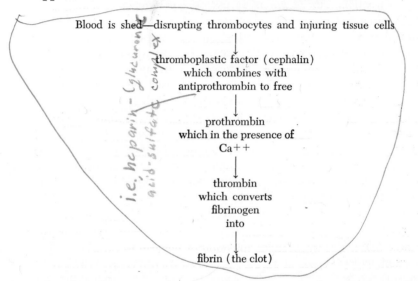

Blood is shed—disrupting thrombocytes and injuring tissue cells

↓

thromboplastic factor (cephalin)
which combines with
antiprothrombin to free

↓

prothrombin
which in the presence of
Ca++

↓

thrombin
which converts
fibrinogen
into

↓

fibrin (the clot)

i.e., heparin—(glucuron-acid-sulfate complex)

The thrombocytes and tissue cells contain a *thromboplastic factor* (probably a cephalin-protein complex) which effectively neutralizes the action of *antiprothrombin,* which normally prevents *prothrombin* from being converted into *thrombin.* Many other factors have been proposed as essential for the conversion of prothrombin to thrombin. For example, the reaction is accelerated by a substance present in the plasma called *accelerator globulin.* Other factors are *antihemophilia globulin,* which is lacking in patients with hemophilia, and possible factors in the thrombocytes. Prothrombin is released when thrombocytes and tissue cells are disrupted and reacts with Ca++ present in the blood to form thrombin. The thrombin acts as an enzyme to convert the *fibrinogen* of the plasma into *fibrin,* which is the clot. A common antiprothrombin is *heparin,* a glucuronic acid-sulfate complex which is formed in the liver and circulates in the blood.

Blood drawn from a normal person usually clots within five minutes.

The clotting time of blood flowing from an injury varies from about two to six minutes. In the disease known as hemophilia, the clotting time may be prolonged to forty or fifty minutes. This is obviously a serious situation, since a nosebleed, tooth extraction, or minor injury may threaten the life of a hemophilic person. The disease is hereditary, occurring only in males, although it is transmitted by females. All of the blood-clotting factors are present in normal amounts in hemophilia, but the thrombocytes are more resistant to disruption than those in normal blood. Also the conversion of prothrombin to thrombin is abnormally slow, suggesting a deficiency in the thromoplastic mechanism.

As can be seen from the outline of the clotting process, blood should not clot in the blood vessels. Nevertheless, intravascular clotting occurs occasionally, and such a clot is called a *thrombus*. For example, after an operation or injury to blood vessels or tissue, a local concentration of thromboplastin might occur, causing a clot within the vessel. If the thrombus clings to the blood vessel, it is gradually absorbed with no serious consequences. If, however, the thrombus breaks loose and is carried by the blood stream, it becomes an *embolus* and may cause paralysis or death if it obstructs certain vessels in the brain or heart. The intravenous injection of heparin to prevent *thrombosis* after certain types of surgery has been tried recently with promising results.

Anticoagulants

The simplest way to prevent drawn blood from clotting is to remove the calcium ions or repress their ionization. An oxalate removes the calcium by precipitation, whereas a citrate represses the ionization of calcium ions. When blood is drawn for analysis, oxalates are almost always used as the *anticoagulant*. Blood for transfusion is protected from clotting by citrates (Fig. 85), since oxalates are poisonous. A recent development in the preservation of blood for transfusions is the use of ion exchange resins for the removal of Ca^{++}. These resins are similar to those used in softening water, which were discussed earlier. Heparin is sometimes used as an anticoagulant since it acts as an antiprothrombin substance and prevents the formation of prothrombin. Blood-sucking leeches secrete a substance called *hirudin*, which acts as an antithrombin and prevents the conversion of fibrinogen to fibrin.

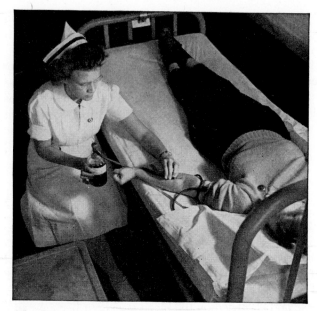

Figure 85. Citrates are used to prevent clotting when blood is drawn for transfusions.

Hemoglobin

Hemoglobin is a conjugated protein composed of the pigment *heme* and the protein *globin*, which is a histone. Heme is a complex molecule containing iron, four pyrrole groups, and hydrocarbon chains as shown below.

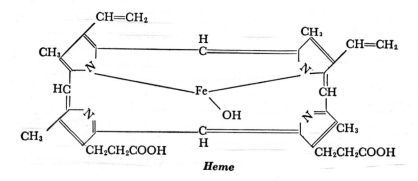

Heme

It has been determined that four heme molecules combine with one globin to form hemoglobin with a molecular weight of approximately 68,000. The point of attachment of the heme and globin is not certain, but the hemoglobin molecule may be represented as follows:

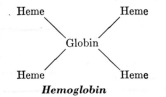

Hemoglobin

The normal concentration of hemoglobin in the blood varies from 14 to 16 gm. per 100 cc. This means that a 120-pound person would have a total of approximately 750 gm. of hemoglobin. Since the red blood cells which contain the pigment are constantly being broken down, there is a continuous degradation of hemoglobin into other pigments in the body, for example, *bilirubin* which is converted into pigments responsible for the characteristic color of bile, urine, and feces.

Hemoglobin is often called the *respiratory pigment* of the blood and has the property of combining with gases to form various derivatives. Most important of these is *oxyhemoglobin,* a combination of oxygen and hemoglobin.

$$\underset{\textit{Hemoglobin}}{Hb} + O_2 \ \rightleftarrows \ \underset{\textit{Oxyhemoglobin}}{HbO_2}$$

It can be seen from the equation that the reaction is reversible, a very important consideration in respiration since hemoglobin combines with oxygen in the lungs and carries it to the tissues where it gives up its oxygen to form hemoglobin again. Another derivative of oxygen and hemoglobin is *methemoglobin,* which is more stable than oxyhemoglobin, containing only one-half the oxygen in a form that is not readily given up to the tissues. Methemoglobin can be represented as HbO and is produced in the body by the action of certain drugs and poisons such as antipyrine, iodine, sulfa drugs, and nitrobenzene. Since it does not act as a respiratory pigment, its production in excessive amounts would cause respiratory difficulties. Another derivative, *sulfhemoglobin,* may be formed from the excess production of hydrogen sulfide in the intestine and possibly from an overdose of sulfa drugs.

Sulfhemoglobin formation interferes with normal respiration since the reaction is irreversible and binds the hemoglobin for the life of the red blood cell.

Carbon monoxide hemoglobin, HbCO, sometimes called carboxy-hemoglobin, is a combination of the colorless, odorless gas and hemoglobin. Since the affinity for *carbon monoxide* is over 200 times that for oxygen, hemoglobin will combine with small concentrations of carbon monoxide and accumulate in the blood. The compound is more stable than oxyhemoglobin; and if sufficiently large amounts are formed, death will occur from respiratory failure. Carbon monoxide is found in the gaseous products of combustion, as in automobile exhaust gas, furnace gases, and in illuminating gas. To illustrate the danger of breathing carbon monoxide gas, death may occur in five to ten minutes if illuminating gas is escaping in a small closed kitchen or if an automobile motor is kept running in a one-car garage without ventilation.

The recent technic of *paper electrophoresis,* in which the electrophoresis of a drop of whole blood or plasma may be carried out on a strip of special filter paper, has been applied to the separation of hemoglobin. At present, adult hemoglobin, fetal hemoglobin, and hemoglobin in sickle cell anemia are called hemoglobin a, f, and s, respectively. In addition, there are hemoglobins b, c, d, and e, which are present in various blood abnormalities. Under proper conditions, the various forms of hemoglobin exhibit different rates of migration in electrophoresis.

Anemia

There are many types of anemia, but they are all characterized by a decrease in the red cell count or in the concentration of hemoglobin. Primary, or *pernicious anemia,* is caused by a deficiency of the red blood cell producing mechanism in the bone marrow. In this disease, the erythrocytes are formed more slowly than they are destroyed, with a resultant decrease in red cell count and hemoglobin concentration. Considerable research has been directed at the problem of pernicious anemia and has resulted in a more satisfactory treatment of this disease. At present, pernicious anemia can be controlled by the ingestion of liver and stomach extract and the vitamin, folic acid.

Secondary anemia is caused by more indirect factors, such as loss of blood by hemorrhage, cancer, certain infections, and intestinal parasites. This type of anemia is readily cured by removing the cause. *Nutritional anemia* usually results from the lack of iron in the diet and may appear in severe malnutrition or protein deprivation. A diet containing adequate quantities of iron, proteins, and vitamins is used to treat nutritional anemia.

Respiration

By far the most important function of hemoglobin is in respiration, to help carry *oxygen* from the lungs to the tissues and *carbon dioxide* from the tissues to the lungs. The transportation of oxygen by the blood depends on the reversible reaction between hemoglobin and oxygen.

$$Hb \;+\; O_2 \;\rightleftarrows\; HbO_2$$

The oxygen capacity of the blood, about 1000 cc., is sufficient for normal tissue requirements. Some conception of the role of hemoglobin may be gained by a comparison of the oxygen capacity of plasma and whole blood. One liter of plasma can carry only 3 cc. of oxygen in solution. In the absence of hemoglobin, our circulatory system would have to contain over 300 liters of fluid to supply oxygen to the tissues. This would represent a system four to five times our body weight.

In the process of respiration, hemoglobin comes into contact with a relatively rich oxygen atmosphere in the alveoli of the lungs to form oxyhemoglobin. The oxyhemoglobin is carried by the arterial circulation to the tissues where a low oxygen concentration and high carbon dioxide concentration combine to release the oxygen to the tissues. The carbon dioxide is then carried back to the lungs for excretion and the cycle is repeated.

The complete detailed mechanism of respiration is very complicated; however, in view of its importance, the essential points will be outlined. Oxygen from the air is breathed into the alveoli of the lungs. Because of the difference in oxygen pressure in the alveoli and capillaries and because of the affinity of hemoglobin for oxygen, the gas passes into the red blood cells and combines with hemoglobin to form oxyhemoglobin. Before leaving the capillaries of the lungs, the oxyhemoglobin, which is an acid compound (represented as $HHbO_2$), reacts with bicarbonates to form carbonic acid and a basic form of oxyhemoglobin (represented as $KHbO_2$).

Lungs   Plasma   **Cell**   *Plasma   Lungs*

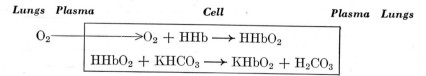

O_2 —————— $\rightarrow O_2$ + HHb $\longrightarrow$ HHbO$_2$

$HHbO_2 + KHCO_3 \longrightarrow KHbO_2 + H_2CO_3$

The oxyhemoglobin is then carried to the tissues where carbon dioxide is being formed as a result of tissue metabolism. The carbon dioxide diffuses into the red blood cell where the enzyme *carbonic anhydrase* catalyzes its combination with water to form carbonic acid. Because of the difference in oxygen pressure between the capillaries and the tissues, the oxyhemoglobin breaks into oxygen and hemoglobin and the gas diffuses into the tissues to be used in the oxidative reactions of metabolism. As the carbon dioxide continues to diffuse into the red cell from the tissues, it first forms more carbonic acid and then the carbonic acid is neutralized by the basic hemoglobin to form bicarbonates. As the bicarbonate concentration increases, it diffuses out of the cell into the plasma. The loss of negative ions from the cell is then balanced by a migration of chloride ions into the cell from the plasma to establish ionic or electrolyte equilibrium. This process is known as the *chloride shift*. In addition, some of the carbon dioxide that diffuses into the cell combines with hemoglobin to form *carbaminohemoglobin* as shown in the following reaction.

$$HbNH_2 + CO_2 \rightarrow HbNHCOOH$$
Hemoglobin   *Carbaminohemoglobin*

Thus the carbon dioxide, partly as carbonic acid, partly as carbaminohemoglobin and the rest as bicarbonates in the cells and plasma, is carried back to the lungs.

Tissue   Plasma   **Cell**   *Plasma   Tissue*

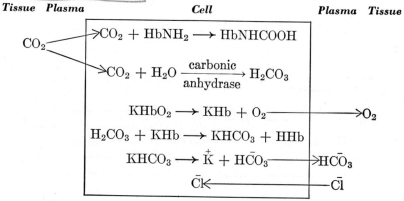

CO_2 $\rightarrow CO_2$ + HbNH$_2$ $\longrightarrow$ HbNHCOOH

$\rightarrow CO_2 + H_2O$ $\xrightarrow[\text{anhydrase}]{\text{carbonic}}$ H_2CO_3

$KHbO_2 \longrightarrow KHb + O_2$ ————— $\rightarrow O_2$

$H_2CO_3 + KHb \longrightarrow KHCO_3 + HHb$

$KHCO_3 \longrightarrow \overset{+}{K} + H\overset{-}{C}O_3$ ——— $\rightarrow HCO_3$

$\overset{-}{C}l$ ←————————— Cl

In the lungs, the carbaminohemoglobin releases its carbon dioxide which diffuses into the alveoli for excretion. The freed hemoglobin along with other hemoglobin that had given up its oxygen in the tissues then combines with oxygen from the alveoli as described previously. The oxyhemoglobin that is formed is an acid substance and reacts with bicarbonates to form carbonic acid. The carbonic acid is rapidly converted into carbon dioxide and water by the reversible enzyme, *carbonic anhydrase*. This carbon dioxide also diffuses into the alveoli for excretion. In addition to these reactions, the bicarbonate in the plasma diffuses into the cell to replace the bicarbonate that was converted into carbon dioxide, thus forming more of the gas for excretion by the reactions just discussed. To balance the loss of negative ions from the plasma, the chloride ions diffuse out of the cell into the plasma causing a chloride shift opposite in direction to that in the tissues. The carbon dioxide is thus carried to the lungs and excreted and the respiratory cycle is ready to be repeated. This cycle is often called the *isohydric cycle*, since oxygen is carried to the tissues, and the acid-forming substance, carbon dioxide, is carried to the lungs with little change in hydrogen ion concentration.

Lungs	Plasma	Cell	Plasma	Lungs

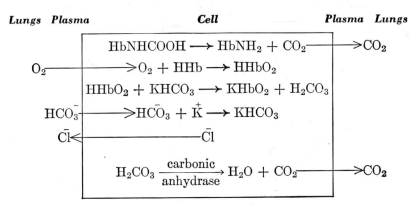

Acid-Base Balance

The pH of the blood is maintained slightly on the alkaline side of neutrality between 7.35 and 7.45. Since a change to a more acid or alkaline pH causes serious disturbances in the *acid-base balance* of the body, several factors combine to maintain the pH of the blood within these narrow limits. The reactions in the isohydric cycle, including the chloride shift and the formation of carbaminohemoglobin, are major factors in the maintenance of acid-base balance. The buffer systems in the plasma and cells are also important factors. *Buffers* are combinations of weak acids and their salts which are able to withstand additions of acid or alkali without appreciable change in *p*H. The following buffers operate to maintain the reaction of the blood. (H represents the acid salt and B the basic salt of a compound):

$$\frac{H_2CO_3}{BHCO_3} \qquad \frac{BH_2PO_4}{B_2HPO_4} \qquad \frac{HHb}{BHb} \qquad \frac{HHbO_2}{BHbO_2} \qquad \frac{H\ Protein}{B\ Protein}$$

To illustrate buffer action, let us assume that an excess of a strong base, NaOH, enters the blood. Using the important *carbonic acid-bicarbonate buffer,* the reaction would be as follows:

$$NaOH + H_2CO_3 \rightleftarrows NaHCO_3 + H_2O$$

The strong base would therefore be neutralized by being converted into a salt of a weak acid which in itself is part of the buffer system. If excessive quantities of NaHCO₃ were formed, it would be excreted by the kidney. Conversely, the presence of the strong acid, H₂SO₄, in the blood would result in the following reaction:

$$H_2SO_4 + 2NaHCO_3 \rightleftarrows 2H_2CO_3 + Na_2SO_4$$

The strong acid would be converted into a weak acid which is also part of the buffer system and is excreted as carbon dioxide in the lungs as described in the foregoing section on respiration. The ability of the combined buffer systems of the blood to neutralize acid is expressed as the *alkali reserve* of the blood. If an excess of acid causes the *p*H of the blood to drop below 7.35, a condition of *acidosis* exists; and the alkali reserve would be lower than normal. On the other hand, the opposite condition of *alkalosis* where the *p*H of the blood rises above 7.45 would result in an increase in alkali reserve. The carbonic acid-bicarbonate buffer system is an extremely effective blood buffer because of its intimate connection with the lungs and the process of respiration. In a patient, decreased respiration will result in an increased concentration of CO₂ and H₂CO₃ for use in the buffer system, while increased respiration will decrease the CO₂ and H₂CO₃, and therefore decrease the acidity of the buffer. *Respiratory control,* coupled with the action of this buffer in the blood, accounts for the rapid changes that are necessary to preserve the acid-base balance of the blood.

The *phosphate buffer* is composed of a mixture of an acid salt, NaH_2PO_4, and a basic salt, Na_2HPO_4. These salts buffer acid or alkali in a similar fashion to the carbonic acid and bicarbonate system. Any excess of acid or basic phosphate salt formed in the blood is rapidly excreted by the kidney. In fact, the pH of the urine is closely related to the phosphate buffer system of the blood since many of the acid or alkaline products of metabolism are excreted as phosphate salts.

The acid-base balance of the body is also aided by the ability of the kidney to produce ammonia. This ammonia combines with acid products of protein metabolism forming ammonium salts which are excreted by the kidney, enabling the body to save the sodium and potassium for the blood buffer systems. On a high protein diet or in conditions of acidosis the ammonia excretion increases, thus illustrating another mechanism that operates to maintain the constancy of the pH of the blood.

Changes in the Composition of the Blood

The major components of the blood have already been discussed, as well as some of the changes that occur in disease. *Blood analysis* is extremely important in clinical medicine, and laboratory findings are often used in diagnosis. A multitude of methods have been devised for the determination of the various constituents with emphasis on simplicity, speed, and the use of small samples of blood. The table on page 365 in the Appendix presents normal clinical biochemical values for several important blood constituents.

Review Questions

1. Outline the major functions of the blood.
2. What are the formed elements of the blood? Why are they important?
3. What is the difference between serum and plasma?
4. Briefly discuss the plasma proteins and their functions in the body.
5. Of what value is the technique of electrophoresis in diagnosis and treatment?
6. Why has gamma globulin recently received considerable publicity?
7. Outline a process for the clotting of blood.
8. What is hemophilia and what relation does it have to the clotting of blood?
9. How would you prevent a sample of blood from clotting? Name three anticoagulants.

10. What would be the approximate blood volume of a nurse who weighed 120 pounds? About how many grams of hemoglobin would be present in her blood?

11. Why is it dangerous to breathe carbon monoxide gas?

12. Briefly discuss three types of anemia, their cause, and treatment.

13. Write an equation for the reaction of hemoglobin and oxygen gas. Why is the reversibility of this reaction important?

14. What is carbonic anhydrase and what is its function in the blood?

15. In respiration, what happens to the oxygen that is taken in the lungs?

16. How is the carbon dioxide that is released in the tissues carried to the lungs?

17. What are buffers? How do they help maintain the acid-base balance of the body?

18. Explain the terms: alkali reserve, acidosis, and alkalosis.

19. In what way does the production of ammonia by the kidney help maintain the acid-base balance of the body?

20. Explain the association of the process of respiration with the carbonic acid-bicarbonate buffer.

Buffer system = resists change in pH upon addition of small amt. of either strong acid or strong base — include at least 1 weak electrolyte.

B.S. usually has basis on common ion effect

$$HC_2H_3O_2 + H_2O \rightleftharpoons H_3O^+ + C_2H_3O_2^-$$

adding $H_3O^+ + Cl^-$ (sol)
adding $Na^+ + C_2H_3O_2^-$ (sol)

common ion

adding either common ion will drive equation to left

common ion

Amphoteric buffers

$H_2PO_4^-$ } tends toward acid
both amphoteric
$HPO_4^=$ } tends toward basic

common buffer
$$HC_2H_3O_2 + H_2O \rightleftharpoons H_3O^+ + C_2H_3O_2^-$$
$$+$$
$$Na^+ + C_2H_3O_2^-$$

common buffer
$$NH_3 + H_2O \rightleftharpoons NH_4^+ + OH^-$$
$$^- + NH_4^+$$

Chapter 21

The Urine

The continuous processes of digestion, absorption, and metabolism result in changes in the concentration of nutrient material and waste products in the blood and body fluids. For most efficient operation of metabolic processes in the body, the constituents of the blood must remain within fairly narrow limits of concentration. The body tissues utilize the nutrients, while the waste products must be removed as they are formed. The kidney is the most important organ of excretion, and removes waste products of metabolism, toxic substances, excess water and inorganic salts, and excess acid or basic substances from the blood stream. The kidney, therefore, is essential to the maintenance of blood and tissue fluid volume, to the electrolyte and acid-base balance of the body, and to the maintenance of normal osmotic pressure relationships of the blood and body fluids.

Water, carbon dioxide, and other volatile substances are eliminated from the body by the lungs. The skin excretes small amounts of water, inorganic salts, nitrogenous material, and lipids. Some inorganic salts are eliminated by the intestine, and the liver is involved in the excretion of cholesterol, bile salts, and bile pigments. Compared to the kidney, the other organs of excretion play a minor role. This is especially true of the end products of protein metabolism, which are excreted almost exclusively by the kidney. A quantitative analysis of these nitrogenous constituents yields valuable information about the nutritional status of an individual.

The Formation of Urine

The kidney may be regarded as a filter through which the waste products of metabolism are passed to remove them from the blood. The blood enters the kidney by means of the renal arteries, which

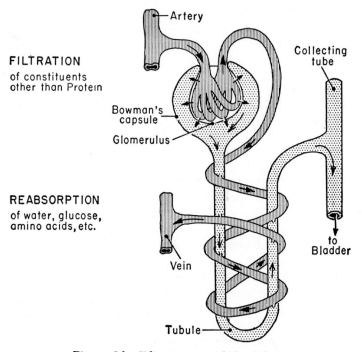

FILTRATION
of constituents
other than Protein

Bowman's
capsule

Glomerulus

REABSORPTION
of water, glucose,
amino acids, etc.

Artery

Collecting
tube

Vein

to
Bladder

Tubule

Figure 86. Filtration unit of the kidney.

break up into smaller branches leading to the small filtration units called *malpighian corpuscles.* Each human kidney contains approximately 4,000,000 to 5,000,000 of these units. A malpighian corpuscle consists of a mass of capillaries from the renal artery which form the *glomerulus.* The glomerulus is enclosed within a capsule called *Bowman's capsule* which opens into a long tubule. Several of these tubules are connected to larger *collecting tubules* which carry the urine to the bladder. These anatomical structures of the kidney are illustrated in Figure 86.

The most generally accepted theory for the formation of urine may be outlined as follows: As the blood passes through the glomerulus, the constituents other than protein filter through the capillary walls and enter the tubules. As this filtrate passes down the tubules, a large proportion of the water and any substances which are of value to the body, such as glucose, certain inorganic salts, and amino acids, are reabsorbed into the blood stream. These substances are called *threshold substances*. Waste products of metabolism, such as urea and uric acid, are not completely reabsorbed, and therefore pass into the collecting tubules for excretion. A few substances, such as creatinine and potassium, are partially removed from the blood through excretion by the tubules in addition to filtration by the glomerulus. It has been estimated that 67 liters of plasma filter through the glomeruli every day to form approximately 1 liter of urine. The other 66 liters are therefore reabsorbed from the tubules to reenter the blood stream. The importance of the reabsorption mechanism cannot be overestimated, because death would result from dehydration if this process failed to function.

The Collection of Urine

An accurate estimation of the quantity of a substance excreted in a day or a qualitative test for its presence in the urine is best carried out on a *twenty-four-hour specimen* of urine. This is due to the variation in urinary excretion at different times during the day, and the fact that some pathological constituents may be excreted only at certain periods of the day. A twenty-four-hour specimen is usually collected by discarding the urine from the first voiding of the morning, and saving all the urine that is passed during the day up to and including the first voiding of the following morning. The specimen is usually preserved by covering it with a thin layer of toluene. When the urine cannot be analyzed at once, it should be kept in a stoppered bottle in a cold place.

General Properties of Urine

Volume

A normal adult will excrete from 600 to 1600 cc. of urine in twenty-four hours. The volume is obviously influenced by the amount of liquids consumed and is decreased in hot weather or by severe muscular exercise. Men as a rule excrete more urine (1200 to 1600 cc. per day) than women (600 to 1200 cc.).

The volume of urine may be decreased below normal in conditions like fevers and diarrhea where excessive amounts of water are lost by other channels of excretion. This decrease in the urinary output is called *oliguria;* a total lack of urinary excretion is known as *anuria,* which is frequently associated with extensive kidney damage. Anuria may be caused by transfusion with the wrong type of blood or by poisoning with salts of heavy metals.

The urine volume may be increased to above normal, a condition known as *polyuria,* by the excessive intake of fluids, and may also be caused by certain diseases. Patients with diabetes mellitus and with nervous disorders show a fairly marked polyuria; however, *diabetes insipidus* is accompanied by an extreme polyuria with volumes ranging from 20 to 50 liters per day. Any substance that causes polyuria is called a *diuretic.* Caffeine is a good example of a diuretic that is widely used in medicine. The end products of protein metabolism, especially urea, are diuretics, which accounts for the increase in the volume of urine excreted by patients on high protein diets.

Color

Normal urine is yellow in color but may vary from a straw to a deep amber color. The chief pigment of normal urine is *urochrome,* a mixture of urobilinogen and urobilin. The amount of urochrome excreted per day is fairly constant, therefore the color of the urine is directly proportional to the volume. A twenty-four-hour specimen with a large volume has a light straw color compared to the brown color of a specimen with a low volume.

The color of the urine is often altered by the presence of abnormal constituents. Hemoglobin causes a brown to a red color when present in the urine. In cases of jaundice, the bile pigments that are excreted in the urine color it a greenish-brown. Brown or black urine may be due to the presence of phenols from carbolic acid poisoning.

Freshly voided urine is usually transparent; it may be turbid after a heavy meal due to the precipitation of calcium phosphate. Infections of the urinary tract are characterized by turbid urines due to the large increase in the number of pus cells present. When urine specimens are allowed to stand, the urine becomes alkaline and phosphates may precipitate.

Reaction

Normal urine is usually slightly acid in reaction, with a *p*H of 6. The acidity of urine is due to acid phosphates, sulfates, and organic acids. Protein foods increase the acidity of the urine because of the increased formation of phosphates and sulfates. The acidity is also increased in diabetes and in starvation, owing to the increased excretion of acetone bodies. Vegetables and fruits usually produce an alkaline urine because of the alkaline ash they form when they are oxidized in the body. The urine is often alkaline following a heavy meal. The formation of hydrochloric acid in the gastric juice is accompanied by an increase in the blood concentration of alkaline salts which are excreted in the urine. This temporary alkalinity of the urine is called *alkaline tide*.

Specific Gravity

The specific gravity of urine depends on its concentration of solid waste products. The lower the volume, the greater the concentration and the higher the specific gravity. The specific gravity of normal urine ranges from 1.008 to 1.030 (grams per cubic centimeter), with an average of about 1.018.

Normal Constituents of the Urine

Most of the normal constituents of the urine are affected by the diet and therefore change in amount from day to day. The average quantity of several important constituents excreted in twenty-four hours is given in the following table:

CONSTITUENT	GRAMS IN TWENTY-FOUR HOURS
Water	1200
Total solids	60
Urea	30
Uric acid	0.6
Creatinine	1.4
Chlorides as NaCl	12.0
Phosphates as PO_4	1.8
Total sulfur as SO_4	2.5
Ammonia	0.7

Organic Constituents

Three important organic constituents excreted in the urine are *urea, uric acid,* and *creatinine:*

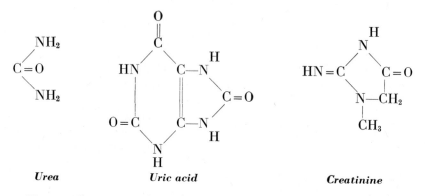

Urea **Uric acid** **Creatinine**

UREA. The principal nitrogen-containing constituent of the urine is urea, which accounts for 80 to 90 per cent of the total nitrogen excretion. The amount of urea excreted depends on the protein in the diet; a high protein intake increases, while a low protein intake decreases the urea output. The urea excretion is decreased in diseases of the liver and acidosis. It may be increased in fevers and diabetes (controlled with insulin).

Urea is usually determined by treating a urine sample with urease, an enzyme that breaks urea into ammonia and carbon dioxide. The ammonia that is formed is estimated by titration with a standard acid and the urea is calculated from this value. Recently colorimetric methods have been devised for the determination of urea which are more rapid and convenient than the enzyme method. Approximately 30 gm. of urea are excreted per day on a mixed diet.

URIC ACID. Uric acid is the end product of purine metabolism in man and is excreted as urates (salts of uric acid) in the urine. The daily excretion of uric acid amounts to about 0.6 gm. If the urine is strongly acidified, the urates will be converted to the very insoluble uric acid, which crystallizes out as red pigmented crystals. An increase in the nucleoproteins of the diet (such foods as liver, sweetbreads, and heart) or in the breakdown of nucleoproteins in the body will cause an increased urinary excretion of uric acid.

The uric acid excretion in man may be increased in conditions where excessive breakdown of nuclear tissue is occurring, as in leukemia and in recovery from pneumonia. The excretion may be decreased in nephritis, uremia, and gout. Gout is characterized by an increase of uric acid in the blood and by the deposition of uric acid or urates in the joints and tissues (Fig. 87). This painful condition was more frequent a few decades ago when larger quantities of meat were consumed.

CREATININE. The urinary excretion of creatinine, the anhydride of creatine, is relatively independent of the protein intake. From 1 to 1.7 gm. of creatinine are excreted per day; the amount is directly proportional to the muscular development of a person. The milligrams of creatinine excreted per day per kilogram of body weight is called the *creatinine coefficient*. In general, the higher the muscular development, the higher the creatinine coefficient. Men have a creatinine coefficient of about 24, women about 18, and children from 9 to 17. Muscularly underdeveloped or obese men may have a low coefficient (15 to 18), while women who are muscularly developed may have a coefficient as high as 24. The creatinine of the urine is thought to have its main origin in the creatine of the muscle. Since the daily urinary creatinine is rather constant in a person, other sources of creatinine must be relatively unimportant.

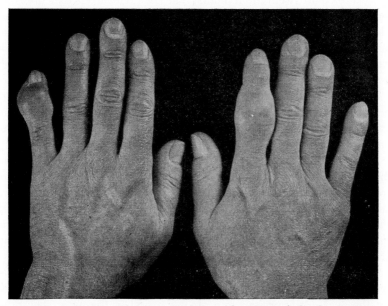

Figure 87. Deposition of urates (tophi) in the joints of the fingers in gout. (From Duncan, C. G.: Diseases of Metabolism.)

Creatine is normally excreted by children up to the age of puberty. It may also be present in the urine during menstruation and in the latter stages of pregnancy. It is not found in the urine of normal men. The pathological excretion of creatine, called creatinuria, occurs in conditions of abnormal carbohydrate metabolism, such as diabetes and starvation. Many diseases of the muscles in which the muscle cells are broken down give rise to the excretion of creatine in the urine. Muscular dystrophy, muscular atrophy, and myasthenia gravis are examples of such diseases. In diseases of the kidney that result in extensive breakdown of kidney cells, the uremia that develops is characterized by an increase in the amount of creatinine in the blood.

Inorganic Constituents

CHLORIDES. Of all the constituents of the urine, chlorides are second only to urea in the amount excreted. There are many inorganic salts in the urine, including the chlorides, phosphates, sulfates, and carbonates of sodium, potassium, ammonium, magnesium, and calcium. Of these, sodium chloride is the most abundant, with 10 to 15 gm. excreted in twenty-four hours. The average mixed diet does not contain sufficient sodium chloride to support life, so salt must be added in the preparation of food. Herbivorous animals are particularly dependent on a supply of salt outside of their diet. Wild animals travel miles to salt licks and will chew the handles of woodsmen's tools to obtain the salt from the perspiration that soaks into the wood.

The excretion of sodium chloride in the urine is decreased in fevers and severe muscular exercise. In certain types of nephritis, the concentration of sodium chloride in the blood and tissues causes more water to accumulate, and a condition of edema results.

PHOSPHATES. The urinary excretion of phosphates amounts to about 1.8 gm. in twenty-four hours. Several types of phosphates are present in the urine. The sodium, potassium, and ammonium salts are called *alkaline phosphates;* the calcium and magnesium salts, *earthy phosphates,* and those in organic combination are known as *organic phosphates.* Alkaline phosphates are the most abundant and make up two thirds of the total urinary phosphates.

The acidity of freshly voided urine is mainly due to the concentration of NaH_2PO_4. The basic salt, Na_2HPO_4, predominates in the blood, but the acid salt is present to a greater extent in the urine. The ratio between these two salts is important in the regulation of the pH of the blood and tissue fluids. The acid salt is formed if acid products in the blood are to be excreted by the kidney, whereas an excess of alkaline substances in the blood would result in the excretion of the basic salt.

The amount of phosphates excreted in the urine varies directly with the quantity of phosphorus-containing foods such as casein, nucleo-protein, and phospholipids in the diet. In diseases of the bone (rickets, osteomalacia) the phosphorus excretion is increased, whereas in con-ditions where bone is being formed (skeletal growth, pregnancy) the excretion is decreased.

SULFATES. As explained under protein metabolism, the end prod-ucts of sulfur metabolism exist in three forms, *inorganic sulfates, ethereal sulfates,* and *unoxidized* or *neutral sulfur.* These products are excreted in the urine, the daily excretion of total sulfur, expressed as SO_4, averaging about 2.5 gm. Over three fourths of the total sulfur is excreted in the form of inorganic sulfates. The sulfur in the urine originates from the sulfur-containing amino acids in the dietary pro-teins and therefore the quantity excreted is influenced by the nature of the diet.

During putrefaction of protein material in the large intestine, indole and skatole are formed. Small amounts of these substances are ab-sorbed into the blood stream and are detoxified in the liver. In this process, indole forms indoxyl potassium sulfate, which is known as *indican.* Indican is an ethereal sulfate that is excreted in the urine, and an increase in its excretion is an indication of abnormal putre-faction in the large intestine.

The neutral sulfur fraction consists mainly of incompletely oxidized sulfur compounds such as cystine, taurine, and sulfides. This fraction is not greatly affected by variation in the diet. In rare cases, large amounts of cystine may be excreted in the urine, a condition known as *cystinuria.*

AMMONIA. Approximately 0.7 gm. of ammonia is excreted in twenty-four hours. It is usually in combination with acids such as hydrochloric, sulfuric, and phosphoric. An increase in the excretion of urinary ammonia is caused by acid-forming foods such as meat and cereals, while it is decreased by base-forming foods like fruits and vegetables. The acidosis resulting from the increased production of acetone bodies in diabetes is accompanied by an increased excretion of ammonia. The acetoacetic and β-hydroxybutyric acids are neutralized by ammonia in the kidney before excretion, thus increasing the ammonia in the urine.

The kidney, therefore, has another valuable mechanism for the regulation of the acid-base balance of the body. When large amounts of acid products have to be excreted, the kidney forms ammonia from the urea of the blood to neutralize them. This protects the body from the loss of excessive amounts of sodium and potassium that are needed in the buffers of the blood.

Pathological Constituents of the Urine

Glucose

Normally the quantity of glucose in the urine is so small that it will not give a positive Benedict's test. Various conditions that cause glycosuria have already been outlined in the discussion of carbohydrate metabolism. Since routine examinations of urine always include a Benedict's test, it may be well to emphasize the conditions that cause glycosuria. In addition to diabetes mellitus, the most common causes for a positive Benedict's test on the urine are alimentary glycosuria, renal diabetes, and emotional glycosuria. If a urine specimen is collected by the patient several hours after a meal, the alimentary and emotional glycosuria and renal diabetes could be ruled out. If large amounts of glucose are present in the urine at this time, diabetes mellitus is strongly suspected.

A positive Benedict's test may be obtained on the urine from pregnant or nursing women, owing to the presence of lactose in the urine. If the sugar is lactose it may be differentiated from glucose by fermentation with yeast. The glucose would be removed from the urine by fermentation, while any lactose present would not be affected. Therefore, a positive Benedict's test after fermentation would indicate the presence of lactose in the urine.

Protein

Normal urine does not contain appreciable amounts of protein because the kidney prevents the passage of such large molecules through the glomeruli when urine is formed. In cases of kidney disease, or *nephritis*, protein escapes from the blood into the urine and causes a *proteinuria*. This condition is sometimes called *renal proteinuria* to distinguish it from *false proteinuria* which is due to protein entering the urine below the kidney as it passes through the urinary tract.

In routine examinations, the heat coagulation test is commonly used to determine the presence of protein in the urine. On heating the upper portion of the urine in a test tube, a cloudiness may result which is due to protein or a precipitate of phosphates. Acidification of the urine with dilute acetic acid will dissolve the phosphate precipitate but not the protein; therefore, if a precipitate remains after acidification, the urine contains protein.

Acetone Bodies

The acetone bodies (acetoacetic acid, β-hydroxybutyric acid, and acetone) are formed in the liver and oxidized in the muscle tissue. As discussed previously, in diabetes and in starvation, they accumulate in the blood and are excreted by the kidney. Before excretion, the two acid products must be neutralized and therefore deplete the body of its alkali reserve, causing an acidosis.

It has already been stated that the kidney has the power to form ammonia from the urea of the blood to combine with these acid compounds, thus sparing the sodium and potassium of the blood buffers. The excretion of acetone bodies is always accompanied by an increase in the output of urinary ammonia. Diabetes mellitus, fevers, prolonged starvation, and the feeding of ketogenic diets are some common causes of acetone body excretion in the urine.

Since the diabetic patient excretes acetone bodies in addition to glucose, a positive Benedict's test and a test for acetone bodies is a fairly certain indication of diabetes. All three of the acetone bodies are usually excreted together; therefore, a positive test for one of them is sufficient to prove their presence in the urine. Acetone is most commonly tested for in routine examinations. When a few drops of sodium nitroprusside are added to the urine specimen and the mixture is made alkaline, a wine-red color develops. This color may be caused by acetone or creatinine; however, if the solution is made acid with acetic acid, the color due to creatinine disappears but that due to acetone becomes more intense.

Bile

In cases of *jaundice,* which is usually caused by an obstruction of the bile duct, the blood contains bile. The bile is excreted by the kidney and imparts a greenish brown color to the urine. When the urine is shaken, the foam is colored yellow if bile is present.

Blood

The condition in which blood is present in the urine is called *hematuria* and results from a hemorrhage in the kidneys or in the urinary tract. Any condition which causes hemolysis of red blood cells in the body, such as scurvy, extensive burns, injection of hypotonic solutions, and purpura, is followed by the excretion of hemoglobin and is known as *hemoglobinuria.*

Appreciable amounts of fresh blood in the urine can be detected by the red color that is produced. Smaller quantities may be detected by adding a solution of benzidine followed by a few drops of hydrogen peroxide. If blood is present, a blue color develops.

Kidney Function Tests

Many tests have been devised to determine how effectively the kidneys function. Two of these tests will be discussed briefly.

Phenolsulfonephthalein Test

Phenolsulfonephthalein or *phenol red* is a nontoxic dye that is rapidly excreted by the kidneys after it is injected into the blood stream. Urine specimens are collected at intervals after the injection and the amount of the dye in the urine is determined colorimetrically. Normally functioning kidneys will excrete 50 to 75 per cent of the dye within two hours. This test for kidney function is perhaps the most widely used in clinics.

Urea Clearance Test

In the urea clearance test, a comparison is made between the concentration of urea in the blood and the rate of its excretion in the urine. By determining the urea in the blood and urine at intervals, the number of cubic centimeters of blood that is cleared of urea in a given time can be calculated. Normally the kidneys clear about 50 to 95 cc. of blood of urea in one minute. This value will be lower if the kidneys are diseased.

Review Questions

1. List several functions of the kidney.
2. Outline the essential processes in the formation of urine.
3. What is a malpighian corpuscle? A tubule? The glomerulus?
4. Why are threshold substances such as glucose and amino acids reabsorbed into the blood stream? What reason would you suggest for calling these substances threshold substances?
5. In an accurate examination of the urine why is it important to collect a twenty-four-hour specimen?
6. Differentiate between the following terms: oliguria, anuria, and polyuria. Which term would you associate with each of the following conditions: diabetes insipidus, nephritis, and diarrhea?
7. Why is caffeine often included in drugs and medications that are taken by mouth?
8. The color of a twenty-four-hour urine specimen is directly proportional to the volume. Explain why this statement is true.
9. Under what conditions would you expect an increase in the acidity of the urine? An alkaline urine?
10. How are the volume, the color, and the specific gravity of urine related to each other?
11. The creatinine coefficient of an athlete is usually higher than that of a businessman. Explain.
12. If a certain diet caused a definite increase in the amount of urea excreted in twenty-four hours, how would it probably affect the excretion of uric acid? Of creatinine? Of phosphates?
13. Why does a high protein diet increase the daily excretion of ammonia in the urine? Of sulfates?
14. In general, what effect would a vegetarian diet have on the excretion of the normal constituents of urine?
15. Name any four of the normal constituents of the urine. Discuss the origin of each of these constituents.
16. If a routine examination of a urine specimen revealed a positive Benedict's test how would you proceed to determine if the patient had diabetes mellitus? (Use only tests on urine.)
17. Pregnant or nursing women often excrete sugar in the urine. What is the nature of the sugar? Why is this sugar excreted at this particular time?
18. Why is albumin normally not present in the urine? Under what conditions may it be excreted?
19. If a urine specimen gave a positive test for the acetone bodies, under what conditions would you suspect diabetes mellitus? Under what conditions would you rule out diabetes mellitus?
20. A positive test for bile in the urine would probably indicate what condition? Why?
21. List four conditions in which blood would be present in the urine.
22. Of what value to the clinician is a kidney function test? What is the principle of such a test?

Chapter 22

Vitamins

In the early years of the twentieth century, nutritional research was still in its infancy. The essential food factors were thought to consist of carbohydrates, fats, proteins, and inorganic salts. Experimental diets composed of these purified food factors not only failed to produce growth in animals, but produced definite abnormal symptoms. When a natural food such as milk or yeast was added to the purified diet the symptoms cleared and the animals grew. These natural foods were thought to contain "accessory food factors" vital to adequate nutrition. We now recognize these accessory food factors as the *vitamins*, which are essential to proper nutrition.

Historical Development

What we now recognize as vitamin deficiency diseases have been observed for centuries, but very little progress has been made in their treatment until recent years. Records show that the Crusaders suffered from *scurvy*. This disease was widespread among sailors on early sailing vessels because of the lack of fresh foods. As early as 1720, citrus fruits were used as a cure for scurvy. The fact that all British ships were later required to carry stores of lime juice to prevent scurvy on long voyages led to the use of the terms, "limey" for sailors, "lime juicers" for ships, and "lime-house district" for the section of the town in which the sailors lived. Another disease that occurred, particularly among sailors on Japanese ships, was *beriberi*. In 1882, one of their medical officers found that beriberi could be prevented by including fruits, vegetables, barley, and meat in the sailors' diet.

In 1897, Eijkman, a Dutch physician working in the East Indies, proved that beriberi was due to a faulty diet instead of an infectious agent as many believed. He cured the disease in chickens by feeding an extract of the rice polishings, the rice bran that forms a coating around each kernel of rice. He was one of the first investigators to use experimental animals for vitamin studies, and thus paved the way for countless future experiments.

About 1911, Funk, a Polish chemist, claimed that the deficiency diseases scurvy and beriberi were caused by the absence of a definite chemical substance from the diet. He succeeded in isolating a crystalline substance from extracts of rice polishings that was very active in preventing and curing beriberi. Since this substance was an amine, he suggested that these essential chemical substances be called "vitamines," from vital amines.

A few years later, other investigators found that certain animal fats such as butter and cod liver oil were capable of promoting growth in young rats fed a purified diet. Since the amine that prevented beriberi was soluble in water and since this substance was soluble in fat, the existence of at least two accessory food factors was suggested. McCollum designated these substances as *fat-soluble A* and *water-soluble B*, respectively. About 1920, when a third factor was established that prevented and cured scurvy, it was suggested that the terminology of Funk and McCollum be combined. Since only water-soluble B was related to amines the letter "e" was dropped from vitamine and the letters were added to give the new terms, vitamin A, vitamin B, and vitamin C. The alphabet of vitamins increased as new factors were discovered.

At the present time, we have over sixteen factors that are included in the category of vitamins. These are commonly classified as either water-soluble or fat-soluble. Among the water-soluble vitamins are included thiamine (vitamin B_1), riboflavin (vitamin B_2), nicotinic acid, pyridoxine (vitamin B_6), pantothenic acid, choline, inositol, p-aminobenzoic acid, biotin (vitamin H), folic acid, vitamin B_{12}, and ascorbic acid (vitamin C), while the fat-soluble vitamins include vitamins A, D, E, and K. Many of these factors have been crystallized and their chemical nature determined. The modern trend, therefore, is to designate vitamins by their chemical names rather than by letters. The water-soluble and fat-soluble vitamins listed above are essential to our knowledge of nutrition and will be discussed in more detail.

Water-Soluble Vitamins

Vitamin B Complex

As has already been stated, the first vitamin to be recognized was water-soluble B, or vitamin B. Because this vitamin has been shown to consist of several dietary factors, it is now called the *vitamin B complex*. As new members of this group were discovered they were designated by subnumbers as B_1, B_2, B_3, etc. Other factors of the B complex were originally known as vitamin G and vitamin H. To overcome the confusion of nomenclature, we commonly call these

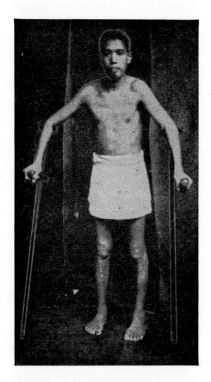

Figure 88. A typical case of beriberi showing the atrophy of arm and leg muscles and the characteristic posture. (From Bicknell, F. and Prescott, F.: The Vitamins in Medicine. New York, Grune & Stratton.)

vitamins by their chemical names, for example vitamin B_1 is thiamine, vitamin B_2 is riboflavin, and so on.

Thiamine

EFFECTS OF DEFICIENCY. Some of the early symptoms that develop on a thiamine-deficient diet are loss of appetite (anorexia), fatigue, loss of weight, and constipation due to decreased motility of the stomach and intestines. Administration of thiamine preparations causes a marked increase in appetite, and an improvement in the condition of constipation. Thiamine is a stimulant to the appetite only when the anorexia is due to lack of this vitamin.

As the deficiency progresses, a nervous disease called *polyneuritis* in animals and *beriberi* in man develops (Fig. 88). This disease, involving the peripheral nerves of the body, is first evidenced by cramps in the muscles, numbness of the extremities, and pain along the nerves. Later the nerves become very painful, and the muscles become paralyzed and atrophied from disuse. Edema, or swelling of the muscles in the arms and legs, and circulatory disturbances are common in advanced beriberi. The heart enlarges and finally death occurs from heart failure.

It has been generally accepted that thiamine is essential to normal oxidation of carbohydrates in the body. In the absence of this vitamin, pyruvic acid is not broken down and accumulates in the blood and tissues. The neuritis that commonly occurs with thiamine deficiency is thought to be due to the accumulation of pyruvic acid. Recently large doses of thiamine have been successfully used in the treatment of several cases of neuritis. *Alcoholic polyneuritis* commonly occurs in people who drink excessive amounts of alcohol. The food intake is diminished in such cases because the alcohol satisfies the appetite, therefore the thiamine intake is decreased and polyneuritis results. Pregnancy and lactation may be accompanied by neuritis, since the demand for the vitamin is high and the food intake may be restricted by nausea and vomiting.

CHEMICAL NATURE. The formula for thiamine was established in 1936, when it was synthesized. It consists of a pyrimidine ring and a sulfur-containing thiazole ring joined as shown on page 308.

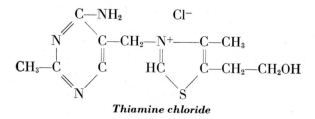

Thiamine chloride

The vitamin is soluble in water, dilute alcohol, and acids, and may be heated in an acid solution with little loss of potency. When heated in an alkaline solution, it rapidly loses its activity. Ordinary cooking procedures destroy 10 to 50 per cent of the thiamine. The loss of thiamine is greatly increased when sodium bicarbonate is added to preserve the color of green vegetables during cooking.

OCCURRENCE. Brewers' yeast, wheat germ, eggs, meat (pork), and whole grains are good sources of thiamine in foodstuffs. Milk, vegetables, and fruits are fair sources, while milled cereals such as white flour are very poor sources of the vitamin. At the present time, large quantities of synthetic thiamine are being used in the fortification of white flour and other commercial foods.

REQUIREMENTS. The daily requirement for thiamine depends somewhat on the type of diet consumed by a person. It has already been shown that thiamine is necessary for normal carbohydrate metabolism; it is also probably used in the catabolism of excess protein for the production of energy. A person who consumes a high carbohydrate and protein diet requires an abnormally large amount of this vitamin, while a high fat diet has a sparing action on thiamine. Since very little storage of thiamine occurs in the body, a thiamine-deficient diet will produce typical symptoms within ten to thirty days. When quantities of this vitamin are taken in excess of body needs, it is excreted in the urine.

The requirements of most people for this vitamin can be met by a daily intake of 1 to 2 mg. of thiamine. During pregnancy and lactation, this amount should be increased to 2 to 3 mg. per day.

Riboflavin

EFFECTS OF DEFICIENCY. Until recently, the need for riboflavin (vitamin B_2 or G) in human nutrition has not been definite. If this vitamin is lacking from the diet for long periods of time, characteristic symptoms occur. Among these are cracks and sores on the lips and in the corners of the mouth (Fig. 89). The eyes show dimness of vision, sensitivity to light, and inflammation of the cornea. Animals such as the rat, dog, chicken, and pig develop definite symptoms on riboflavin-deficient diets. For example, in rats such a diet causes loss of hair, failure to grow, and cataracts of the lenses of the eyes, while dogs exhibit loss of weight, vomiting, diarrhea, muscular weakness, and death. Riboflavin is an essential constituent of the yellow enzyme, which is necessary for the proper oxidation of carbohydrates and proteins in the tissue cells.

CHEMICAL NATURE. Riboflavin is an orange solid that is slightly soluble in water and alcohol, giving a greenish yellow fluorescent solution. It is composed of ribose (a pentose) and flavin (a pigment), as shown in the following formula. The vitamin is stable to acids and heat but is destroyed by light and alkalies. From 10 to 20 per cent of riboflavin in foods may be destroyed by cooking.

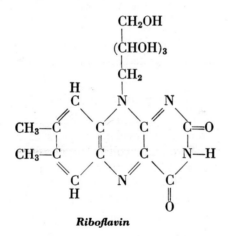

Riboflavin

OCCURRENCE. Riboflavin, closely related to thiamine, is found in many of the same sources. For example, brewers' yeast, liver, eggs, beef muscle, and leafy vegetables are good sources of this vitamin. Milled cereal products lose their riboflavin, and at present the trend is toward the fortification of white flour with riboflavin as well as with thiamine.

REQUIREMENTS. A daily intake of 2 to 3 mg. of riboflavin has been

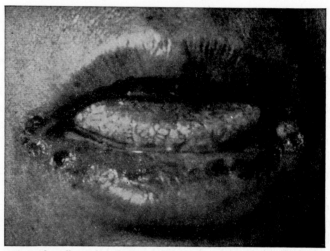

Figure 89. The effect of a riboflavin deficiency on the lips and tongue. (From Bicknell, F., and Prescott, F.: The Vitamins in Medicine. London, William Heinemann Medical Books, Ltd.)

recommended. Riboflavin can be stored to a limited extent, but excessive amounts are merely excreted in the urine.

Nicotinic Acid

EFFECTS OF DEFICIENCY.   Lack of nicotinic acid causes *pellagra* in man (Fig. 90) and blacktongue in dogs. Pellagra is a disease characterized by skin lesions that develop on parts of the body that are exposed to sunlight. Sore and swollen tongues, loss of appetite, diarrhea, nervous and mental disorders are typical symptoms of pellagra.

Nicotinic acid plays a role similar to riboflavin in oxidation-reduction reactions in the tissues. It is a constituent of an enzyme system that is essential in the oxidation of glucose in the body and in the fermentation of glucose by yeast.

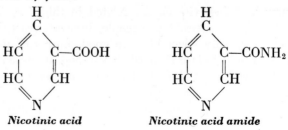

Nicotinic acid   Nicotinic acid amide

CHEMICAL NATURE. Nicotinic acid is a simple derivative of pyridine. It is soluble in water and dilute alcohol and is stable to acid, alkalies, heat, and light. The amide of nicotinic acid is also effective in the treatment of pellagra and is the form that is used clinically.

OCCURRENCE. Liver, lean meat, and yeast are good sources of nicotinic acid, while corn, molasses, and fat meat are very poor sources. Because the latter three foods are the major constituents of the diet of the poorer classes in the South, pellagra is prevalent throughout that region. Nicotinic acid as a chemical has been known for many years and is readily obtainable. The synthetic vitamin is used in large amounts to fortify white flour. The similarity of the terms nicotine and nicotinic acid caused laymen to call bread baked with fortified flour "tobacco bread." To overcome the commercial disadvantage of such a term, the name "niacin" was coined for nicotinic acid.

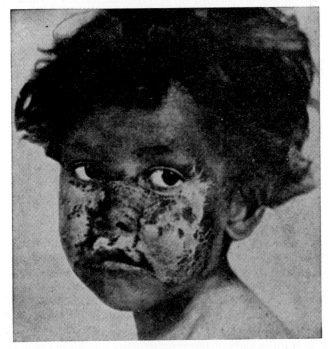

Figure 90. Pellagra in a child. Extensive pigmentation occurs on areas that are exposed to the light. (From Bicknell, F., and Prescott, F.: The Vitamins in Medicine. London, William Heinemann Medical Books, Ltd.)

REQUIREMENTS. The daily recommended requirement for humans is 10 to 20 mg. of nicotinic acid or nicotinic acid amide. While this vitamin is specific for pellagra, most cases of this disease require additional thiamine and riboflavin for a complete cure, because of a multiple deficiency.

Pyridoxine

EFFECTS OF DEFICIENCY. A deficiency of this vitamin in young rats results in a dermatitis characterized by swelling and edema of the ears, nose and paws. Dermatitis of this type, known as "acrodynia," is not cured with niacin. Pigs, cows, dogs, and monkeys show definite deficiency symptoms when their diet lacks pyridoxine. Similar deficiency symptoms have not as yet been observed in man although pyridoxine derivatives are known to be essential for coenzymes involved in amino acid metabolism.

CHEMICAL NATURE. This vitamin was originally called vitamin B_6, which is a general name for pyridoxine and two closely related compounds, pyridoxal and pyridoxamine.

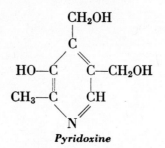

Pyridoxine

The pyridoxines, like nicotinic acid, are pyridine derivatives which are soluble in water and stable to heat when in a slightly acid solution.

OCCURRENCE. Pyridoxine is widely distributed in nature with yeast, eggs, liver, cereal, legumes, and milk representing good sources.

REQUIREMENTS. Although this vitamin is essential for many animals, little is known about the requirements for the human. The daily recommended dose is about 2 mg.

Pantothenic Acid

EFFECTS OF DEFICIENCY. Several animals exhibit deficiency symptoms when raised on a diet lacking pantothenic acid. Rats fail to grow, and develop dermatitis, graying of hair, and adrenal cortical failure. In recent dietary research on pantothenic acid deficiency in man, symptoms such as emotional instability, gastrointestinal tract discomfort, and a burning sensation in the feet and hands have been observed. This vitamin is an essential constituent of coenzyme A and is therefore involved in many metabolic processes.

CHEMICAL NATURE. The structural formula for pantothenic acid has been recently worked out and the compound has been synthesized. It is soluble in water and stable to heat in neutral solutions, but is really hydrolyzed by boiling in acid or alkali. The calcium salt of the vitamin is available commercially.

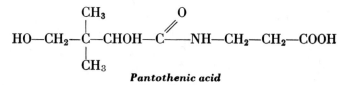

Pantothenic acid

OCCURRENCE. Pantothenic acid is so widespread in nature that it was named from the Greek "pantos," meaning "everywhere." Yeast, eggs, liver, kidney, and milk are good sources of the vitamin.

REQUIREMENTS. No specific requirement of pantothenic acid has been established for the human, but from 3 to 10 mg. a day has been recommended.

Choline

EFFECTS OF DEFICIENCY. A choline-deficient diet will cause an excessive accumulation of fat in the liver (fatty livers) and hemorrhage of the kidneys in young, rapidly growing rats. The fatty livers that develop in young rats and other animals on a choline-free diet may be due to the failure to form sufficient phospholipids for the transportation of fats in the body. Diets deficient in choline also affect the process of lactation in rats, stop hens from laying eggs, and cause lack of appetite in young dogs.

CHEMICAL NATURE. Choline is a strongly alkaline substance soluble in water and alcohol. It is readily available, having been synthesized long before it was known to act as a vitamin.

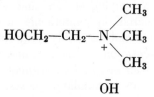

Choline

OCCURRENCE. Choline occurs as a constituent of lecithin in all living cells. Meats such as brain, liver, kidney, and sweetbreads are rich sources of this vitamin. There is no evidence at present that choline is required in human nutrition.

Inositol

EFFECTS OF DEFICIENCY. A synthetic diet containing all the known vitamins failed to support growth in young mice and caused a loss of hair. The administration of inositol cured both of these symptoms. The condition of "spectacled eyes" in rats is prevented by inositol in the diet.

CHEMICAL NATURE. Inositol is a white crystalline solid with the following composition:

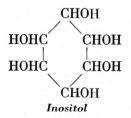

Inositol

OCCURRENCE. The best sources of inositol are muscle tissue, liver, brain, and kidneys. This vitamin has not been suggested as an essential constituent of the human dietary.

Para-aminobenzoic Acid

EFFECTS OF DEFICIENCY. A diet deficient in *p*-aminobenzoic acid retards the growth of young chickens, causes gray hair in black rats and mice, and prevents bacterial multiplication. There is some evidence that gray hair in man may be caused by the lack of vitamins, but experiments with both p-aminobenzoic and pantothenic acids have failed to yield promising results. It has been claimed that p-amino-benzoic acid is essential for the normal pigmentation of the skin.

CHEMICAL NATURE. This compound, known to chemists for many years, has a fairly simple structure. As yet no relationship has been found between p-aminobenzoic acid and human nutrition.

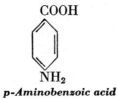

p-Aminobenzoic acid

Since the advent of sulfa drugs, it has been found that this vitamin interferes with the therapeutic action of sulfanilamide. These two compounds are very similar in structure and apparently both fit into an enzyme system in bacteria. Sulfanilamide and the other sulfa drugs stop the action of pathogenic bacteria when present in this enzyme system and are called *bacteriostatic agents.*

Biotin

EFFECTS OF DEFICIENCY. When rats are fed large quantities of raw egg white, they develop a dermatitis around the mouth and show a loss of hair. The addition of biotin to such diets prevents the occur-rence of these symptoms. None of these symptoms has been induced in rats on a biotin-deficient diet in which proteins other than raw egg white were fed, although there is some evidence that hamsters will exhibit characteristic symptoms on a similar diet. Biotin has been found essential for the normal growth of yeast, bacteria, and fungi.

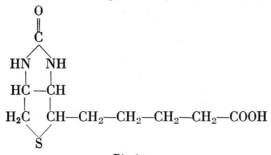

Biotin

CHEMICAL NATURE. Biotin is a sulfur-containing compound that is stable to heat and light and ordinary chemicals, but is hydrolyzed by strong acids or alkalies. The role of biotin in human nutrition has not been established at present.

Folic Acid

EFFECTS OF DEFICIENCY. A lack of this vitamin in the diets of young chickens and monkeys causes anemia and other blood disorders. The beneficial effects of folic acid in the treatment of anemia in animals led to a study of its effectiveness in various types of anemia in man. Recently, favorable clinical results have been reported after the use of this vitamin in *macrocytic anemias*, which are characterized by the presence of giant red corpuscles in the blood. This type of anemia may occur in sprue, pellagra, pregnancy, infancy, and in gastric and intestinal disorders.

CHEMICAL NATURE. The structural formula for folic acid has recently been reported and is a complex molecule consisting of three major parts. Since it is composed of a yellow pigment called a pteridine, *p*-aminobenzoic acid, and glutamic acid, the vitamin is often called *pteroylglutamic acid*.

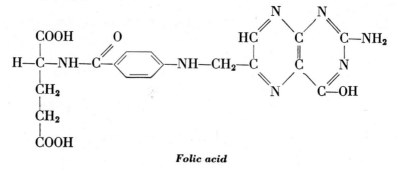

Folic acid

It is a yellow compound only slightly soluble in water and stable to heat in neutral or alkaline solutions but not in an acid solution.

OCCURRENCE. Folic acid occurs in many plant and animal tissues, especially in the foliage of plants, from which it was named. Yeast, soybeans, wheat, liver, kidney, and eggs are good sources of this vitamin.

REQUIREMENTS. No specific requirement of folic acid has been established for humans, although from 100 to 200 mg. per day is given in the treatment of macrocytic anemias.

Vitamin B_{12}

EFFECTS OF DEFICIENCY. This vitamin, like folic acid, is useful in the treatment of the anemias that develop in human beings and animals. Pernicious anemia in particular responds most readily to treatment with vitamin B_{12}. This vitamin is also closely related to the "animal protein factor" that is essential in growth and lactation. Both vitamin B_{12} and folic acid produce an increase in hemoglobin and red cell count while vitamin B_{12} also has a therapeutic effect on the nervous symptoms of anemia.

CHEMICAL NATURE. The exact chemical nature of this vitamin is not as yet known, although it contains a dimethylbenzimidazole group, a ribose phosphate, a derivative of propanolamine, and cobalt. The parent compound is called cobalamine, and is synthesized by microorganisms when cobalt is included in their nutrient medium.

OCCURRENCE. The best source of vitamin B_{12} is liver. Other sources include milk, beef extract, and culture media of microorganisms.

REQUIREMENTS. No specific requirements have been established for this vitamin in human beings. Extremely small quantities are effective therapeutically, and it has been estimated that 1 μg. per day would be sufficient.

Other Vitamins of the B Complex

There are many other factors that have been found essential for the growth of animals, yeasts, and bacteria but have not been definitely established in nutrition to the extent where they are included in the above group of vitamins.

OTHER WATER-SOLUBLE VITAMINS

Ascorbic Acid

EFFECTS OF DEFICIENCY. A deficiency of ascorbic acid (vitamin C) in the diet results in the disease known as *scurvy*. Early symptoms are loss of weight, anemia, and fatigue. As scurvy becomes more severe, the gums become swollen, bleed readily, and the teeth loosen. The bones become brittle and are easily broken. Hemorrhages develop under the skin and in the mucous membrane. In the later stages, the

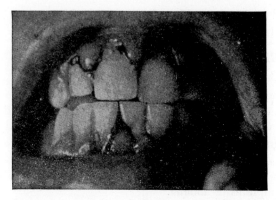

Figure 91. Gingivitis caused by a lack of ascorbic acid in the diet. (From Bicknell, F., and Prescott, F.: The Vitamins in Medicine. London, William Heinemann Medical Books, Ltd.)

teeth fall out, the joints become very painful, headaches and convulsions develop, and the patient may die in a delirium.

One of the essential functions of ascorbic acid is the formation and maintenance of the intercellular substance that cements the cells together. This *intercellular tissue* is particularly important in the capillary walls, cartilage, bones, and teeth. On a diet lacking ascorbic acid, the intercellular substance is lost and structural weakness of capillary walls, bones, and teeth develops (Fig. 91). Since the hemorrhage of small capillary blood vessels occurs early in the disease, capillary resistance tests are often used to detect the early stages of scurvy. These tests are carried out by increasing the intravascular pressure with a tourniquet and observing the skin for hemorrhage spots. Extreme scurvy is not commonly seen today, although many cases of subacute or latent scurvy are recognized. Symptoms such as sore receding gums, sores in the mouth, tendency to fatigue, lack of resistance to infections, defective teeth, and pains in the joints are indicative of subacute scurvy.

Man, monkeys, and guinea pigs are the only species that are known to be susceptible to the lack of ascorbic acid. Other animals apparently possess the ability to synthesize this vitamin.

CHEMICAL NATURE. Ascorbic acid, a simple compound with six carbon atoms, is an oxidation product of a hexose sugar.

The hydrogen atoms on the second and third carbon atoms (from the top) are readily removed by oxidation, forming a ketone called *dehydroascorbic* acid. This reaction is reversible and either compound may be formed from the other. Because of this oxidation-reduction relationship, ascorbic acid probably functions in oxidations and reductions in the body tissues.

Ascorbic acid is a strong reducing agent that is readily destroyed by heat in the presence of atmospheric oxygen. This oxidative destruction is accelerated in alkaline solution and by certain metals such as copper.

OCCURRENCE. The richest sources of vitamin C are paprika and citrus fruits such as lemons, oranges, and grapefruit. Tomatoes, raw cabbage, strawberries, and green leafy vegetables are good sources of this vitamin, while cereals, meats, eggs, and milk are poor sources.

A large percentage of the ascorbic acid in foods is destroyed or lost in cooking. Boiling for thirty minutes will destroy 70 to 90 per cent of the vitamin C content of cabbage and green vegetables. The addition of sodium bicarbonate to maintain the green color of vegetables further increases the loss.

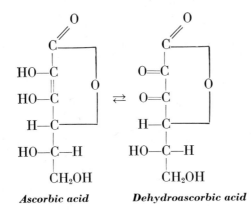

Ascorbic acid   *Dehydroascorbic acid*

REQUIREMENTS. In comparison with other vitamins, large amounts of ascorbic acid are required daily. It has been recommended that 70 to 80 mg. of this vitamin per day would constitute an adequate intake. This amount should be increased during pregnancy and lactation.

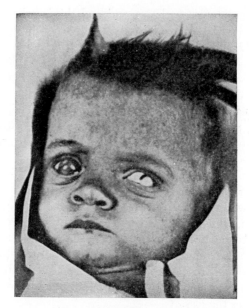

Figure 92.   Xerophthalmia in an infant. (From Marriot, W. K., and
Jeans, P. C.: Infant Nutrition. St. Louis, C. V. Mosby Company.)

The Fat-Soluble Vitamins

Vitamin A

EFFECTS OF DEFICIENCY.   A diet deficient in vitamin A will not
support growth, a fact which led to its discovery. The lack of this
vitamin causes other more specific symptoms; for example, it affects
the epithelial cells of the mucous membrane of the eye, the respiratory
tract, the digestive tract, and the genito-urinary tract. When the epithelial cells lose their ability to secrete normally, the mucous membrane hardens and dries up, a process known as *keratinization.* The
eye is first to show the effect of a deficiency and develops a disease
called *xerophthalmia* (Fig. 92). This disease is characterized by in-
flamed eyes and eyelids. The eyes finally become infected and when
this infection involves the cornea and lens, sight is permanently lost. A
continued deficiency of vitamin A results in extensive infection in the
respiratory tract, the digestive tract, and the urinary tract. This vitamin has often been called the *anti-infective* vitamin because it prevents infections that are caused by the drying of mucous membrane.

It should be emphasized that this vitamin is not anti-infective in the sense that it combats the infectious organisms, but because it maintains a healthy condition of the mucous membrane. Vitamin A deficiency also causes sterility since it affects the lining of the genital tract. It is therefore necessary for normal reproduction and lactation.

One of the first symptoms of the lack of vitamin A is *night blindness*. The retina of the eye contains a pigment called visual purple, a protein combined with vitamin A, responsible for vision in dim light. This pigment is bleached on exposure to light and is regenerated only slowly in the absence of this vitamin. The eye is therefore unable to adapt itself to rapid changes of light and the vision is impaired. Recent studies indicate that night blindness is more common than was formerly suspected.

CHEMICAL NATURE. Vitamin A is closely related to a group of pigments called carotenoids. The pigments occur widely in plants and includes the carotenes, which are responsible for the color of yellow corn, carrots and butter. Four of these pigments, alpha-, beta-, and gamma-carotene and cryptoxanthin, can be converted into vitamin A in the animal body. This vitamin is soluble in fat and fat solvents and is a liquid at room temperature. It has recently been synthesized.

Chemically it represents one half of the beta-carotene molecule ($C_{40}H_{56}$) with the end carbon oxidized to form a primary alcohol group.

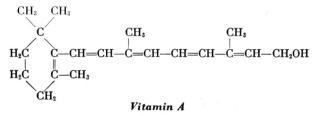

Vitamin A

Vitamin A is stable to heat, acids, and bases but not to oxidation. Thus, when fats become rancid through oxidation, the vitamin A content is destroyed. Ordinary methods of cooking do not appreciably reduce the vitamin A content of foods.

OCCURRENCE. Food sources of the vitamin consist of the four carotenoid pigments in plants and the free vitamin in animal products. No differentiation will be made between the two forms in this discussion. Fish liver oils are very potent sources of vitamin A. Eggs, liver, milk and dairy products, green vegetables, and tomatoes are good food sources of the vitamin.

The body has the ability to store vitamin A in the liver when it is present in the food in excess of the body requirements. Infants obtain a store of the vitamin in the first milk (colostrum) of the mother, which is 10 to 100 times as rich in vitamin A as ordinary milk.

REQUIREMENTS. The recommended daily requirement of vitamin A is approximately 5000 international units (3 mg. of beta-carotene). This value is increased to about 8000 international units a day during pregnancy. One to two teaspoons of cod liver oil would furnish the normal daily requirement of this vitamin.

Vitamin D

EFFECTS OF DEFICIENCY. The lack of vitamin D in the diet of infants and children results in an abnormal formation of the bones, a disease called *rickets;* therefore the vitamin is often known as the *antirachitic vitamin.* Calcium and phosphorus, the most important mineral elements present in bone, and vitamin D, are all involved in proper bone formation. In rickets, the bones are improperly calcified and are weak and soft. The weight of the body causes the legs to bow. The joints become enlarged and the ribs become beaded, forming the familiar "rachitic rosary" (Fig. 93), or they may become deformed, producing the condition known as "pigeon breast." This malformation of the chest combined with weak abdominal muscles causes a pot-bellied appearance.

Rickets does not occur in adults after bone formation is complete, although the condition of *osteomalacia* may occur in women after several pregnancies. In osteomalacia, the bones soften and abnormalities of the bony structure may occur. Vitamin D deficiency is also associated with poor tooth development. Since the composition of bones and teeth is similar, it is not surprising that a lack of this vitamin during formation of the permanent teeth will result in defective teeth. Tooth decay (dental caries) has been reduced considerably by the administration of sufficient vitamin D during childhood.

CHEMICAL NATURE. Several compounds with vitamin D activity exist, although only two of them commonly occur in antirachitic drugs and foods. These two compounds are produced by the irradiation of ergosterol and 7-dehydrocholesterol with ultraviolet light. Ergosterol is a sterol that occurs in yeast and molds, while 7-dehydrocholesterol is found in the skin of animals. Irradiated ergosterol is called *calciferol* or vitamin D_2; irradiated 7-dehydrocholesterol is called vitamin D_3. The structures of the two forms of vitamin D are very similar, as shown on pages 324 and 325.

OCCURRENCE. The fish liver oils are the most potent sources of vitamin D, while fish such as sardines, salmon, and herring are the richest food sources. Although eggs and butter contain appreciable quantities of the vitamin, the majority of foods are very low in vitamin D. For this reason, children are given additional amounts of this substance in their diet.

The ultraviolet rays in sunlight form vitamin D by irradiation of 7-dehydrocholesterol in the skin; thus children who play outdoors in the summer or are exposed to ultraviolet lamps materially increase the

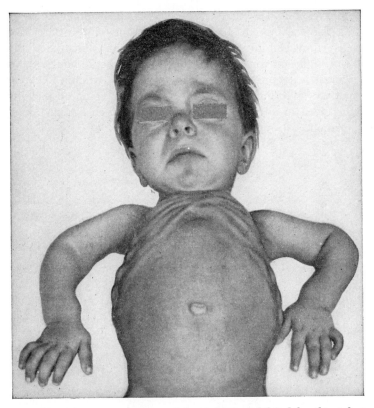

Figure 93. The pigeon breast and beaded ribs exhibited by this infant are characteristics of rickets. (Dept. of Pediatrics, University of Iowa Hospitals.)

vitamin D content of their bodies. If their diet contains sufficient calcium and phosphorus, bone formation will proceed normally. It should be emphasized that sunshine or vitamin D will not take the place of these two mineral elements in the diet. The main function of vitamin D in the body is to increase the utilization of calcium and phosphorus in the formation of bones and teeth.

Irradiation of foods is often used to increase their vitamin D content. Milk may be irradiated or a small amount of irradiated ergosterol may be added. Several products on the market today have their vitamin D content increased in this manner. In addition to fish liver oils, more potent sources of vitamin D such as calciferol, viosterol and drisdol (all three from irradiated ergosterol) and liver oil concentrates are on the market.

REQUIREMENTS. The daily requirements for vitamin D in young children may be met by 10 to 20 micrograms of the pure vitamin, which is equivalent to 400 to 800 international units. This amount should be sufficient for older children and adults, although the adult requirement is not agreed upon. This amount of vitamin D cannot be supplied by an ordinary diet so additional sources of the vitamin must be given to growing children and to women during pregnancy and lactation.

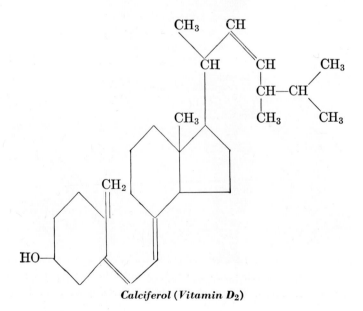

Calciferol (Vitamin D₂)

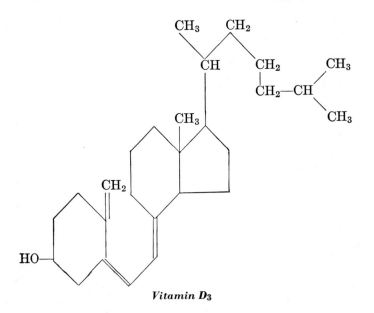

Vitamin D₃

Vitamin E

EFFECTS OF DEFICIENCY. A diet deficient in vitamin E produces sterility in animals. The male rat, for example, loses his ability to make spermatozoa, and continued lack of this vitamin results in permanent sterility. The female rat shows a normal ovulation and mating. The fetuses grow for about two weeks, at which time they die and are resorbed by the female. If sufficient vitamin E is given after resorption occurs, the female rat recovers and may give birth to a normal litter after another mating.

A lack of vitamin E results in the condition of *muscle dystrophy* in such animals as the rat, rabbit, dog, and hamster. Muscle dystrophy is characterized by degenerative changes in the muscle fibers, resulting in paralysis. The administration of vitamin E will cure the condition in its early stage.

CHEMICAL NATURE. Vitamin E is related to a group of compounds called tocopherols. At least three, alpha-, beta-, and gamma-tocopherol, have vitamin E activity. Alpha-tocopherol is the most potent and has recently been synthesized. Vitamin E is stable to heat but is destroyed by oxidizing agents and ultraviolet light. Oxidative rancidity of fats rapidly destroys the vitamin potency.

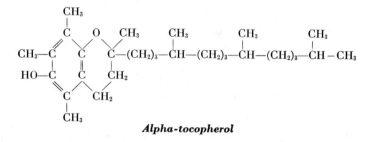

Alpha-tocopherol

OCCURRENCE. The richest source of vitamin E is wheat germ oil. Other plant oils such as corn oil and cottonseed oil contain appreciable quantities of the vitamin. Green leafy vegetables, egg yolk, and meat are good sources of this substance.

DEFICIENCY OF VITAMIN E IN HUMANS. As yet evidence is not conclusive that vitamin E is required in human nutrition. Large doses of this vitamin in the form of wheat germ oil have been administered to women in an attempt to prevent habitual abortion. While the clinical evidence is meager, it is doubtful that habitual abortion is due to a dietary deficiency in view of the widespread distribution of vitamin E in nature.

Vitamin K

EFFECTS OF DEFICIENCY. A diet lacking in vitamin K will cause an increase in the clotting time of the blood. This condition leads to the occurrence of hemorrhages under the skin and in the muscles. The abnormality in the clotting mechanism is due to a reduction in the formation of *prothrombin*, one of the factors in the normal process.

In man, obstructive jaundice reduces the prothrombin level of the blood because vitamin K cannot be properly absorbed from the intestine in the absence of bile. In these cases, post-operative hemorrhage is frequent, but it can be controlled if vitamin K and bile are given for several days before the operation. Other intestinal conditions that are accompanied by a low prothrombin level in the blood may be benefited by the administration of this vitamin.

Hemorrhages of newborn babies often result from injuries at birth, since the prothrombin level of infant blood is usually low (Fig. 94). These hemorrhages have been controlled by giving vitamin K to the baby, or to the mother prior to childbirth.

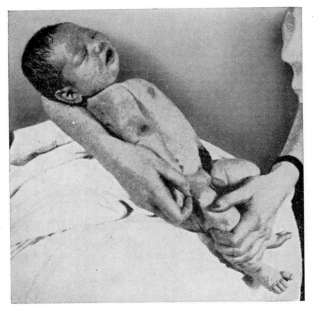

Figure 94. Hemorrhage in a three-day-old infant caused by the lack of vita-min K. The right arm and shoulder and the umbilical cord show evidence of hemorrhage. (From Bicknell, F., and Prescott, F.: The Vitamins in Medicine. London, William Heinemann Medical Books, Ltd.)

CHEMICAL NATURE. Vitamin K, a derivative of 1,4-naphthoquinone, exists in at least two active forms. Vitamin K_1 is represented as shown below:

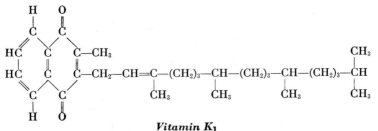

Vitamin K_1

Vitamin K is a fat-soluble substance and therefore is soluble in the ordinary fat solvents. It is stable to heat but is destroyed by alkalies, acids, oxidizing agents, and light.

OCCURRENCE. Rich sources of vitamin K are alfalfa, spinach, cabbage, and kale. The bacteria present in putrefying fish meal are capable of synthesizing vitamin K and are potent sources of this vitamin.

Summary of Important Vitamins in Human Nutrition

VITAMIN	MAIN DEFICIENCY SYMPTOMS	FUNCTION IN THE BODY	AVERAGE DAILY REQUIRE- MENT	GOOD SOURCES
B₁, thiamine	Beriberi	Oxidation of carbohydrates	1–2 mg.	Yeast and wheat bran
B₂, riboflavin	Cracked, sore lips, impaired vision	Oxidation in the tissues	2–3 mg.	Yeast and liver
Nicotinic acid	Pellagra	Oxidation in the tissues	10–20 mg.	Liver, meat and yeast
C, ascorbic acid	Scurvy	Maintenance of intercellular tissue	70–80 mg.	Citrus fruits, tomatoes and cabbage
A, carotenes	Xerophthalmia, night blindness	Maintenance of normal epithe- lial cells	5000 I.U. 3 mg. beta- carotene	Fish liver oils and green vegetables
D, calciferol	Rickets	Regulates calci- um and phos- phorus me- tabolism	400–800 I.U. 10–20 μg. calciferol	Fish liver oils and fish
E, alpha-to- copherol	Sterility, muscle dystrophy (in animals)	Essential for normal muscle metabolism	Not known	Wheat germ oil and leafy vegetables
K	Increased clotting time of blood	Production of prothrombin	Not known	Alfalfa, spinach, and kale

Review Questions

1. What two dietary deficiency diseases were known long before modern vitamin studies began? How were these diseases treated?
2. Who initiated the use of experimental animals in vitamin studies? What vitamin was he working with?

3. Why were vitamins originally called vitamines? What caused the "e" to be omitted from the name?

4. Why is the modern trend to designate vitamins by their chemical names rather than by letters?

5. List the important water-soluble vitamins. Which of these belong in the vitamin B complex?

6. Name several of the main symptoms that develop on a diet deficient in thiamine. What disease is associated with a lack of thiamine in the diet of man?

7. Why is thiamine frequently of value in the treatment of neuritis?

8. Name three dietary sources of thiamine. What is the average daily requirement for this vitamin?

9. What observations would lead you to conclude that a person lacked riboflavin in his diet?

10. Why is riboflavin sometimes used in the fortification of white flour?

11. Why is pellagra more prevalent in the South than in the North?

12. What steps have been taken to prevent pellagra in the United States? What is niacin?

13. Solutions of pantothenic acid are sold for the prevention of gray hair. If you were to prepare a remedy for the loss of hair and the graying of hair what vitamins would you include in your preparation?

14. Of what importance is vitamin B_{12}? How does it differ chemically from all other vitamins?

15. What are some of the symptoms of subacute scurvy? What common type of diet may produce subacute scurvy?

16. How does ascorbic acid function in the body?

17. Why is the modern trend toward cooking vegetables in as short a time as possible?

18. How would you characterize the disease called xerophthalmia?

19. Why is it misleading to advertise vitamin A as the anti-infective vitamin?

20. What is night blindness? This condition has been cured by the ingestion of large amounts of carrot juice. What source would be more convenient and more concentrated?

21. How are young babies protected against vitamin A deficiency?

22. Why is vitamin D known as the antirachitic vitamin?

23. What are the factors involved in the proper formation of bones and teeth?

24. Why is it unnecessary to feed cod liver oil to children in the summer time?

25. Why are children and pregnant women often given extra sources of vitamin D?

26. Vitamin E is often called the antisterility vitamin. What is the reason for such a term?

27. Recently several cases of muscle dystrophy in children have been attributed to the lack of vitamin E in the diet. How would you treat these cases?

28. What conditions are benefited by the administration of vitamin K?

29. How does vitamin K function in the body?

30. Make a list of the vitamins that are required by man and give the average daily requirement for each vitamin.

Chapter 23

Nutrition

Recently a symposium was held on the subject, "The Nutritional Ages of Man." Qualified research workers presented material on the nutritional problems, requirements, and status of infants, adolescents, adults, and the aged. In the past fifty years, the science of nutrition has advanced considerably beyond "three square meals a day" and the requirement for carbohydrates, fats, proteins, and inorganic salts. The many factors that are required in a proper diet will be the subject of this chapter.

Carbohydrate Requirement

Carbohydrates are not essential dietary constituents, because they may be formed from certain amino acids and from the glycerol portion of fats. They furnish the major source of energy in the average diet, however, and add to the variety and palatability of the food. It has been estimated that over one half of the energy supplied by the diet is due to the carbohydrates in the food. The cellulose portion of many fruits and vegetables is indigestible and makes up the bulk of the material in the large intestine after absorption has occurred. This roughage is essential for the prevention of constipation.

Lipid Requirement

As yet, there is no definite evidence that lipids are required in the human dietary. It is reasonable to assume that on a lipid-free diet, the body would be unable to synthesize essential lipids such as lecithin, cephalin, sphingomyelin, and the cerebrosides. White rats, for example, on a lipid-free diet cease to grow, develop a dermatitis, and a characteristic scaly tail, and finally die. These symptoms may be prevented or alleviated by the presence of certain unsaturated fatty acids.

These unsaturated fatty acids, called *essential fatty acids*, consist mainly of linoleic, linolenic, and arachidonic acids. White rats also require choline for normal nutrition and develop fatty livers when it is absent from the diet. Since choline is a constituent of the phospholipid lecithin, which is widely distributed in dietary fats, a choline deficiency in the human has not been recognized.

Recently there has been considerable interest in the nature of the fat in the diet. The combination of lipids with certain plasma proteins, called lipoproteins, has been assigned several important functions in the body. Changes in the concentration of the lipoproteins and of cholesterol in the plasma have been associated with such diseases as atherosclerosis. Since atherosclerosis is more prevalent in older persons, the lipid components of their diet have received intensive study. Fats and oils rich in unsaturated fatty acids apparently reduce the lipoprotein and cholesterol concentration when added to the diet.

Lipids supply more than twice as much energy per gram as carbohydrates or protein. About one third of the calories of an adequate diet are supplied by lipids. From a practical standpoint, fats are the most economical source of energy, whereas proteins are the most expensive.

Protein Requirement

Sufficient protein is required in the diet to provide adequate amounts of the essential amino acids for the growth of new tissue, the repair of old tissue, and the synthesis of hormones, enzymes, pigments, and similar substances. Growing children require more protein than adults because they are continually forming new body tissue from the available amino acids.

Dietary proteins vary considerably in their content of the essential amino acids and may therefore be classed as adequate or inadequate. Plant proteins usually lack sufficient amounts of certain of the essential amino acids and as a general rule are more *inadequate proteins* than those from animal tissues. *Adequate proteins* are found in such animal products as eggs, milk, liver, and kidney, while the plant proteins present in cereals, vegetables, and legumes are termed inadequate. On a mixed diet, it is safe to include from 70 to 90 gm. of protein per day for an adult. Children require more protein and are usually fed 2 to 2.5 gm. of protein per kilogram of body weight compared to the value of slightly more than 1 gm. per kilogram for adults.

General Dietary Requirements

According to nutritional authorities, the following dietary plan will provide an adequate diet for the majority of people:

TYPE OF FOOD	RECOMMENDED CONSUMPTION
Eggs	One or two per day.
Milk	One pint or more daily for adults; one quart daily for children.
Meat	One serving per day. Liver and fish at least once a week.
Vegetables	Potatoes and two cooked vegetables daily. Yellow leafy and green vegetables, cooked or raw, should be eaten frequently.
Fruits	One or more servings daily, cooked or raw. Citrus fruits once a day, if possible.
Remainder of diet	Selected according to taste. Will usually contain a large amount of cereals, breads, fats, and a moderate amount of sweets.
Vitamin D source	Children should be exposed to sunshine or be given fish liver oils, vitamin D concentrates, or vitamin D milk.

Energy Requirements

The body requires relatively large amounts of energy to maintain a constant temperature, to carry out processes of digestion, and metabolism, and other processes involving muscular movement. This energy is obtained from the oxidation of foodstuffs and is measured in large calories. The large calorie (Cal.) is the amount of heat energy required to raise the temperature of 1 liter of water 1 degree centigrade (from 15° to 16° C.). When burned in the body the major foodstuffs yield the following calorific values:

	CAL./GM.
Carbohydrates	4
Lipids	9
Proteins	4

The transformation of the potential energy of the food into muscular contractions and other forms of kinetic energy by the body is a relatively efficient process. About 20 per cent of our food may be converted into energy of motion; while the remaining 80 per cent is liberated as heat. There are several factors which contribute to the total energy requirement or heat production of the body. The most important of these are the heat derived from the metabolism of the body at rest, the energy required for work or exercise and that due to the specific dynamic action of food.

The minimum amount of energy required by the body at rest, when no digestion or muscular movement is occurring, is called the basal energy requirement or, more often, the *basal metabolism.* It has been found that the energy production of the body is more closely related to the surface area of the body than to the weight. For convenience, the basal requirement is referred to as the *basal metabolic rate* (BMR), which is the number of large calories eliminated from each square meter of body surface in one hour under the conditions outlined above. A series of average basal metabolic rates has been determined for normal persons of all ages. The basal metabolic rate of a person (Fig. 95) is not considered abnormal unless it varies more than 10 per cent from the normal standard value. In general practice, basal metabolic rates are expressed as percentage variations from the normal; for example, a basal metabolic rate of +5 would indicate a

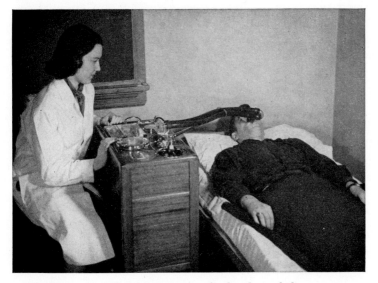

Figure 95.   The determination of a basal metabolic rate.

value 5 per cent higher than the normal value for a specific sex and age, while a basal metabolic rate of −10 would represent a value 10 per cent below the normal standard.

The amount of energy required in a day consists of the basal requirement plus the energy expended for muscular activity. In addition to these two requirements, a source of energy must be supplied to account for the *specific dynamic action* in metabolism. Protein foods, especially, stimulate the rate of metabolism and require energy for their oxidation in the tissues. On an average mixed diet, this energy for the specific dynamic action of foods amounts to about 10 per cent of the basal energy.

The requirement for muscular activity obviously depends on the occupation of the person. Most professional people require between 500 and 1000 calories daily for this purpose. In general, a total daily energy requirement of from 2000 to 3000 calories will include the majority of the people in this class. In occupations where continuous hard physical labor is involved, the daily energy requirement may exceed 5000 calories.

Inorganic Salt Requirement

Of the inorganic substances required by the body, water is by far the most important. Many inorganic elements are essential for the normal functions of the body, and must be present in the diet. We will briefly discuss the requirements for some of the important mineral elements.

Calcium

Some of the major functions of calcium in the body include: (1) formation of bones and teeth, (2) clotting of blood, (3) formation of milk, (4) formation of calcium paracaseinate curd in digestion. Milk, probably the best source of dietary calcium, contains this element in a readily absorbable form, whereas the calcium of vegetables is sometimes absorbed with difficulty. The daily requirement for calcium is approximately 1 gm. for growing children and 0.7 gm. for adults.

Phosphorus

Since bones and teeth are composed mainly of a compound of calcium and phosphorus, this element is essential in their formation.

An adequate amount of vitamin D is also required for proper calcium and phosphorus metabolism in the body. Other functions of phosphorus are (1) formation of milk, (2) formation of organic phosphorus compounds such as phospholipids, nucleoproteins, and casein, (3) formation of phosphate buffers, and (4) formation of esters of phosphoric acid that function in the oxidation of carbohydrates. For maximum bone and tooth formation, the ratio of calcium to phosphorus in the diet should be approximately 2 to 1.

There are many foods that contain phosphorus, so a dietary deficiency of this element is much less likely than a deficiency of calcium. A daily intake of 1.3 gm. of phosphorus is thought to be adequate for children and adults.

Iodine

The main purpose of iodine in the body is in the development and functioning of the thyroid gland. As shall be seen later, a deficiency of this element results in hypothyroidism and simple goiter. The daily requirement of iodine is about 0.1 to 0.15 mg. Seafood and crops grown in coastal areas contain sufficient iodine to meet this requirement, but in the Great Lakes region the iodine content of the crops is extremely low. To overcome this deficiency and to prevent goiter, small amounts of an iodine salt (potassium iodide) are added to ordinary table salt.

Iron

Hemoglobin, the pigment of blood, requires iron for its formation in the body. A deficiency of this element results in anemia. Normally the body requires from 10 to 15 mg. of iron daily. This requirement is increased by menstruation, pregnancy, and lactation. The body of a newborn infant contains enough iron to last approximately six months. Since milk is deficient in this element, additional sources of iron must be fed after the first few months.

Copper

Copper is essential for the formation of hemoglobin. It probably acts as a catalyst because no copper is present in the pigment itself. Very small amounts of copper are required per day (2 to 3 mg.), and it is doubtful that an ordinary diet would lack sufficient quantities of this element.

Sodium

The body requires sodium for several purposes. The buffer systems in the blood and tissue fluids are usually sodium salts, as for example, sodium bicarbonate and the sodium phosphates. The first named salt also produces the proper pH for enzyme action in the saliva and the pancreatic and intestinal juices. This element assists in the elimination of carbon dioxide by the lungs, and of acid products by the kidney.

The daily requirement of sodium, as sodium chloride, has been suggested as 1.7 gm. for children and 10 gm. for adults.

Potassium

Potassium is probably essential for proper cell formation in the body, since it occurs as a constituent of all animal cells. It functions with sodium in the relaxation of muscles. Salts of this element are found inside of the red blood cell, whereas sodium is present mainly in the blood plasma. Potassium therefore replaces sodium in the buffer salts used inside of the cells.

The requirement for this element may be met by a daily intake of 1.5 gm. for children and 3 gm. for adults.

Vitamin Requirement

The vitamin requirement in human nutrition has been discussed in the preceding chapter. In the past few years, the use of vitamins and vitamin products by the general public has increased tremendously. It has been estimated that over $300,000,000 worth of synthetic vitamins and multiple vitamin preparations were sold in the United States in 1957.

It cannot be stressed too strongly that adequate nutrition concerns food and not synthetic products that are taken as cure-alls. The proper source of vitamins in the diet is food, because there are many other requirements in an adequate diet besides vitamins.

Special Dietary Requirements

In Pregnancy and Lactation

An adequate diet during pregnancy and lactation is essential for the development of the fetus, the placenta, the uterus, and breasts, and for the formation of milk. Obviously this calls for an increased intake of proteins. Inorganic salts and vitamin D are often given to pregnant women to insure proper bone development of the fetus.

In the Growing Child

An improper diet in childhood does not produce symptoms as striking as those shown in an infectious disease, but may result in far more serious handicaps when the child reaches maturity. Many of the common diseases that affect children are more prevalent among those suffering from malnutrition (Fig. 96). The proper development of bones and teeth is closely related to an adequate intake of calcium, phosphorus, and vitamin D. The size of the adult body is partially hereditary, but may be influenced markedly by the diet in childhood. The malnutrition so extensive in parts of Europe is certain to influence the stature of the present generation of children.

In Disease and Abnormal Conditions in the Body

Variations in the diet are often advantageous in the treatment of disease and abnormal conditions in the body. A careful control of the diet in diabetes mellitus will result in less frequent glycosuria and

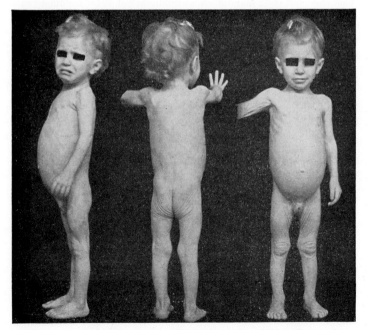

Figure 96. Typical potbelly and wrinkled skin of a child suffering from malnutrition. (Dept. of Pediatrics, University of Iowa Hospitals.)

acidosis, and will enable the patient to maintain a fairly constant blood sugar level with a minimum number of insulin injections.

Anemia is usually treated by a diet that contains additional amounts of iron salts, liver, and vitamins. Diseases of the liver and gallbladder respond more rapidly to a diet that is low in fat and moderately rich in protein. In nephritis, a nearly salt-free diet is fed and the protein intake is sometimes restricted. Since considerable quantities of protein are often lost in the urine, it has recently become the practice to include relatively large amounts of protein in the diet to maintain the protein content of the plasma.

Many hospitalized patients are given diets that contain bland, quickly digested foods to prevent upsets and intestinal disturbances from adding to their discomfort. The nature and amount of food given to patients after a major operation are important factors in recovery.

Review Questions

1. What was your conception of an adequate diet at about the time you started high school?
2. Why has the past war greatly influenced our practical knowledge of nutrition?
3. Which of the three major foodstuffs is used mainly for energy in the diet?
4. Explain the meaning of the following terms: basal metabolism, basal metabolic rate, a basal metabolic rate of 0, and specific dynamic action.
5. How many calories would you estimate the average student nurse requires per day?
6. Why would it be unwise to exist on a lipid-free diet for long periods of time?
7. If your daily calorific requirement was 2250 calories, how many grams of fat would you have to eat to supply your energy requirement? Approximately what fraction of a pound is this amount of fat?
8. Give three examples of an adequate protein. Of an inadequate protein.
9. Why are children fed more than twice the amount of protein per kilogram of body weight than adults?
10. List the functions of calcium in the body. Of phosphorus.
11. Why are calcium and phosphorus so closely interrelated in nutrition?
12. For what reason is potassium iodide added to the table salt in certain regions of the United States?
13. What are iron and copper used for in the body?
14. List the abnormalities that might occur in the body if the diet lacked sodium and potassium.
15. Why is an adequate diet much more important than the ingestion of multiple vitamin preparations?
16. The nutritional requirements in pregnancy and lactation are similar to those of the growing child. Explain.
17. Briefly discuss three conditions that will respond more favorably when the proper foods are fed to the patient.

Chapter 24

Hormones

Hormones are catalysts that are similar in action to enzymes. Enzymes are formed in the gastrointestinal tract or in glandular organs with ducts to carry these agents to their site of action. Hormones, in contrast, are formed in glandular organs called *ductless glands* because they have no external ducts. These glands are also called *endocrine glands* or *glands of internal secretion,* since they produce secretions that diffuse directly into the blood stream. *Hormones* are compounds that are effective in regulating bodily processes. While they do not initiate a process, they exhibit an enzyme-like action in controlling the rate of the process, and are thought to exert their action by influencing enzyme systems in the body. Hormones are called "chemical messengers" because they are formed in an endocrine organ and carried by the blood stream to another part of the body where they exert their effect. They are specific in action, like enzymes, and, in addition, affect the action of other hormones. In a normal individual, the integrative functioning of the endocrine glands results in a high degree of hormonal balance. When this balance is disrupted, abnormal metabolic processes result. In this chapter, the hormones will be discussed in connection with the glands that produce them (Fig. 97).

Hormones of the Digestive Tract

These hormones have been briefly discussed in the chapter on digestion because of their function in the production of digestive juices. The three most important hormones of the digestive tract are *gastrin, secretin,* and *cholecystokinin.*

Gastrin is manufactured in the mucosa of the pyloric end of the stomach. The presence of food in the stomach causes this hormone to diffuse into the blood and to stimulate the secretion of gastric juice. Many investigators believe that gastrin is chemically identical to hista-

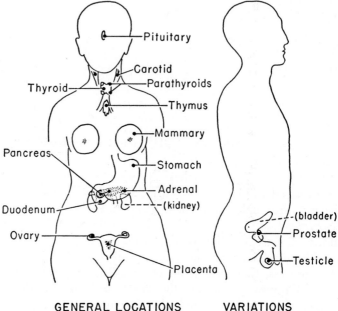

GENERAL LOCATIONS
in the male & female
plus female characteristics

VARIATIONS
in the male

Figure 97.   The location of the endocrine glands in the body.

mine. The injection of histamine causes an increased flow of gastric juice and is often used to collect specimens for gastric analysis.

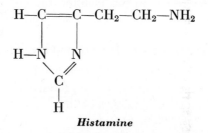

Histamine

Secretin is formed in the walls of the duodenum and is liberated into the blood stream whenever the acid gastric contents pass through the pyloric valve. It is carried by the blood to the pancreas, where it stimulates the flow of pancreatic juice. It has also been shown to increase the flow of bile and intestinal juice. Secretin has been isolated in crystalline form and found to be a polypeptide with a molecular weight of 5000, containing a high percentage of the basic amino acids, lysine and arginine.

Cholecystokinin is also produced in the walls of the duodenum. The presence of fat or acid in this section of the intestine causes this hormone to stimulate the gallbladder to contract and pour bile into the duodenum. Its chemical nature is unknown.

Two other hormones have been found in extracts of the intestinal mucosa. *Enterogastrone,* a hormone which inhibits gastric secretion when large quantities of fat are present in the duodenum, has not been chemically characterized, although its activity is associated with a polypeptide structure. *Pancreozymin* is a hormone that stimulates the secretion of enzymes by the pancreas. Its chemical nature is unknown.

The Hormone of the Pancreas

We have already seen that *insulin* is produced by the pancreas and that its main function is to regulate the metabolism of carbohydrates. If this hormone is not produced in sufficient quantity by the pancreas, the disease known as *diabetes mellitus* develops.

Anatomically, the pancreas is made up of two types of tissue, the acinous and the islet tissue. The former produces the pancreatic juice which pours into the intestine through external ducts, whereas the latter is responsible for the formation of insulin.

Although it was demonstrated as early as 1889 that removal of the pancreas of an animal would result in diabetes, it was not until 1922 that Banting and Best developed a method for obtaining active extracts of the pancreas. Within a short time insulin became available in sufficient quantities for the treatment of diabetes. The hormone was crystallized in 1926 and was found to be a protein with a molecular weight of about 35,000. It contains a relatively large amount of the sulfur-containing amino acid, cystine, which is believed to be involved in the physiological activity of insulin. Since it is a protein, it is not effective when taken by mouth, because the proteolytic enzymes of the gastrointestinal tract hydrolyze it and destroy its insulin activity. Insulin is usually injected into the muscles when administered to a diabetic (Fig. 98).

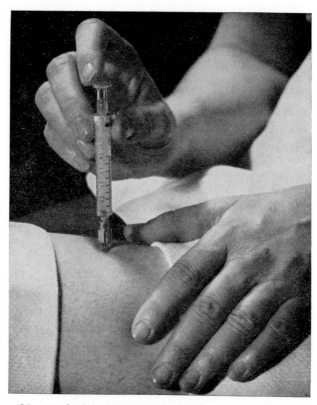

Figure 98.   Insulin being injected into the muscles by a diabetic patient.
(Bortz: Diabetes Control. Philadelphia, Lea & Febiger.)

The strength of an insulin solution is expressed in units. Originally a *unit of insulin* was one-third the amount of insulin required to decrease the blood sugar level of a 2-kilogram fasting rabbit to a point where the rabbit went into convulsions (45 mg. per 100 cc. of blood). As used today, the unit is somewhat stronger than originally employed. In man, 1 unit of insulin will cause the oxidation of about 2 gm. of glucose. Crystalline insulin has a potency of 24 units per milligram.

The main function of insulin is to control the oxidation of glucose in the body. If insulin is injected into the diabetic, the blood sugar level falls, the glycogen storage in liver and muscles increases, and the rate of production of acetone bodies is decreased. The action of insulin is rapid, however, and its effect soon wears off. This results in variations of the blood sugar level from hour to hour during the day and necessitates frequent injections in severe diabetes. In 1935, Hagedorn combined insulin with protamine (a simple protein) and found that it produced a more prolonged effect on injection. The addition of zinc to protamine insulin still further prolongs the effective action of insulin. Instead of two and three injections a day, many diabetic persons are able to control the blood sugar level with one injection of protamine zinc insulin. However, there are cases in which insulin alone is more effective, for example when severe hyperglycemia must be rapidly reduced to a normal blood sugar level. The protamine zinc insulin may also cause prolonged hypoglycemia that is difficult to overcome.

It should be emphasized that insulin injections will not cure diabetes but will merely allow the diabetic to regulate his carbohydrate metabolism, thus preventing glycosuria, acetone body excretion, acidosis, diabetic coma, and loss of body weight.

Considerable interest has been stimulated recently by the development of two drugs that may be taken orally to help control the blood sugar level in certain types of diabetic patients. One is a derivative of sulfanilamide known as BZ-55, the other a tolylsulfonylbutylurea known as *Orinase*. After extensive clinical trials the new compounds appear to be effective only if the diabetic produces some insulin of his own. Children, thin patients, or those who take large doses of insulin are not benefited. It has been suggested that these drugs exert their effect either by blocking the action of insulinase, which would indirectly permit the pancreas to produce more insulin, or by extending the effectiveness of a given amount of insulin. With an estimated 2,000,000 diabetics in the United States, an orally ingested drug that would benefit even 25 per cent of the patients creates tremendous interest.

The Hormone of the Thyroid

The Thyroid

The thyroid gland, located on either side of the trachea, consists of two lobes connected by a strip of tissue. It weighs about 20 gm. and its cells are filled with a colloidal material that contains the active principle. This colloid is composed mainly of the protein *thyroglobulin*.

Thyroxin

The active hormone of the thyroid gland is the iodine containing compound *thyroxin*. It has been shown to be the functional part of the *thyroglobulin* molecule, and is released from the protein by the action of intestinal enzymes when thyroglobulin is taken orally. Thyroxin is related to the amino acid, tyrosine, and has the following structure:

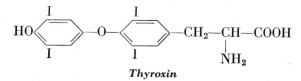

Thyroxin

The function of thyroxin is to regulate the rate of metabolism of the body tissues. If extra thyroxin is injected into the body, the rate of metabolism is increased, the heart beat is increased, and the patient loses weight unless the food intake is increased. Destruction of part of the thyroid by disease results in a slowing down of the metabolic rate and heartbeat and the patient usually becomes sluggish and overweight.

Hypothyroidism

A congenital absence of the thyroid gland or a failure to develop a normal gland in infancy results in *cretinism*. The child grows neither physically nor mentally in a normal fashion but becomes a dwarf with thick dry skin, a wide flat nose, and coarse, scanty hair (Fig. 99). Continued treatment with thyroxin, if started at an early age, will cause the child to develop normally.

Hypothyroidism in the adult is called *myxedema* and is characterized by thick dry skin, subnormal temperature and pulse rate, coarse hair, and decreased physical and mental activity (Fig. 100). The metabolic rate is lowered and there is a tendency toward increased weight. This condition is also benefited by the injection of thyroxin.

The thyroid gland requires iodine for the manufacture of thyroxin and will not develop properly in the absence of this element. In regions where the iodine content of the soil and drinking water is low, a simple hypothyroidism occurs. In this condition, patients become sluggish and overweight; in general they show symptoms similar to those in myxedema but not as severe.

Hyperthyroidism

In cases of overdevelopment of the thyroid gland, sometimes caused by an *adenoma* or tumor, the gland becomes enlarged and produces excessive amounts of thyroxin. The symptoms in these cases are opposite to those observed in myxedema. The metabolic rate and the heartbeat are increased, the body temperature is above normal, and the patient is usually underweight. Nervous irritability and an increase in mental activity are usually observed. A common symptom of this disease is a bulging of the eyes, which gives it the name *exophthalmic goiter.*

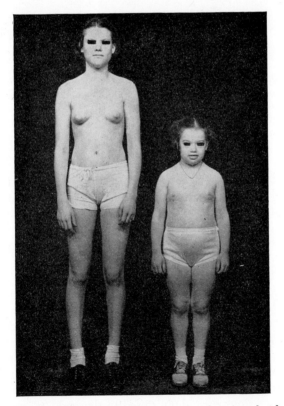

Figure 99. A comparison of a cretin, age 16, with a normal girl, age 15. (Dept. of Pediatrics, University of Iowa Hospitals.)

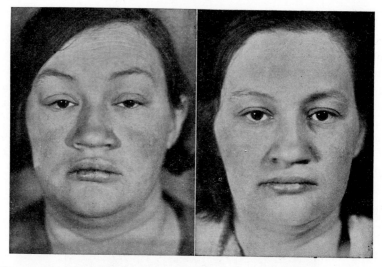

Figure 100. Twenty-six year old woman with myxedema, before treatment. Basal metabolic rate,—36.

Same patient as in Figure 100, two months later, after treatment with desiccated thyroid gland. Basal metabolic rate,—5.

(Cecil & Loeb: Text of Med. 9th Ed.)

Goiters

The term goiter refers to an enlargement of the thyroid gland, which is evidenced by a swelling in the neck. *Simple goiter,* often called *endemic goiter* or *colloid goiter,* is prevalent in regions of the country where there is a lack of iodine in the crops and drinking water. The thyroid increases in size in an attempt to produce the proper amount of thyroxin. This type of goiter responds favorably to an increase in the iodine intake. Patients suffering from cretinism or myxedema usually have goiters.

The goiters that result from hyperthyroidism are due to an abnormal enlargement of functional thyroid gland tissue which produces excessive amounts of the thyroid hormone. Exophthalmic goiter (Fig. 101), for example, is usually treated by surgery or x-ray to remove or destroy part of the gland. In recent years, considerable research on thyroid disorders has been carried out with radioactive iodine. When this radioactive isotope is administered to the body, it concentrates in the thyroid gland as does ordinary iodine. The radiations given off by

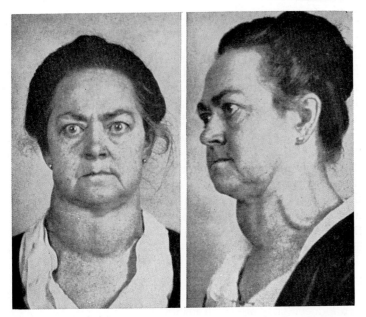

Figure 101. This patient exhibits enlarged thyroid gland and characteristic bulging eyes caused by an exophthalmic goiter. (Crile, G. W.: The Thyroid Gland.)

the isotope have been found very effective in the treatment of exophthalmic goiter.

Diagnosis of hyper- or hypothyroidism is somewhat difficult in the early stages of the disease before definite physical signs have become apparent. The speed of metabolism, or *basal metabolic rate* (BMR), has long been used as a diagnostic aid. More recently, the rate at which the thyroid gland takes up a dose of *radioactive I¹³¹* has been found to be diagnostically significant. Also, a determination of the *protein-bound iodine* of the plasma yields information that is more significant than BMR values.

The Hormone of the Parathyroids

The Parathyroids

The parathyroid glands are small organs, weighing about 0.1 gm., which are attached to the thyroid. Two of these are embedded in the thyroid while two others lie on the surface of this gland. Removal of the parathyroids causes death within a few days.

Parathyroid Secretion

The hormone of the parathyroid, *parathyroid secretion,* is probably a protein. Its main function is to maintain a normal level of calcium in the blood. When the parathyroids are removed, the blood calcium decreases and muscle twitches are observed. Within a few days, tetany develops and the patient dies in convulsions. Injections of parathyroid secretion will bring about recovery even when the patient is already in tetany, by transferring calcium from the bones into the blood.

Overactive parathyroids may be caused by an adenoma; this results in increased calcium in the blood with subsequent excretion of this element in the urine. A continuation of this process results in decalcification of the bones, making them soft and weak.

The Hormones of the Adrenals

The Adrenals

The adrenals, sometimes called suprarenals, are located on the top of each kidney. They are small glands weighing approximately 3 gm. each. Each adrenal gland consists of two parts, an inner portion called the *medulla* surrounded by an outer layer called the *cortex.*

Epinephrine

The medulla manufactures a hormone known as *adrenalin,* or *epinephrine.* This compound has been prepared synthetically and is a relatively simple substance that is probably made from the amino acid, tyrosine.

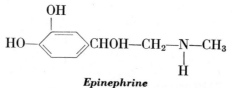

Epinephrine

The injection of epinephrine (adrenalin) causes a stimulation of the sympathetic nervous system. The arterioles are constricted and thus cause an increase in blood pressure. The heart muscle is stimulated and the beat is faster than normal. The blood sugar level is increased because the hormone causes glycogenolysis in the liver and muscles; it also causes relaxation of smooth muscle. In general, an injection of epinephrine produces effects similar to those observed in the emotional stress of an emergency.

Epinephrine is frequently injected in patients to counteract insulin shock because of its ability to increase the blood sugar level. It is often mixed with a local anesthetic and injected around the site of an operation to constrict the small blood vessels and check the loss of blood. Epinephrine is useful in combating shock because it produces a temporary increase in the blood pressure. It is sometimes injected directly into the heart muscle when the heart stops beating during surgical anesthesia. The heart of a newborn baby that is not beating may be started by this method. Small doses of epinephrine are frequently used to relieve the spasm in bronchial asthma by relaxing the muscle of the bronchi.

A second hormone of the adrenal medulla, *norepinephrine,* has recently been isolated. Chemically it differs from epinephrine in that the methyl group on the nitrogen atom is replaced by a hydrogen. The action of norepinephrine is similar in some respects to that of epinephrine, but fundamental differences exist. For example, it does not affect carbohydrate metabolism nor relax smooth muscle as does epinephrine. Commercial extracts of epinephrine contain from 10 to 20 per cent of norepinephrine.

Hormones of the Cortex

The cortex of the adrenal gland produces a group of hormones known as *cortin.* Several of these hormones have been isolated from the gland and are similar in structure, being derivatives of the sterol nucleus. Typical steroid hormones related to the adrenal cortex are represented as follows:

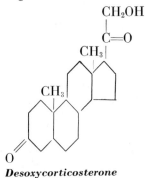

Desoxycorticosterone

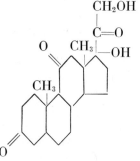

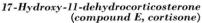

17-Hydroxy-11-dehydrocorticosterone
(compound E, cortisone)

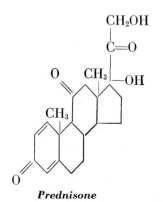

Prednisone

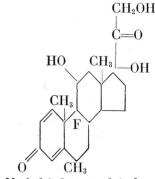

6-Methyl-9-fluoroprednisolone

Addison's disease results from the failure of the adrenal cortex to produce sufficient hormones (Fig. 102). This disease is characterized by many complex changes in the body. The skin becomes bronze in color, there is loss of weight, extreme muscle fatigue, emaciation, the metabolic rate and body temperature are lowered, and the blood volume is decreased. The two most important changes are: (1) a low concentration of sodium and a high concentration of potassium in the blood, accompanied by the excretion of large amounts of sodium in the urine; (2) an improper utilization of carbohydrates, evidenced by a fall in the blood sugar level. The injection of cortin into a patient with Addison's disease results in the alleviation of the above symptoms. Desoxycorticosterone alone corrects the abnormal metabolism of sodium but does not affect the carbohydrate utilization, whereas 17-hydroxycorticosterone is active only in adjusting the metabolism of carbohydrates.

In recent years, the adrenal cortex hormone, 17-hydroxy-11-dehydro-corticosterone, which is also known as compound E or *cortisone*, has obtained considerable publicity. The early clinical trials of this compound produced dramatic results in the treatment of rheumatoid arthritis (Fig. 103). It was soon learned, however, that after a brief period of relief, the original symptoms returned, and severe side effects were observed. Extensive research by the pharmaceutical industry resulted in *prednisone* and *prednisolone* which have structures closely related to cortisone and hydrocortisone. Prednisone was found to be 4 to 5 times as effective as cortisone in the treatment of arthritis and to exhibit fewer side effects such as salt retention, loss of calcium and nitrogen, and gastrointestinal disturbances. In 1957, the fluoro derivatives of prednisolone were reported to possess 3 to 9 times the potency of prednisone in the treatment of arthritis. The 6-methyl-9-fluoro-prednisolone is reported to 30 to 50 times as potent as predni-

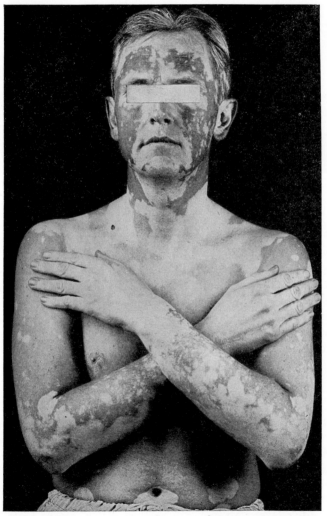

Figure 102. Addison's disease. Note the areas of extensive pigmentation of the skin. (Loeb, R. F.: Bull. N. Y. Acad. Med.)

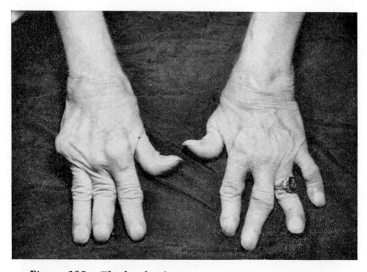

Figure 103. The hands of a patient with rheumatoid arthritis.

sone. These derivatives are undergoing clinical trial to determine the extent of side effects. This type of research could result in safe therapeutic agents for the treatment of rheumatoid arthritis.

Overactivity of the adrenal cortex may be caused by a cortical tumor and produces an overdevelopment of masculine characteristics in male and female. A man becomes a "paragon of virility" while a woman loses her feminine characteristics and becomes a "masculine caricature of her former self." In children, sexual development occurs at an early age; completely developed secondary sexual characteristics may appear at the age of six.

Female Sex Hormones

The female sex hormones formed in the ovaries are responsible for the development of the secondary sexual characteristics (development of the breasts, appearance of body hair, and changes in the uterus and vagina) that occur at puberty. These hormones regulate the *estrus cycle* or *menstrual cycle* (Fig. 104) and function in pregnancy. Before discussing the individual hormones, it may be well to consider the changes that occur in the normal menstrual cycle in women.

The ovaries are small almond-shaped organs that are located in the pelvic cavity on each side of the uterus. At birth, they are filled with numerous immature ova. At puberty, an ovum matures and is discharged into the uterus. In the ovary, the ovum is located in a small spherical-shaped body called the *follicle*. As the ovum matures, the follicle grows and at ovulation it ruptures to release the ovum. During the development of the follicle, the hormone *estrone* is produced.

After the follicle ruptures, it first fills with blood, then is replaced by large yellow cells forming the *corpus luteum* (yellow body). A second hormone, *progesterone*, is formed in the corpus luteum. If the discharged ovum is not fertilized by spermatozoa in the uterus, the corpus luteum is soon replaced by scar tissue. If pregnancy occurs, however, this gland is active throughout the period of pregnancy. This process of ovulation and development of the corpus luteum is repeated every four weeks in a normal woman, if pregnancy does not occur.

Prior to ovulation, changes are also occurring in the uterus. The walls and epithelial lining of the uterus become thicker in preparation for the implantation of the fertilized ovum. If the ovum is not fertilized, the lining of the uterus is maintained for about two weeks after ovulation, then the endometrium (epithelial lining) sloughs off and is discharged. This process, called *menstruation*, is accompanied by bleeding and continues for four or five days.

The entire menstrual cycle may be summarized briefly as follows: Normally, the length of each cycle is four weeks and the days of the

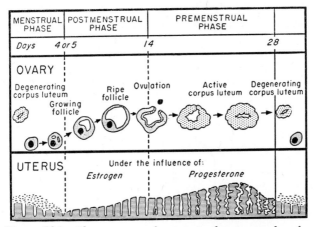

Figure 104. The sequence of events in the menstrual cycle.

cycle are numbered from the onset of menstruation. From the cessation of menstruation until the fourteenth day, the ovum and follicle are maturing in the ovary. During this time, the uterine endometrium is growing under the influence of estrone. Ovulation occurs about the fourteenth day and the ovum is expelled into the uterus. If pregnancy does not occur, the corpus luteum that develops in the ovary disappears after about a week. The endometrium is maintained by progesterone until menstruation occurs and removes the endometrium from the uterus. The cycle then repeats itself.

If pregnancy occurs, the corpus luteum continues to develop, preventing further ovulation or menstruation.

Hormones of the Follicle

The liquid within the follicle contains at least two hormones, known as *estrone* and *estradiol*. Estrone (theelin) was the first principle to be isolated from the follicular liquid; however estradiol (dihydrotheelin) is more potent than estrone and may be the principal hormone. These compounds are related chemically to the sterols.

These two compounds are excreted in the urine in increased amounts during pregnancy. Similar compounds such as *estriol* have been isolated from urine during pregnancy, although their estrogenic activity is low compared to the follicular hormones. As has already been stated, the function of the estrogens is the development of the secondary sexual characteristics at puberty and the regeneration of the endometrium of the uterus in the first half of the menstrual cycle.

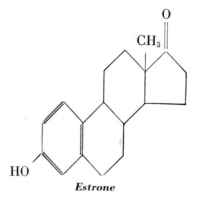

Estrone

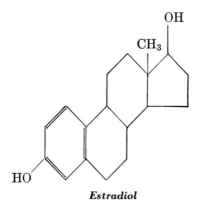

Estradiol

A synthetic compound, stilbestrol, a derivative of *p*-hydroxybenzene exhibits 3 to 5 times the potency of estrone.

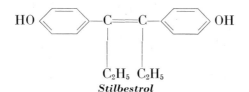

Stilbestrol

Its low cost and effectiveness when administered orally make stilbestrol a valuable therapeutic agent. It is used extensively in the poultry industry for its estrogenic action in caponizing young cockerels.

The Hormone of the Corpus Luteum

The hormone produced by the corpus luteum is called *progesterone*. In the body, progesterone is converted into *pregnanediol* by reduction, before it is excreted in the urine. These two compounds are similar to the estrogens in chemical structure.

The main function of progesterone is the preparation of the uterine endometrium for implantation of the fertilized ovum. If pregnancy occurs, this hormone is responsible for the retention of the embryo in the uterus and for the development of the mammary glands prior to lactation.

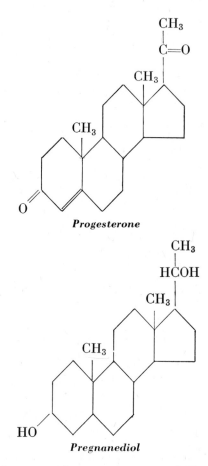

Progesterone

Pregnanediol

During the early stages of pregnancy, a round, flat organ called the *placenta* is formed in the uterus. The placenta is the attachment between the mother and the fetus. The placenta produces hormones during pregnancy, especially estrone and a hormone that inhibits the continuance of the normal menstrual cycle.

Male Sex Hormones

The male sex hormones are produced by the testes, which are two oval glands located in the scrotum of the male. Small glands in the testes form spermatozoa which are capable of fertilizing a mature ovum. Between the cells that manufacture spermatozoa are the *inter-stitial cells* which produce a hormone called *testosterone*. This hor-mone is probably converted into other compounds such as *androste-rone* before being excreted in the urine. *Dehydroandrosterone* has also been isolated from male urine but is much less active than the other two hormones. The male sex hormones or *androgens* have structures similar to the estrogens.

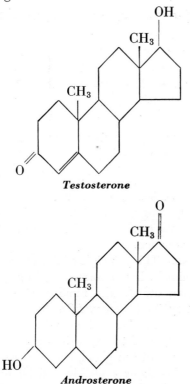

Testosterone

Androsterone

The main function of the androgens is the development of mascu-line sexual characteristics, such as deepening of the voice, the growth of a beard, and distribution of body hair at puberty. They also control the function of the glands of reproduction (seminal vesicles, prostate, and Cowper's gland).

If the testes are removed before puberty, masculine characteristics fail to develop, the voice is high pitched, the beard fails to grow, and the fat deposition of the body resembles that of the female. The castration of young animals is commonly practiced in the raising of livestock. Such animals put on weight more rapidly and produce a higher quality of meat.

Hormones of the Pituitary

The Pituitary Gland

The pituitary gland (hypophysis) is a small organ that is located at the base of the brain. It is composed of an *anterior lobe* and a *posterior lobe,* which are connected by a strip of tissue known as the *pars intermedia.* The anterior lobe produces several hormones that are necessary for the proper functioning of the other endocrine glands. For this reason, the anterior lobe of the pituitary is often referred to as the master gland of the endocrine system. Since the two lobes form different hormones, they will be discussed separately.

Hormones of the Anterior Lobe

The hormones of the anterior lobe are protein in nature and are therefore not characterized chemically as are many of the other hormones. Many physiological functions have been attributed to this gland. However, we will confine our discussions to those that exhibit a definitely accepted function.

GROWTH HORMONE.   This principle of the anterior lobe controls the growth of young animals. If the hormone is lacking in childhood, the individual becomes a dwarf. The familiar circus dwarf is usually the result of pituitary insufficiency. In contrast to the cretins, these dwarfs have well-formed bodies and normal intellect.

An excessive formation of the growth hormone in childhood may result from an adenoma of the gland, and causes gigantism. Most of the giants seen in the circus probably had an overactive pituitary during their childhood. If this hormone is produced in excessive amounts in an adult, the condition of *acromegaly* develops. Acromegaly (Fig. 105) is characterized by an increased disproportional growth of the bones in the face, hands, and feet.

GONAD-STIMULATING HORMONES.   The ovaries in women, and testes in men, are sometimes called the gonads. The anterior pituitary contains substances that regulate the formation of sex hormones. The *follicle-stimulating hormone* controls the growth of the follicles and stimulates the production of follicular hormones. In the male, this hormone regulates the function of the cells that make spermatozoa. The formation of corpus luteum and progesterone are stimulated by the *luteinizing hormone,* while in the male this factor controls the production of androgens by the interstitial cells of the testes. The different stages of the menstrual cycle and the normal course of pregnancy depend on the balance between these two hormones.

LACTOGENIC HORMONE. This hormone, called *prolactin,* has been isolated in a crystalline form. Prolactin is a protein that initiates lactation. During pregnancy this hormone is inhibited by the principle in the placenta that stimulates the growth of the mammary glands. When the placenta is removed, the prolactin is free to stimulate milk formation, and lactation occurs.

THYROTROPIC HORMONE. The development and secretion of the thyroid gland is stimulated by the thyrotropic hormone. If the anterior lobe of the pituitary is removed, the thyroid atrophies and fails to produce sufficient thyroxin, thereby causing a drop in the metabolic rate. When extracts of this hormone are injected into experimental animals, the thyroid gland enlarges and a condition similar to exophthalmic goiter is produced.

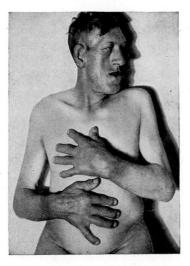

Figure 105. Acromegaly. (Major & Delp: Physical Diagnosis, 5th Edition.)

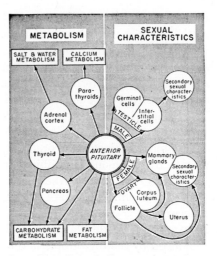

Figure 106. The relationship of the anterior pituitary to metabolism and sexual characteristics.

ADRENOTROPIC OR ADRENOCORTICOTROPIC HORMONE. This hormone stimulates the growth and function of the adrenal cortex. Some cases of Addison's disease have benefited more from injections of this factor than from cortin itself. The adrenocorticotropic hormone, commonly called *ACTH*, is a protein that has recently been isolated in purified form. It is being used in the therapeutic treatment of rheumatoid arthritis, acute rheumatic fever, and other diseases benefited by cortisone. When ACTH is injected into the body, it stimulates the adrenal cortex to produce cortisone as well as other adrenal cortical hormones.

PANCREATROPIC HORMONE. Extracts of the anterior lobe of the pituitary when injected into animals cause an increased production of insulin by the pancreas. Continued injections result in an exhaustion of the islet tissue and insulin formation decreases markedly. Experimental animals have been made permanently diabetic by this factor, therefore it may also be called the diabetes-producing hormone.

DIABETOGENIC HORMONE. This hormone stimulates the breakdown of liver glycogen and causes an increase in the blood sugar level. If the anterior lobe of the pituitary is removed from a diabetic animal there is a temporary lowering of the blood sugar level due to the lack of the diabetogenic hormone.

The relationship of the anterior pituitary to sexual characteristics and metabolism is summarized in Figure 106.

Hormones of the Posterior Lobe

The posterior lobe of the pituitary gland produces at least two hormones, *pitocin* and *pitressin*. Pitocin or *oxytocin* is a factor that causes a contraction of the smooth muscle of the uterus when it is injected. This hormone is often used in obstetrics to contract the uterus after the birth of the child and thus aid in the control of hemorrhage.

Pitressin or *vasopressin* stimulates the peripheral blood vessels and causes a gradual, prolonged increase in blood pressure. It is sometimes used instead of epinephrine to combat shock, because of its prolonged effect. Pitressin also controls the formation of urine. Injection of this substance in a patient with diabetes insipidus greatly decreases the urine volume. It is believed to influence the process of reabsorption of water by the kidney tubules.

The Pars Intermedia

This small strip of tissue produces a hormone that increases the size of the pigment spots on the skin of frogs and fish but has not been shown to function in the human.

Review Questions

1. Why are the endocrine glands also called ductless glands and glands of internal secretion?
2. Name the three main hormones of the digestive tract. What is the function of each hormone in digestion?
3. Why are gastrin and histamine thought to be the same compound?
4. Discuss the effectiveness and importance of the recently developed insulin substitutes.
5. How many units of insulin would a diabetic require if he oxidized an amount of carbohydrate equivalent to 100 gm. of glucose in a day?
6. What advantages does the use of protamine zinc insulin have over ordinary insulin? What disadvantages?
7. At one time preparations containing thyroxin were used for removal of excess body weight. How would the hormone accomplish this? Can you suggest a reason for the fact that it is not used for this purpose today?

8. Name and describe the conditions that result from hypothyroidism. From hyperthyroidism.

9. Is there a logical connection between the parathyroid gland and bone formation? Explain. Why is tetany sometimes observed in cases of rickets?

10. Name five uses of epinephrine in medicine.

11. What disease results from the lack of function of the adrenal cortex? What are the outstanding symptoms of this disease?

12. Name and describe three steroid hormones that are effective in the management of patients with rheumatoid arthritis.

13. Explain the following terms: estrus cycle, follicle, corpus luteum, and menstrual cycle.

14. What process occurs at ovulation? At menstruation?

15. Why do ovulation and menstruation cease when pregnancy occurs?

16. What are the main functions of the estrogens? Of progesterone?

17. Name two androgens and give their main functions.

18. Why is the anterior lobe of the pituitary gland often called the master gland of the endocrine system?

19. What similarities exist in the conditions caused by a lack of the growth hormone in childhood and hypothyroidism in infancy? What differences?

20. Why are the gonad-stimulating hormones important in reproduction?

21. Compare the activity of the pancreatropic and the diabetogenic hormones.

22. In what way are ACTH and cortisone related? How are they used therapeutically?

23. Pitocin is often injected immediately before or immediately after childbirth. Explain its use in both cases.

24. In what way are hormones related to enzymes?

Appendix

Chemical Properties of the Important Elements

	Element	Outstanding Properties	Reduction of Sulfide	Reduction of Oxide	Electrolysis	Occurs Free	Liquid Air	Industrial Uses of Compounds
				Preparation by				
Metals	Sodium Potassium Calcium	Soft, reactive			■			Glass, soap, paper, soda Photography, fertilizers Plaster of paris, cement, glass
	Magnesium Zinc	Easily ignited	■	■				Alloys, asbestos, talc, dyes Galvanized iron, alloys, paint
	Arsenic Bismuth	Brittle, crystalline	■					Insecticides, glass, dyes Type metal, Babbitt metal
	Iron Nickel Tin	Malleable		■				Construction, blue prints Alloys, hydrogenation of oils Solder, dyes
	Lead Copper Mercury Silver	Soft, malleable	■					Paint, storage batteries, alloys Conductors, alloys, fruit sprays Explosives, illumination Photography, mirrors
	Gold Platinum	Non-reactive				■		Dentistry alloys, jewelry X-ray tubes, dental alloys
	Aluminum Manganese Chromium	Both acid- and base-forming			■			Alloys, electric conductors, paint Alloys, dry-cell batteries Chrome plating, pigments
	Radium	Radioactive			■			Luminous materials
Non-metals	Hydrogen Oxygen	Reactive gases			■			Ammonia, hydrogenating oils Oxyacetylene torches
	Nitrogen Neon	Inert gases					■	Ammonia, explosives, fertilizers Illumination
	Phosphorus Fluorine Chlorine Bromine Iodine	Very reactive acid-forming		■	■			Matches, fertilizers Etching of glass, catalysts, jet fuels Purifying of water, bleaching Dyes, gasoline, photography Dyes, photography
	Sulfur Carbon	Crystalline and amorphous				■		Acids, dyes, paper pulp Rubber products, phonograph records
	Silicon	Hard and cryst.		■				Cement, glass, carborundum, plastics

Biological Significance of the Important Elements

	Element	Per Cent in Earth's Crust	Per Cent in Human Body	Occurrence in Body				Medical Uses of Compounds
				Bones and Teeth	Enzymes	Muscle	Blood	
Essential in Diet	Calcium	3.39	2.0	■	■			In rickets, tetany
	Carbon	0.08	18.0		■	■	■	In all organic compounds
	Chlorine	0.19	0.15	■		■		Germicides, anesthetics
	Cobalt	....	Trace		■		■	For hematopoiesis
	Copper	....	0.00015		■		■	Germicides; hematopoiesis
	Fluorine	0.03	Trace	■			■	Blood anticoagulants
	Hydrogen	0.87	10.0	■	■	■	■	In organic compounds
	Iodine	....	0.00004	■	■	■	■	Germicides; in goiter
	Iron	4.71	0.004	■			■	In anemia; astringents
	Magnesium	1.93	0.05	■	■			Antacids, cathartics
	Manganese	0.09	0.0003	■		■		Antiseptics
	Nitrogen	0.03	3.0	■	■	■	■	Constituent of proteins
	Oxygen	49.20	65.0	■	■	■	■	Gas used in anoxias
	Phosphorus	0.11	1.1	■	■			Cathartic; lead poisoning
	Potassium	2.40	0.35		■	■	■	Making soluble salts
	Sodium	2.63	0.15		■	■	■	Making soluble salts
	Sulfur	0.06	0.25	■		■		Skin diseases; germicides
	Zinc	....	Trace		■			With insulin; astringents
Non-essential	Aluminum	7.50	Trace	■				Antacids, astringents
	Antimony	....	....					Parasiticides, emetics
	Arsenic	....	Trace				■	In syphilis, leukemia
	Barium	0.04	....					X-ray, antidiarrhetics
	Bismuth	....	....					Antisyphilitic, adsorbents
	Boron	....	Trace					Disinfectants, protectives
	Bromine	....	Trace				■	Sedatives, blood dyes
	Gold	....	....					Arthritis
	Lead	....	Trace					Astringents
	Mercury	....	....					Antisyphilitics, germicide
	Nickel	0.02	Trace			■		Toxic
	Radium	....	Trace					Destruction of carcinomas
	Selenium	....	Trace					Toxic
	Silicon	28.06	Trace	■				Antacids

Normal Clinical Biochemical Values

Constituent	Normal Range	Changes Associated with Pathological Conditions
Whole blood:		
Creatinine	0.8–2 mg. per 100 cc.	Increases in nephritis and uremia.
Glucose	65–100 mg. per 100 cc.	Increases in diabetes. Decreases in Addison's disease.
Hemoglobin	14–16 gm. per 100 cc.	Increases in polycythemia. Decreases in anemias.
Oxygen content (venous)	10–19 vol. %	Increases in polycythemia. Decreases in respiratory diseases and anemia.
Urea nitrogen	8–20 mg. per 100 cc.	Increases in nephritis, cardiac failure and intestinal or urinary obstruction.
Uric acid	2–3.5 mg. per 100 cc.	Increases in nephritis, gout, leukemia and eclampsia.
Blood plasma:		
Ascorbic acid (Vitamin C)	0.75–2.5 mg. per 100 cc.	Decreases in scurvy.
CO_2 content	25–30 mEq./l.	Increases in vomiting, tetany. Decreases in diabetes and nephritis.
Chlorides	100–105 mEq./l.	Increases in nephritis and cardiac conditions. Decreases in vomiting, diarrhea and pneumonia.
Fibrinogen	0.2–0.4 gm. per 100 cc.	Increases in pneumonia and infections. Decreases in typhoid fever.
Blood serum:		
Albumin	3.5–5.6 gm. per 100 cc.	Decreases in cirrhosis and nephrosis.
Amylase	50–150 units	Increases in acute pancreatitis.
Bilirubin	0.0–0.2 mg. per 100 cc. (direct)	Direct: Increases in obstructive jaundice.
	0.2–1 mg. per 100 cc. (total)	Indirect: Increases in hemolytic jaundice.
Calcium	9–11 mg. per 100 cc. 4.5–5.5 mEq./l.	Increases in multiple myeloma. Decreases in tetany, nephritis and celiac disease.
Cholesterol (total)	150–200 mg. per 100 cc.	Increases in diabetes, nephrosis and biliary obstruction. Decreases in pernicious anemia.
Cholesterol esters	60–80% of total	

Normal Clinical Biochemical Values (continued)

CONSTITUENT	NORMAL RANGE	CHANGES ASSOCIATED WITH PATHOLOGICAL CONDITIONS
Blood serum (cont.):		
Globulin	1.3–3.2 gm. per 100 cc.	Increases in cirrhosis, nephrosis and chronic infections.
Phosphatase (acid)	0.1–1.5 units	Increases in carcinoma of prostate.
Phosphatase (alkaline)	1.5–4 units	Increases in obstructive jaundice, rickets and diseases of the bone.
Phospholipids	60–350 mg. per 100 cc.	Increases in diabetes and nephrosis.
Phosphorus	3–5 mg. per 100 cc.	Increases in tetany and nephritis. Decreases in rickets and myxedema.
Potassium	4–6 mEq./l.	Increases in pneumonia and acute infections. Decreases in nephritis and diabetic coma.
Protein, total	6–8 gm. per 100 cc.	Increases in multiple myeloma. Decreases in nephrosis and liver disease.
Sodium	130–145 mEq./l.	Decreases in Addison's disease and severe nephritis.
Cerebrospinal fluid:		
Chlorides	110–130 mEq./l.	Decreases in meningitis.
Glucose	40–80 mg. per 100 cc.	Increases in encephalitis. Decreases in meningitis.
Protein	15–40 mg. per 100 cc.	Increases in meningitis and myxedema.
Liver function tests:		
Bilirubin (Van den Bergh)	0.0–0.2 mg. per 100 cc. (direct)	Direct: Increases in obstructive jaundice.
	0.2–1.0 mg. per 100 cc. (total)	Indirect: Increases in hemolytic jaundice.
Bromsulfalein test	0–10% retention in blood in 30 minutes.	Increases in extrahepatic obstructive jaundice.
Cephalin flocculation	24 hr.—0–1+ 48 hr.—0–1+	Increases in infectious hepatitis.
Thymol turbidity	0–5 units	Increases in jaundice and infectious hepatitis.
Zinc sulfate flocculation	0–8 units	Increases in parenchymal jaundice and cirrhosis.

Index

A

Absorption, from the digestive tract, 244
Acetaldehyde, 153
Acetanilid, 182
Acetic acid, 155, 157
Acetoacetic acid, 263, 301
Acetone, 154, 263, 301
  bodies, 263, 301
    formation of, 263
    in urine, 299, 301
Acetophenone, 178
Acetylene, 139
  series, 138
Acetylsalicylic acid, 180
Achroodextrin, 201
Acid(s), 102
  acetic, 155, 157
  acetoacetic, 263
  acetylsalicylic, 180
  ascorbic, 317
  benzoic, 178
  beta-hydroxybutyric, 263
  binary, 106
  boric, 102
  burns, treatment of, 108
  butyric, 205, 263
  carbolic, 174
  chaulmoogric, 206
  citric, 156, 158
  definition of, 74, 102
  dehydroascorbic, 319
  dibasic, 156
  effect on tissue, 108
  fatty, 204

Acid(s)—*Continued*
  formic, 155, 156
  glutamic, 223
  hydrochloric, 102, 103
  hydroxy, 156
  inorganic, 102
  ionization of, 118
  lactic, 156, 158
  monobasic, 156
  naming of, 106
  nicotinic, 184, 310
  nitric, 102
  nucleic, 273
  oleic, 205
  organic, 155, 178
  oxalic, 156, 158
  palmitic, 205
  phosphoric, 102
  phosphotungstic, 232
  picric, 174, 176
  properties of, 103
  propionic, 155
  radical, 102
  reaction with amines, 162
    with bases, 104
    with carbonates and bicarbonates, 105
    with metals, 103, 104
    with oxides, 104
    with salts, 110
  ricinoleic, 205
  salicylic, 179
  salts, 111
  stearic, 205
  strength of, 119

367

Acid(s)—*Continued*
  sulfuric, 102
  tannic, 231
  tartaric, 156
  ternary, 106
  tribasic, 156
  tungstic, 231
  uric, 186, 274
Acid-base balance, 287
Acidosis, 264, 288
Acrodynia, 312
Acrolein tests, 212
Acromegaly, 358
ACTH, 360
Activators, 235
Acyl group, 161
Addison's disease, 350
Adenine, 186, 273
Adequate proteins, 331
Adipose tissue, 261
Adrenal cortex, 348
  hormones, 349
  medulla, 348
Adrenalin, 256, 348
Adrenocorticotropic hormone, 360
Adrenotropic hormone, 360
Adsorption, 97
Aeration of water, 79
Agammaglobulinemia, 279
Agar-agar, 198
Alanine, 162, 223
Albumin, 226
  in plasma, 278
Albuminoids, 227
Alcoholic fermentation, 196
Alcohols, 143
  aliphatic, 143
  aromatic, 173
  denatured, 147, 148
  ethyl, 147
  methyl, 144, 146
  oxidation of, 145
  polyhydric, 149
  primary, 145
  propyl, 145, 146
  reactions of, 145
  secondary, 145
  tertiary, 145
  wood, 146
Aldehydes, 152, 176
  as reducing agents, 152
Aldose, 192

Alimentary glycosuria, 258
Aliphatic compounds, 136
  saturated, 138
  unsaturated, 138
Alkali reserve, 288
Alkalies, 107
Alkaline tide, 295
Alkaloidal reagents, 231
Alkaloids, 187
  table of, 187
Alkalosis, 288
Alkanes, 136
Alkyl halides, 143
  radicals, 143
Allantoin, 274
Allotropic forms of elements, 62
Alpha amino acids, 222
  particles, 23
  tocopherol, 326
Americium, 29
Amides, 161
Amine(s), 161
  aralkyl, 173
  aromatic, 180
  ethyl, 161
  methyl, 161
Amino acids, 162, 222
  absorption of, 247
  amphoteric nature of, 224
  anabolism of, 267
  catabolism of, 268
  essential, 270
  metabolic pool, 266
Amino group, 161
Aminopolypeptidase, 242
Ammonia, formation of, 300
  urinary excretion of, 299
Ammonium hydroxide, 107
  radical, 44
Amphoteric compounds, 224
Amylopectin, 200
Amylopsin, 242
Anabolism, 251
Androgens, 357
Androsterone, 357
Anemia, 284
  macrocytic, 316
  nutritional, 285
  pernicious, 284
  secondary, 284
Anesthesia, 150, 151
Anhydrous, 75

Aniline, 181
Animal protein factor, 317
Anthracene, 171
Anticoagulants, 281
Antidotes for acid burns, 108
  for alkali burns, 108
  for salts of heavy metals, 231
Antienzymes, 235
Anti-freeze, 90
Antihemophilia globulin, 280
Anti-infective vitamin, 320
Antioxidants, 213
Antiprothrombin, 280
Antirachitic vitamin, 322
Antiseptic agents, 67
  soaps, 216
Anuria, 294
Aqueous solutions, 82
Aralkyl amines, 173
Argyrol, 231
Aromatic compounds, 172
Arrhenius, theory of ionization, 116
Arthritis, 350–352
Aryl group, 166
Ascorbic acid, 317
  requirements of, 319
Asphyxiation, 59
Aspirin, 180
Atabrine, 189, 190
Atomic bomb, 28, 29
  energy, 30
    peacetime applications, 30
  number, 19
  pile, 28, 29
  power plant, 30
  structure, 19
  symbols, 36
  theory, 15
  weight, 16
    table of, Inside Back Cover
Atoms, composition of, 15
  definition of, 16
  structure of, 19
Atropine, 187, 188
Avogadro, 19

B

Bacteria, action of, in intestine, 248
  in water, 78
Bacteriostatic agents, 315
Baking soda, 105

Balancing chemical equations, 46
Barbiturates, 185
Barium sulfate, use in medicine, 110
Basal metabolic rate, 333
Bases, 107
  definition of, 107
  effect on tissues, 108
  ionization of, 119
  naming of, 108
  properties of, 109
  reaction with acids, 108
  strength of, 119
Becquerel, 23
  rays, 23
Beeswax, 208
Benedict's solution, 195
  test, 195
    on urine, 300
Benzaldehyde, 176, 177
Benzedrine, 174
Benzene, 165
  formula for, 166
  halogen derivatives of, 167
  homologs of, 169
  ring, 166
    positions in, 168
  structure of, 168
Benzidine test for blood, 302
Benzoic acid, 178
Benzophenone, 178
Benzyl alcohol, 173
Benzyl amine, 173
Beriberi, 307
Berkelium, 29
Beta carotene, 321
  oxidation of fatty acids, 262
  particles, 24
Beta-hydroxybutyric acid, 263
Bicarbonates, 104
Bile, 242
  composition of, 242
  functions of, 243
  in urine, 302
  pigments, 243
  salts, 243
Bilirubin, 243, 283
Biliverdin, 243
Binary acids, 106
Biological value of proteins, 270
Biotin, 315
Biuret test, 229
Bleaching agents, 67

Blood, 276
  acidosis in, 288
  analysis, 289
  buffers, 288
  clotting, 280
  composition of, 277
  constituents, 289, 365
  formed elements of, 277
  functions of, 276
  in urine, 302
  pH, 287, 288
  sugar levels, 251
  volume of, 277
Boiling point of solutions, 89
Boric acid, 102
Bottled gas, 140
Bowman's capsule, 292
Brownian movement, 96
Buffer salts, 288
Buffers, 125, 288
Burning, definition of, 55
Burns, acid, treatment of, 108
  alkali, treatment of, 108
  treatment with alkaloidal reagents,
    232
Butesin picrate, 176
Butyric acid, 205, 263

C

Caffeine, 186, 294
Calciferol, 212, 324
Calcium, in tetany, 348
  metabolism, parathyroids in, 348
  requirement in body, 334
  soap, 216
Californium, 29
Calorie, definition of, 332
  requirement in body, 332
Cancer, of stomach, 239
Cane sugar, 198
Carbaminohemoglobin, 286
Carbocyclic compounds, 165
Carbohydrates, 191
  absorption of, 246
  classification of, 193
  conversion to fat, 259
  definition of, 192
  digestion, summary of, 245
  metabolism of, 251
  reactions of, 195
  reducing power of, 195
  requirement in nutrition, 336

Carbohydrates—*Continued*
  synthesis of, 191
Carbolic acid, 174
Carbon atom, diagram of, 21, 130
Carbon, 130
  black, 140
  dioxide, 57, 58, 60
  monoxide, 59, 284
    hemoglobin, 59, 284
  properties of, 130
  radioactive, 30, 31
  tetrachloride, 134, 142
Carbonates, reaction with acid, 105
Carbonic acid, 102
Carbonic anhydrase, 287
Carbonyl group, 153
Carboxyl group, 155
Carboxypolypeptidase, 241
Carnauba wax, 208
Carotenes, 321
Carotenoid pigments, 321
Casein, 228
Casts, surgical, 76
Catabolism, of amino acids, 268
  definition of, 251
Catalyst, definition of, 54
  use of, 54
Celiac disease, 216
Cellophane, 202
Celluloid, 202
Cellulose, 201
Centigrade temperature, 12, 13
  conversion to Fahrenheit, 13
Centimeter, 10
Cephalins, 209, 210
Cerebrosides, 211
Charcoal, 97
Chaulmoogric acid, 206
Chemical, changes, 8, 9
  energy, 7
  equation, 46
    balancing, 46
  formulas, 37
  mixtures, 9
  properties, 7, 8
  radicals, 44
  reactions, types of, 49
  symbols, 36
Chemistry, definition of, 7
  divisions of, 3
  history of, 2
  importance of, 4

Chloramine T, 179
Chloride shift, 286, 287
Chlorides, 109
  in urine, 298
  test for, 109, 110
Chlorine, 22, 23
  molecule, 40, 41
Chloroform, 142
Chlorophyll, 191
Cholecystokinin, 242, 341
Cholesterol, 211, 243
Choline, 313, 314
Chromoproteins, 228
Chyme, 240
Chymotrypsin, 241
Chymotrypsinogen, 241
Cinnamic aldehyde, 177
Citric acid, 156, 158
Clearance test for urea, 302
Clinical biochemical values, table of, 365
Clotting of blood, 280
  time of, 281
Coagulation of proteins, 230
Coal, 171
  gas, 172
  tar, 172
Cobalt bomb, 33, 34
  radioactive, 34
Cocaine, 187, 188
Cod liver oil, 322, 324
Codeine, 187, 190
Coenzymes, 235
Coke, 171
Collecting tubules, 292
Colloid goiter, 346
Colloids, 92–101
  adsorption by, 97
  electrical charge on, 95
  importance of, 100
  mill, 95
  movement of, 96
  properties of, 95
  size, 95
Coma, diabetic, 256, 264
Combustible substances, 55
Combustion, 55
  spontaneous, 56
Complete proteins, 270
Compound(s), 9
  aliphatic, 136
  aromatic, 172
  carbocyclic, 165

Compound(s)—*Continued*
  cyclic, 165
  definition of, 9
  heterocyclic, 165, 182
  organic, 128
Concentrated solution, 84
Concentration of solutions, 84
Conductivity of solutions, 115
Conductors, 115
Coniine, 187
Conjugated proteins, 226, 228
Conversion factors, weights, and
      measures, 11, 12
  of centigrade to Fahrenheit, 13
Copper in nutrition, 335
Corn syrup, 197
Corpus luteum, 353, 355
Cortin, 349
Cortisone, 349
Cottonseed oil, 208, 214
Covalence, 40
Creatine, 272, 298
  phosphate, 272
Creatinine, 272, 297
  coefficient, 297
Creatinuria, 298
Crenation, 92
Cresol, 174, 176
Cretinism, 344, 345
Crisco, 214
Cryptoxanthine, 321
Crystallization, 75
  water of, 75
Crystalloids, 97
Cubic centimeter, 10
Curdling of milk, 240
Curie, Madame, 23, 24
Curium, 29
Cyclic compounds, 165
Cyclohexane, 167
Cyclopentanoperhydrophenanthrene
      nucleus, 211
Cyclotron, 26, 27, 29
Cystine, 223, 273
Cystinuria, 273, 299
Cytosine, 185

D

Dalton's atomic theory, 15
Deamination, 268
Deficiency diseases, 305

Dehydroandrosterone, 357
Dehydroascorbic acid, 319
7-Dehydrocholesterol, 322
Deliquescent, 75
Demineralized water, 81
Denatured alcohol, 147, 148
Dental caries, 322
Depot fat, 261
Derived proteins, 226
Desiccating agent, 75
Desoxycorticosterone, 349
Detergents, 217
Deuterium, 22, 74
Deuterons, 27
Dextrins, 201
Dextrose, 197
Diabetes insipidus, 294, 361
Diabetes mellitus, 256, 341
    acidosis in, 256
    caused by phlorhizin, 259
    coma in, 256, 264
    diet in, 337
    glucose tolerance in, 257
    insulin in, 256
Diabetogenic hormone, 360
Dialysis, 97, 98
Dialyzing membrane, 98
Diarrhea, 248
Dibasic acids, 156
Diet, general requirements of, 332
    in anemia, 338
    in childhood, 337
    in diabetes mellitus, 337
    in lactation, 336
    in nephritis, 338
    in pregnancy, 336
Diethyl ether, 150
    in anesthesia, 150, 151
Diffusion, 89
Digestion, 236
    gastric, 238
    intestinal, 241
    salivary, 237
Digestive enzymes, table of, 245
Digestive system, diagram of, 238
Dihydrotheelin, 354
Dilute solution, 84
Dipeptidase, 242
Dipeptides, 225
Disaccharides, 193, 198
Distillation of water, 77

Diuretic, 294
Divinyl ether, 151
Drisdol, 212, 324
Ductless glands, 339
Duodenum, 241
Dwarfs, 358
Dynamite, 150
Dystrophy of muscles, 325

E

Edema, 271, 279
Efflorescent, 75
Eijkman, 304
Einsteinium, 29
Electric charge, on electrons, 115
    on protons, 115
Electric current, conductance of, 115
Electrolytes, 116, 117
    ionization of, 117
    strength of, 119
Electromotive series, 104
Electron microscope, 93, 94, 95
Electrons, 19
    planetary, 19
    shells of, 20
    transfer of, 39, 40
Electrophoresis, 96, 278
Electrovalence, 39
Elements, 9
    allotropic forms, 62
    properties of, table, 363, 364
    radioactive, 23
        production of, 30
        use in industry, 34
        use in research, 31
    symbols for, 36
    valence of, 39
Embolus, 281
Emotional glycosuria, 258
Empirical formula, 129
Emulsifying agents, 100
Emulsions, 99
Endemic goiter, 346
Endocrine glands, 339
    location in the body, 340
Energy, 7
    chemical, 7
    requirements in nutrition, 332
Enterogastrone, 341
Enterokinase, 241

Enzymes, 55, 233
  activation of, 235
  classification of, 235
  common, table of, 236
  definition of, 233
  digestive, table of, 245
  factors, influencing action of, 234
  nature of, 233
Ephedrine, 174
Epinephrine, 174, 256, 348
  action of, 348, 349
Equations, chemical, 46
  methods of balancing, 46
  writing, summary of, 49
Ergosterol, 211, 212
Erythrocytes, 277
Erythrodextrin, 201
Essential amino acids, 270
  fatty acids, 331
Ester, aliphatic, 159
  aromatic, 180
Estradiol, 354, 355
Estriol, 354
Estrogenic hormones, 354, 356
Estrone, 354
Estrus cycle, 352, 353
Ethane, 137
  molecular model of, 137
Ether, 150
  diethyl, 150
  divinyl, 151
Ethereal sulfates, 273, 299
Ethyl, acetate, 160
  alcohol, 147
  amine, 161, 162
  cellulose, 203
  chloride, 142
  nitrite, 160
Ethylene, 139
  dibromide, 142
  glycol, 148
  series, 138
Excretion, routes of, 291
Exophthalmic goiter. 345–347
Extinguishing fires, 56

F

Factors, conversion, for weights and
    measures, 11, 12
Fahrenheit temperature, 13
  conversion to centigrade, 13

False glycosuria, 259
Fat(s), 207
  absorption of, 247
  calorific value of, 332
  composition of, 207
  constants, 214
  definition of, 207
  depot, 261
  digestion of, 245
  formation from carbohydrates, 259
  hydrogenation of, 214
  hydrolysis of, 212
  metabolism of, 260
  rancidity of, 213
  -soluble vitamins, 320
Fatty acids, 204
  essential, 331
  oxidation of, 262
  table of, 205
Feces, 247
Female sex hormones, 352
Fermentation, 147, 196
  alcohol, 147, 196
  intestinal, 248
Fermium, 29
Fibrin, 279, 280
  film, 279
  foam, 279
Fibrinogen, 278, 279, 280
  plastics, 279
Fields of chemistry, 3
Filtration, 78
Fire extinguishers, 57, 58
Foamite, 58
Folic acid, 316
Follicle, 353, 354
  -stimulating hormone, 358
Foods, residue of, 247
  specific dynamic action of, 334
Formaldehyde, 152, 153
Formalin, 153
Formic acid, 155, 156
Formulas, chemical, 37
  empirical, 129
Freezing point of solutions, 89
Fructose, 195, 198
Fruit sugar, 198
Fuel oil, 141
Functional tests of the kidney, 302
Funk, 305

G

Galactose, 195, 198
Gallbladder, 244
Gallstones, 244
Gamma, 10
  globulins, 279
  rays, 24
Gas, bottled, 140
  oil, 141
  natural, 139
Gases, solubility of, 84
Gasoline, 141
Gastric acidity, 239
  digestion, 238
  enzymes, 239, 240
  juice, 239
  lipase, 245
Gastrin, 239, 339
Geiger tube, 31
Geiger-Müller counter, 31
Gel, 99
Gigantism, 358
Glands, digestive, 238
  ductless, 339
  endocrine, 339
Globin, 227, 282, 283
Globulins, 227, 278
Glomerulus, 292
Glucose, 195, 197
  in blood, 251
  in urine, 257, 300
  oxidation of, 254
  tolerance test, 257
Glucuronic acid, 196
Glutamic acid, 223
Glutelins, 227
Glycerides, mixed, 207
  simple, 207
Glycerol, 149, 206
  test for, 212
Glycine, 162, 222
Glycogen, 201
  formation of, 253
Glycogenesis, 253, 254
Glycogenolysis, 253, 254
Glycolipids, 210
Glycoproteins, 228
Glycosuria, 258, 300
  alimentary, 258
  emotional, 258
  false, 259

Goiter, 346
  colloid, 346
  endemic, 346
  exophthalmic, 345–347
  simple, 346
Gonad-stimulating hormone, 358
Gout, 296, 297
Grain alcohol, 147
Gram, 10
  atomic weight, 18, 37
  equivalent weight, 87, 88
  molecular weight, 18, 19
Grape sugar, 197
Graphite, in atomic pile, 28, 29
Growth, anterior pituitary in, 358
Guanine, 186, 273
Guncotton, 202
Gypsum, 75, 76

H

Half-life of radioactive elements, 25, 30
Halogen, derivatives of hydrocarbons, 142
Hard soap, 215
  water, 79, 80
Heat, coagulation of proteins, 230
Heavy chlorine, 23
  hydrogen, 22
  metal salts, 231
  water, 22, 74
Helium atom, 21
Heller's ring test, 231
Hematuria, 302
Heme, 282
Hemoglobin, 59, 282
Hemoglobinuria, 302
Hemolysis, 91, 92
Hemophilia, 281
Heparin, 280
Heterocyclic compounds, 165, 182
Heterocyclic nucleus, 183
Hexosans, 200
Hexoses, 194
Hirudin, 281
Histamine, 239, 340
Histones, 227
History of chemistry, 2
Homologs, 137, 164
Homologous series, 137
  of alcohols, 144, 145
  of hydrocarbons, 137

Hopkins-Cole test, 230
Hormones, 339
  of adrenals, 348
  of digestive tract, 339
  of ovary, 352
  of pancreas, 341
  of parathyroids, 347
  of pituitary, 358
  of testes, 356
  of thyroid, 343
Hydrates, 75
Hydration, water of, 75
Hydrocarbons, aliphatic, 136
  aromatic, 165
    sources of, 171
  halogen derivatives, 142
  paraffin, 137
  saturated aliphatic, 138
  sources of, 139
  unsaturated aliphatic, 138
Hydrochloric acid, 102, 103
  in gastric juice, 239
Hydrogen, atom, 20, 21
  ion concentration, 122
  ions in acid solution, 118
  peroxide, 67
  replaceable, 104
Hydrogenation of liquid fats, 214
Hydrolysis, 74
  of disaccharides, 199
  of fats, 212
  of polysaccharides, 200, 201
  of proteins, 222
  of salts, 74, 121
Hydrolytic rancidity, 213
Hydronium ions, 118
Hydroxides, 107
Hydroxy-acids, 156
β-Hydroxybutyric acid, 263
17-Hydroxycorticosterone, 350
17-Hydroxy-11-dehydrocorticosterone,
    349, 350
Hydroxyl ions, 119
Hygroscopic, 75
Hyperacidity, of gastric juice, 239
Hyperglycemia, 251
Hyperthyroidism, 345
  use of radioactive iodine in, 32, 347
Hypertonic solution, 92
Hypoacidity, of gastric juice, 239
Hypoglycemia, 251

Hypophysis, 358
Hypothyroidism, 344
Hypotonic solution, 91

I

Ileum, 241
Importance of chemistry, 4
Inadequate proteins, 331
Incombustible substances, 55
Incomplete proteins, 271
Indican in urine, 299
Indicators, 103
Indole, 248, 249
Inhibitors, 235
Inorganic, acids, 102
  bases, 107
  salts, 109
    requirement in nutrition, 334
  sulfates, 273, 299
Inositol, 314
Insoluble soaps, 216
Insulators, 115
Insulin, 341, 556
  action of, 256, 342
  protamine, 343
  unit of, 342
Intercellular tissue, 318
Internal secretions, 339
Interstitial cells, 357
  fluid, 276
Intestinal, absorption, 244
  digestion, 241
  enzymes, 242
  fermentation, 248
  juice, 242
  putrefaction, 248
Iodides in salt, 335
Iodine, as antiseptic, 67
  color with polysaccharides, 200, 201
  in nutrition, 335
  in thyroid gland, 344
  number, 215
  radioactive, 32, 347
Iodoform, 142
Ion(s), definition of, 116
  exchange resins, 80
  formation of, 39, 40
  hydrogen, 118, 122
  hydroxyl, 119
  importance of, 122
Ionic valence, 40

Ionization, 115, 116
    degree of, 120
    of acids, 118
    of bases, 119
    of electrolytes, 117
    of salts, 120
    theory of, 116
Iron, in hemoglobin, 282
    radioactive, 33
    requirement in the body, 335
Islet tissue in pancreas, 341
Isohydric cycle, 287
Isomerism, 137
Isomers, 130, 137
Isotonic solution, 91
Isotopes, 22, 23
    radioactive, 23, 30
    stable, 23

J

Jaundice, 243, 302
Javelle water, 67
Jejunum, 241
Juice, gastric, 240
    intestinal, 242
    pancreatic, 241

K

Kerasin, 210
Keratinization, 320
Kerosene, 141
Ketones, 153, 178
Ketose, 192
Kidney, filtration, unit of, 292
    function tests, 302
    in urine formation, 291
Kilogram, 10
Kindling temperature, 56
Kjeldahl method, 228
Knoop's theory of β-oxidation, 262

L

Lactase, 242
Lactation, diet in, 336
Lacteals, 246
Lactic acid, 156, 158
    in muscular contraction, 253, 254
Lactogenic hormone, 359
Lactose, 199
    in urine, 259, 300

Laked blood, 92
Lanolin, 208
Large calorie, definition of, 332
Law of definite proportions, 18
Lead acetate, 159
Lecithins, 209
Length, units of, 11
Leprosy, 206
Leukocytes, 277
Levulose, 198
Linseed oil, 208
Lipase, gastric, 245
    pancreatic, 241
Lipids, 204
    classification of, 204
    metabolism of, 260
    requirement, in nutrition, 330
Lipoproteins, 228
Liquid air, 52, 53
Liter, 10
Litmus, 103
Liver, in anemia, 284
    glycogen storage in, 253
Lubricating oils, 141
Luteinizing hormone, 359
Lye, 107, 108
Lymph, 276
Lysine, 223
Lysol, 176
Lysolecithin, 209

M

Macrocytic anemia, 316
Magnesia, milk of, 111
Magnesium salts, 112
    uses in medicine, 113
Male sex hormones, 357
Malnutrition, 337
Malpighian corpuscles, 292
Malt sugar, 199
Maltase, 242
Maltose, 199
Manganese dioxide, catalyst, 54
Matter, states of, 7
Membrane, dialyzing, 98
Mendelevium, 29
Menstrual cycle, 352, 353
Menstruation, 353
Meta isomer, 168
Metabolism, basal, 333
    inorganic, 334

Metabolism of carbohydrates, 251
  of fats, 260
  of proteins, 266
  of purines, 273
  of pyrimidines, 273
Metals, activity of, 104
  heavy, in precipitation of proteins, 331
  reaction with acids, 103–104
Meter, 10
Methane, 131, 137
  halogen derivatives of, 142
  molecular model of, 133
  series, 136
Methemoglobin, 283
Methionine, 273
Methods of study, suggested, 4
Methyl alcohol, 144, 146
  amine, 161
  cellulose, 203
  chloride, 142
  molecular model of, 144
  salicylate, 180
Metopryl, 151
Metric system, 10
Microgram, 10
Milk, casein of, 228, 240
  curdling of, 240
  sugar, 199
  vitamin D in, 324
Milligram, 10
Milliliter, 10
Millimeter, 10
Millimicron, 93
Millon's test, 229
Mixed glycerides, 207
Mixtures, 9
Molar solution, 87
Mole, 87
Molecular models, of carbon, 132
  of ethane, 137
  of methane, 133
  of methyl alcohol, 144
  of propane, 137
Molecular weight, 17
  of proteins, 221
Molecules, 16
Monobasic acids, 156
Monosaccharides, 196
  absorption of, 246
Morphine, 190
Mucin, in saliva, 237

Muscle glycogen, 255
  metabolism, 255
Muscular atrophy, 298
  dystrophy, 298, 325
Myxedema, 344

N

Naming of acids, 106
  of bases, 108
  of salts, 111
Naphthalene, 170
Natural gas, 139
  composition of, 140
Nephritis, 300
Nephrosis, 278
Neptunium, 28
Neutralization, 104, 119
Neutral sulfur, 273, 299
Neutron, 19
  in atomic pile, 28, 29
Niacin, 311
Nicotine, 187
Nicotinic acid, 184, 310
  amide, 184, 310
Night blindness, 321
Nitric acid, 102
Nitrocellulose, 202
Nitrogen balance, 269
Nitrogen cycle, 220
Nitroglycerin, 150, 161
Nitrous oxide, 59, 60
Nobelium, 29
Nonelectrolyte, 117
Norepinephrine, 349
Normal salts, 111
  solutions, 87
Novocain, 179, 189
Nuclear fission, 28
Nucleic acid, 273
Nucleoproteins, 228
  metabolism of, 273
Nucleus of the atom, 19
Nutrition, 330
  in childhood, 337
  in diseases, 337
  in pregnancy and lactation, 336
Nutritional anemia, 285

O

Obesity, 261
Obstructive jaundice, 243

Oils, gas, 141
  fuel, 141
  hydrogenated, 214
  liquid fats, 207, 208
  lubricating, 141
  vegetable, 208, 214
Oleic acid, 205
Oliguria, 294
Optimum pH, 234
  temperature, 234
Organic acids, aliphatic, 155
  aromatic, 178
Organic compounds, 128
  aliphatic, 136
    saturated, 138
    unsaturated, 138
  aromatic, 172
  comparison with inorganic, 129
  cyclic, 165
  heterocyclic, 165, 182
  importance of, 128
  molecular models of, 133, 137, 144
Organic salts, 159
Orinase, 343
Ortho isomers, 168
Osmosis, 90
Osmotic pressure, 91
Osteomalacia, 322
Ovary, hormones of, 352
Oxalic acid, 156, 158
Oxidation, definition, 64
  loss of electrons in, 64, 65
  of alcohols, 145
  of carbohydrates, 195, 196
    in the body, 254
  of fats, 262
  of proteins, 268
Oxidation and reduction, 65
  reactions, 49, 66
Oxidative rancidity, 213
Oxides, definition of, 55
  reaction with acids, 104
    with water, 74
Oxidizing agents, definition of, 64
Oxyacetylene flame, 60
Oxygen, 52
  administration of, 59–62
    with nitrous oxide, 59, 60
  in breathing, 59
  in industry, 60
  occurrence of, 52
  preparation of, 52

Oxygen—*Continued*
  properties of, 54
  use in therapy, 59
Oxyhemoglobin, 59, 283
Oxytocin, 361
Ozone, 62
  preparation, 63
  properties, 63
  uses of, 64

P

Palmitic acid, 205
Pancreas, hormone of, 341
Pancreatic enzymes, 241
  juice, 241
Pancreatropic hormone, 360
Pancreozymin, 341
Pantothenic acid, 313
Paper electrophoresis, 284
Para isomer, 168
Para-aminobenzoic acid, 179, 314
Paracasein, 240
Paraffin series, 137
Paraformaldehyde, 153
Paraldehyde, 153
Paralysis, in vitamin E deficiency, 325
Parathyroids, 347
  secretion of, 348
Particles, alpha, 23
  beta, 24
Pellagra, 310
Penicillin, 183
Pentose, 194
Pepsin, 239
Pepsinogen, 235, 239
Peptidases, 242
Peptide linkage, 225
Peptides, 225
Peptones, 239
Percentage solutions, 85
Periodic table, Inside Back Cover
Permanent hard water, 80
  emulsions, 99
Pernicious anemia, 284
Petroleum, 140
  distillation fractions of, 141
  gases from, 141
pH, of body fluids, 124
  determination and meaning of, 124
  optimum, 234
Phenacetin, 182

Phenanthrene, 171
Phenol red, 302
Phenols, 174
Phenolsulfonephthalein, 179
    kidney function test, 302
Phenyl radical, 166
Phlorhizin diabetes, 259
Phosphates, as buffers, 298, 299
    in urine, 298
Phosphocreatine, 272
Phospholipids, 208
Phosphoproteins, 228
Phosphoric acid, 102
Phosphorus, in nutrition, 334
    radioactive, 33
Phosphotungstic acid, 232
Photosynthesis, 191
Phrenosin, 210
Physical change, 8
    properties, 7
Physiological properties of elements, 364
    salt solution, 91
Picric acid, 174, 176
Pitocin, 361
Pitressin, 361
Pituitary gland, 358
    anterior lobe hormones, 358
    pars intermedia, 361
    posterior lobe hormones, 361
Placenta, 356
Planetary electrons, 19
Plasma, 278
    proteins, 278
Plaster of paris, 75, 76
    casts, 76
Platelets, 277
Plutonium, 28
Pneumonia, oxygen therapy in, 59
Poisoning, carbon monoxide, 59, 284
Polyhydric alcohol, 149
Polyneuritis, 307
    alcoholic, 307
Polypeptides, 225
Polysaccharides, 193, 200
    reaction with iodine, 200, 201
Polyuria, 294
Potassium, in nutrition, 336
    permanganate, 67
    soaps, 215
Precipitation of proteins, 230
Prednisolone, 350
Prednisone, 350

Pregnancy, diet in, 338
    hormones in, 355, 356
Pregnandiol, 355, 356
Pressure, cooking, 71
    influence on solubility of gas, 84
Primary alcohols, 145
Procaine, 179, 180, 189
Proenzyme, 235
Progesterone, 355, 356
Prolactin, 359
Prolamines, 227
Propane, 140
    molecular model of, 137
Properties, chemical, 7, 8
    of acids, 103
    of bases, 109
    of carbon, 130
    of oxygen, 54
    of water, 72
    physical, 7, 8
Propionic acid, 155
Propyl alcohol, 145, 146
Prosecretin, 241
Protamine insulin, 343
Protamines, 227
Proteases, 236
Proteins, 219
    absorption of, 247
    adequate, 331
    anabolism of, 267
    biological value of, 270
    bound iodine, 347
    catabolism of, 268
    classification of, 226
    color reactions of, 229
    complete, 270
    composition of, 219
    conjugated, 226, 228
    derived, 226
    digestion of, 245
    hydrolysis of, 221
    in growth, 267
    in urine, 300
        test for, 301
    inadequate, 331
    incomplete, 271
    metabolism of, 266
    minimum, 270
    molecular weights of, 221
    plasma, 278
    precipitation of, 230
    requirement in nutrition, 331

Proteins—*Continued*
  simple, 226
  structure, 225
  synthesis, 219, 267
Proteinuria, 301
  false, 301
  renal, 301
Proteoses, 239
Prothrombin, 280, 326
Protons, 19
Pteroylglutamic acid, 316
Ptyalin, 237, 238
Purification of water, 76
Purines, 186
  metabolism of, 273
Putrefaction, intestinal, 248
Pyridine, 184
Pyridoxine, 312
Pyrimidines, 184
  metabolism of, 273
Pyroxylin, 202
Pyrrole, 183

Q

Quinine, 189, 190

R

Rachitic rosary, 322
Radicals, 44
  table of, 44, 45
Radioactive carbon, 30, 31
  elements, 23
    half-life of, 25
    in cancer therapy, 33, 34
    production of, 30
    table of, 30
    transmutation of, 25, 26
    use in industry, 34
      in medicine, 31–33
      in research, 31–33
  iodine, 32, 347
  isotopes, 23, 30
Radium, 23, 33, 34
Rancidity of fats, 213
Rayon, 202
Rays, alpha, 23
  beta, 24
  gamma, 24
Reaction, types of, 49
  chemical, 49
  oxidation-reduction, 49, 66

Red blood cells, 277
  crenation of, 92
  hemolysis of, 91, 92
Reducing agent, 65
Reduction, 65
  gain of electrons in, 65
  of carbohydrates, 195
Renal, diabetes, 258
  proteinuria, 301
  threshold, 257
Rennin, 239, 240
Replaceable hydrogen, 104
Resins, ion exchange, 80
Resorcinol, 174, 175
Respiration, 285
Rheumatic fever, 360
Rheumatoid arthritis, 350, 352, 360
Riboflavin, 308
  requirement, 310
Ricinoleic acid, 205
Rickets, 322, 323
Röntgen, 23
Routes of excretion, 291
Rutherford, 23

S

Saccharin, 179, 180
Salicylic acid, 179
Saliva, 237
  composition of, 237
Salivary, digestion, 237
  glands, 237
Salt solution, physiological, 91
Salting out of proteins, 231
Salts, 109
  acid, 111
  bile, 243
  hydrolysis of, 74, 121
  importance of, 112
  ionization of, 120
  naming of, 111
  normal, 111
  organic, 159
  reactions of, 109
  uses in medicine, 113
Sand filter for water purification, 113
Saponification, 213, 215
  number, 214
Saturated aliphatic hydrocarbons, 138
Saturated fatty acids, 205
Saturated solutions, 84

Scurvy, 317
Seaborg, 29
Secondary, alcohols, 145
  anemia, 284
Secretin, 241, 340
Secretions, internal, 339
Semipermeable membrane, 90
Series, acetylene, 138
  electromotive, 104
  ethylene, 138
  homologous, 137
  methane, 136
Serum, 278
Sex characteristics, secondary, 352, 357
Shell, electron, 20
Shortenings, 214
Silver nitrate, 109
  uses in medicine, 113
Simple, glycerides, 207
  goiter, 346
  proteins, 226
  sugars, 193
Skatole, 248, 249
Soaps, antiseptic properties of, 216
  formation of, 215
  hard, 215
  insoluble, 216
  soft, 215
Soda, baking, 105
  washing, 105
Sodium, acetate, 159
  atom, 21
  bicarbonate, 105, 106, 113
  carbonate, 105
  chloride, 39, 40
    in urine, 298
  hydroxide, 107
  glycocholate, 243
  radioactive, 30, 32
  requirement in body, 336
  salicylate, 179
  soaps, 215
  taurocholate, 243
Soft, soaps, 215
  water, 79
Softening of water, 79
Solubility, factors affecting, 83
Solute, 82
Solution, Benedict's, 195
  physiological, salt, 91
Solutions, 82
  aqueous, 82

Solutions—*Continued*
  colloidal, 92–101
  concentrated, 84
  dilute, 84
  hypertonic, 92
  hypotonic, 91
  isotonic, 91
  molar, 87
  normal, 87
  percentage, 85
  physical properties of, 89
  saturated, 84
  supersaturated, 85
  true, 92
  types of, 84
Solvent, 82
Souring of milk, 196
Specific dynamic action, 334
Specific gravity, 71
  of urine, 295
Specificity of enzyme action, 234
Spermaceti, 208
Sphingomyelins, 210
Spontaneous combustion, 56
Stable isotopes, 23
Stains, removal of, 67
Starch, 200
  digestion of, 245
  reaction with iodine, 200, 201
Steapsin, 241
Stearic acid, 205
Stercobilin, 243
Sterility, 325
Sterols, 211
  nucleus of, 211
Stilbestrol, 355
Stomach, digestion in, 238
  evacuation of, 240
Strong, acids, 119
  bases, 119
Structure of atoms, 19
  of benzene, 168
Substrate, 233
Sucaryl, 179
Succus entericus, 242
Sucrase, 242
Sucrose, 198
Sugar, cane, 198
  malt, 199
  milk, 199
  simple, 193
Sulfadiazine, 182

Sulfanilamide, 182
Sulfates, in urine, 299
Sulfathiazole, 182
Sulfhemoglobin, 283
Sulfonic acids, 179
Sulfur metabolism, 273
   neutral, 273, 299
   oxidized, 273
   radioactive, 33
Sulfuric acid, 102
Supersaturated solution, 85
Surface, adsorption on, 97
   tension, 90
Surgical casts, 76
Suspensions, 92
Symbols, atomic, 36
   table of, 37
Synthesis, of carbohydrates, 191
   of complex lipids, 260
   of enzymes, 267
   of fats, 260
   of hormones, 267
   of proteins, 219, 267
System, metric, 10

T

Table of atomic weights,
      Inside Back Cover
Tannic acid, 231
Tartaric acid, 156
Taurocholic acid, 243
Temperature, centigrade, 12, 13
   critical, 55
   effect on solubility, 83
   Fahrenheit, 12, 13
   kindling, 56
   optimum, 234
Temporary, hard water, 79
   emulsions, 99
Ternary acids, 106
Tertiary alcohols, 145
Testes, hormones of, 356
Testosterone, 357
Tests, for acetone, 301
   for bile, 302
   for blood, 302
   for glucose, 195, 300
   for kidney function, 302
   for protein, 229, 301

Tetany, 348
Theelin, 354
Theory, atomic, 15
   of ionization, 116
Thermometer, centigrade, 12, 13, 71
   Fahrenheit, 12, 13
Thiamine, 185, 307
   requirement, 308
Threonine, 223
Threshold, renal, 257
   substances, 293
Thrombin, 280
Thrombocytes, 278
Thromboplastic factor, 280
Thrombosis, 281
Thrombus, 281
Thymine, 185
Thymol, 174, 176
Thyroglobulin, 343
Thyroid gland, hormone of, 343
   uptake of radioactive iodine by,
      32, 33, 347
Thyrotropic hormone, 359
Thyroxin, 344
Tincture of green soap, 215
Tissue, adipose, 261
   fluid, 276
Tocopherols, 326
Toluene, 169, 170
Transamination, 268
Transmutation of radioactive elements,
      25, 26
Treatment, of acid burns, 108
   of alkali burns, 108
   of heavy metal poisoning, 231
Tribasic acids, 156
Tricarboxylic acid cycle, 255, 262, 275
Triose, 193, 194
Tripalmitin, 207
Tripeptide, 225
Trisaccharide, 193
Tropane nucleus, 187
True solutions, 92
Trypsin, 241
Trypsinogen, 235, 241
Tryptophan, 183, 224
Tubules, kidney, 292
Tungstic acid, 231
Twitchell's reagent, 213
Tyndall effect, 96
Tyrosine, 223

U

Ulcers, gastric, 239, 240
Ultraviolet irradiation, 323, 324
Unoxidized sulfur test, 229
Unsaturated, aliphatic hydrocarbons, 138
  fatty acids, 205
Uracil, 185
Uranium, 23, 28, 29
  isotopes, 25, 28
  pile, 28
Urates in urine, 296
Urea, 269
  clearance test, 302
  formation of, 269
  in urine, 296
Urease, 296
Uremia, 296
Uric acid, 186, 274
  in gout, 296, 297
  in urine, 296
Urine, 291
  collection for analysis, 293
  color of, 294
  constituents of, 295
    normal, 295
    pathological, 300
  formation of, 291
  reaction of, 294
  specific gravity of, 295
  volume of, 293
Urobilin, 243
Urobilinogen, 243
Urochrome, 243, 294

V

Valence, 36
  application of, 45
  co-, 40
  electro-, 39
  ionic, 40
  number, 42
    negative, 43
    positive, 43
  of carbon atom, 130
  table of, 44, 45
  zero, 64, 66
Vanillin, 177
Vasopressin, 361
Vegetable oil, 208, 214
Villus, 244, 246

Vinethene, 151
Viosterol, 212, 324
Visual purple, 321
Vitamin A, 320
  precursors of, 321
  requirement, 322
  B complex, 306
    B_{12}, 317
    biotin, 315
    choline, 313
    folic acid, 316
    inositol, 314
    nicotinic acid, 310
    p-aminobenzoic acid, 314
    pantothenic acid, 313
    pyridoxine, 312
    riboflavin, 308
    thiamine, 185, 307
  C (ascorbic acid), 317
    requirement in nutrition, 319
  D, 322
    requirement in nutrition, 324
    D_2, 323, 324
    D_3, 323, 325
  E, 325
  K, 326
Vitamins, 304
  fat-soluble, 320
  historical development, 304
  water-soluble, 306
Volume, units of, 10, 12

W

Washing soda, 105
Waste materials, excreted by kidney, 291
Water, 70
  aeration of, 79
  as polar compound, 72
  boiling of, 71, 78
  chemical properties of, 72
  distillation of, 77
  effect on ionic compounds, 72, 73
  electrolysis of, 53
  filtration of, 78
  freezing of, 71
  hard, 77
    permanent, 80
    temporary, 79
  heavy, 22, 74
  impurities of, 76, 77
  Javelle, 74

Water—*Continued*
  occurrence of, 70
  of crystallization, 75
  of hydration, 75
  physical properties, 71
  purification of, 76
  reactions, with metals, 73
    with oxides, 73, 74
    with salts, 74
  soft, 77
  softening of, 79
  -soluble vitamins, 306
Waxes, 208
Weak, acids, 119
  bases, 119
Weight, gram atomic, 18, 37
  gram molecular, 18, 19
  units of, 10, 11
Weights and measures, 11, 12
  conversion factors for, 11, 12

Welding, 60
Wöhler, 127
Wood alcohol, 146

X

Xanthoproteic test, 230
Xerophthalmia, 320
X-rays, 23
Xylene, 170

Y

Yeast, 328
Yellow enzyme, 309

Z

Zeolite, 80
Zero valence, 64, 66
Zwitterions, 224
Zymase, 196
Zymogen, 235

$$K_{eq} = \frac{\text{"product" of products used to an appropriate}}{\text{"product" of reactants}}$$

"product" = concentration in moles/liter
of each solution involved.

solubility

$$K_{sp} = [Ag^+][Cl^-] \qquad \overset{constant}{AgCl \rightleftharpoons Ag^+ + Cl^-}$$

water

$$K_w = [H_3O^+][OH^-] \qquad 2 \overset{constant}{H_2O} \rightleftharpoons H_3O^+ + OH^-$$

$$[H_3O^+] = 1 \times 10^{-7} \text{ moles/liter} \qquad [OH^-] = 1 \times 10^{-7} \text{ moles/liter}$$

$$K_w = 1 \times 10^{-14}$$

ionic

$$HC_2H_3O_2 + H_2O \rightleftharpoons H_3O^+ + C_2H_3O_2^-$$

$$K_{eq} = \frac{[H_3O^+][C_2H_3O_2]}{(HC_2H_3O_2)[H_2O]} = K_i \frac{[H_3O^+][C_2H_3O_2^-]}{[HC_2H_3O_2]}$$

for weak electrolytes only because strong electrolyte is completely ionized

experimentally found for k_i of acetic acid

$$1 \times 10^{-5} = \frac{X^2}{0.01 \times X} = \frac{X^2}{1 \times 10^{-2}}$$

$$1 \times 10^{-7} = X^2$$

$$1 \times 10^{-3.5} = X \qquad pH = 3.5$$

adding .01 $Na^+ Ac^-$

$$k_i = \frac{[H_3O^+] + [C_2H_3O_2^-]}{(HC_2H_3O_2)}$$

k_i usually in range of 10^{-4} to 10^{-15}

$$1 \times 10^{-5} = \frac{X + [X .01]}{0.01 \times \text{ or } 1 \times 10^{-2}}$$

$$1 \times 10^{-7} = 1 \times 10^{-1} X$$

$$X = 1 \times 10^{-6} \qquad pH = 6$$

Buffers (see p. 290)

Buffers HAc

Na^+Ac^- $\begin{cases} \text{adding } H_3O^+ + Cl^- = \text{excess } Ac^- \text{ takes care of added } H_3O^+ \\ \text{adding } Na^+ OH^- = \text{excess } H_3O^+ \text{ takes care of added } OH^- \end{cases}$

only in small amt.

Other buffers = CO_2 - bicarbonate system - phosphate system
amino acids weak electrolytes + ~~slight~~ buffer

amphoteric or amphoprotic - substance
which has equal ability to donate or to
accept protons, i.e., H_2O

$H_3O^+ = $ strongest acid $OH^- = $ strongest base

$$K_i = \frac{[HCO_3^-][OH^-]}{(CO_3^=)}$$

$K_i = \dfrac{x^2}{1\times10^{-2}}$

1×10^{-12}

$1\times10^{-14} = x^2$

$1\times10^{-7} = x \, [OH^+]$

pH 7

$$K_i = \frac{[NH_4^+][OH^-]}{[NH_3]} :$$

$1\times10^{-5} = \dfrac{x^2}{1\times10^{-4}}$ $1\times10^{-5} = \dfrac{x^2}{1\times10^{-2}}$

$1\times10^{-6} = x^2$ $1\times10^{-7} = x^2$

$1\times10^{-3} = x \, [OH^-]$ $1\times10^{-3.5} = x \, [OH^-]$

$14-3 = 11 \text{ pH}$ $\begin{array}{r} 14.0 \\ 3.5 \\ \hline 10.5 = pH \end{array}$

K^+, MnO_4^- purple

$Cu(NH_3)_4^{+2}$ blue

Ca^{++}
$Ca^{++}(H_2O)_4$ } change color with moisture

tend to show colored ions

(transition elements)

Wilson's disease
Cu, instead of bound to ceruloplasm is partly found in free ions

$Ba^{++}, SO_4^{=}$ ↓ x-rays enemas

BaS toxic - forms ↓ OH^- deposit

Mg OH - milk of mag
~~antacid~~ antiacid - laxative

$NaHCO_3$ - ~~antacid~~ antiacid

$Al(OH)_3$↓ - " amphoteric

H_3AlO_3 or $HAlO_2$

Sulfur - imp. in enzymes structure - in ~~two~~ one essential amino acid

P - buffer - utilization of glucose.

hybridization

$C^6 - 1S^2, 2S^2, 2P^1, 2P^1$

1st step } $2S^1, 2P^1, 2P^1, 2P^1$

2nd step above e^- have equal energy levels

hybridization = redistribution of e^- in energy levels during chem. reaction

period 2 - small atoms
prop. vary greatly in period

antacids

amphoteric
insoluable

expanded periodic

physical center of 1

table = transition elements

chem. center = Carbon

group — Dr. T. det.

TRANSITIONAL

Some have varying valence —

and react with valence of $+2$ or $+3$

$4s^2 4s 4p$ fill partially before 3D

properties change slightly from L. to R. between each

most tend toward metals

colored ions

Heavier element in group,

more metalic are properties

compared with that group

Elements less metalic in

right of period

---

char. of metals

tend to be solid

lus ter

density

tensile strength

left of table

non metal

F — most active

opposite of metals

Cs — most active

metal most active state would tend

to be electrovalent in binary

compound — tend to form

ionic compounds — tend to

form strong bases —

group I alkaline metals

group II — alkaline earth metals

Rare Earths

Closer alike than transitional

4F series = lanthanide

5F series = Actinides after each other

Filling in F levels

levels

In a group

Higher wt. — more metalic —

more poisonous in sm. quantities

period 3

Long Form of the Periodic Table

EXPLANATION. This table is based on the atomic numbers of the elements. Groups of similar elements are easy to locate; for example, nonmetals are located in the upper right corner and are bounded by a diagonal line drawn from carbon through phosphorus, selenium, iodine and radon. Light metals are located in the upper left portion, including the upper elements in Group IIIB; heavy metals are in the bottom half. The most active metals are located at the extreme left in Groups IA, IIA, and IIIA. The most active nonmetals are located on the extreme right in Groups VB, VIB, and VIIB. Transitional elements, which are metals with more than one valence or combining number, are located in the central portion of the bottom half in Group IIIA to Group VII inclusive. Rare earth elements are very similar in properties and are located in Groups IIIA; however, for convenience, they are listed in a separate section at the bottom. Actinides are also located in Group IIIA and are listed at the bottom. Within each group the elements exhibit approximately the same valence. The elements in Group O show a 0 valence; in Group I, a valence of 1; Group II, a valence of 2; Group III, a valence of 3; and Group IV, a valence of 4. The elements of Group V have a valence of 3 or 5; those of Group VI, a valence of 2, 4, or 6; and Group VII, a valence of 1, 3, 5, or 7.

Period	IA	IIA	IIIA	IVA	VA	VIA	VIIA	VIIIA			IB	IIB	IIIB	IVB	VB	VIB	VIIB	O
1	1 H 1.008																1 H 1.008	2 He 4.003
2	3 Li 6.940	4 Be 9.013											5 B 10.82	6 C 12.001	7 N 14.008	8 O 16.00	9 F 19.00	10 Ne 20.183
3	11 Na 22.991	12 Mg 24.32											13 Al 26.98	14 Si 28.09	15 P 30.975	16 S 32.066	17 Cl 35.457	18 Ar 39.944
4	19 K 39.100	20 Ca 40.08	21 Sc 44.96	22 Ti 47.90	23 V 50.95	24 Cr 52.01	25 Mn 54.95	26 Fe 55.85	27 Co 58.94	28 Ni 58.71	29 Cu 63.54	30 Zn 65.38	31 Ga 69.72	32 Ge 72.60	33 As 74.91	34 Se 78.96	35 Br 79.916	36 Kr 83.80
5	37 Rb 85.48	38 Sr 87.63	39 Y 88.92	40 Zr 91.22	41 Nb 92.91	42 Mo 95.95	43 Tc 99	44 Ru 101.1	45 Rh 102.91	46 Pd 106.4	47 Ag 107.880	48 Cd 112.41	49 In 114.82	50 Sn 118.70	51 Sb 121.76	52 Te 127.61	53 I 126.91	54 Xe 131.30
6	55 Cs 132.91	56 Ba 137.36	57-71 La-Lu Rare Earths	72 Hf 178.50	73 Ta 180.95	74 W 183.86	75 Re 186.22	76 Os 190.2	77 Ir 192.2	78 Pt 195.09	79 Au 197.0	80 Hg 200.61	81 Tl 204.39	82 Pb 207.21	83 Bi 209.00	84 Po 210	85 At 210	86 Rn 222
7	87 Fr 223	88 Ra 226	89-96 Ac Actinides															

Rare Earths

57 La 138.92	58 Ce 140.13	59 Pr 140.92	60 Nd 144.27	61 Pm 147	62 Sm 150.35	63 Eu 152.0	64 Gd 157.26	65 Tb 158.93	66 Dy 162.51	67 Ho 164.94	68 Er 167.27	69 Tm 168.94	70 Yb 173.04	71 Lu 174.99

Actinides

89 Ac 227	90 Th 232.05	91 Pa 231	92 U 238.07	93 Np 237	94 Pu 242	95 Am 243	96 Cm 247	97 Bk 249	98 Cf 251	99 Es 254	100 Fm 253	101 Md 256	102 No 253